Charles

FUNDAMENTAL
CONCEPTS
OF
ARITHMETIC

FUNDAMENTAL
CONCEPTS
OF
ARITHMETIC

Sidney G. Hacker

Wilfred E. Barnes

Calvin T. Long

Department of Mathematics
Washington State University

Prentice-Hall, Inc., Englewood Cliffs, N. J.

PRENTICE-HALL INTERNATIONAL, INC., *London*
PRENTICE-HALL OF AUSTRALIA, PTY., LTD., *Sydney*
PRENTICE-HALL OF CANADA, LTD., *Toronto*
PRENTICE-HALL FRANCE, S.A.R.L., *Paris*
PRENTICE-HALL OF INDIA, PRIVATE LIMITED, *New Delhi*
PRENTICE-HALL OF JAPAN INC., *Tokyo*
PRENTICE-HALL DE MEXICO, S.A., *Mexico City*

Library of Congress Catalog Card Number 63–20708
Printed in the United States of America
C–91322

PREFACE

This is a book for both practicing and prospective elementary school teachers. The material has been used in mimeographed form by the authors and other instructors for over two years in both the in-service training of elementary school teachers in several school systems as well as in classes for college students who are preparing to be elementary school teachers.

The purpose of the book is simply to provide an understanding and appreciation of the fundamental concepts which underlie the operations and applications of arithmetic. It is not a book on how to teach arithmetic. Neither is it a book on what the professional mathematician calls the "foundations of arithmetic," that is to say a meticulously argued and rigorous examination of the logic which is the basis for arithmetic and thus for mathematics generally. Nor is it a book on the "theory of numbers," which some mathematicians call "the higher arithmetic." This book is none of these things, but occasionally such matters are necessarily touched upon. It is hoped that some readers will go on to significant studies in pedagogical disciplines, some to the exacting studies of the logical foundations of arithmetic, and some to the study of the many beautiful aspects of number theory. Our primary objective, however, is to provide the teacher or the prospective teacher of what we commonly call arithmetic with a real understanding of the *what, how,* and *why* of the subject so that he or she may be a better equipped and better informed teacher.

A brief description of the origin of this book may help to emphasize its purpose and to distinguish the class of readers for which it is intended. For several consecutive summers the authors have been engaged in a sequential series of Summer Institutes for High School Teachers of Mathematics under the sponsorship of the National Science Foundation. In the course of this work it occurred to us that the benefits of such institutes could be broadened if certain carefully selected high school teachers from among the participants could be given special instruction in the fundamental concepts of arithmetic and could be called upon subsequently by their local school boards to teach these things to their elementary school colleagues. In this way it was hoped to meet the great demand of the very large number of elementary school teachers who are today seeking such training. We have succeeded in carrying out this project in many communities both large and small. At the same time, in our own university we began to prepare those undergraduate students who are prospective elementary school teachers along these same lines. Mimeographed notes were prepared and distributed to large classes of in-service teachers and prospective teachers.

In the course of writing, teaching, and revising this material we found that this subject, within the framework of its limited and particular objective, is a surprisingly difficult one for intelligible description when that description is to impart not only accurate information but enthusiasm as well. We had to learn once again that although arithmetic is a science, the teaching of it at any level is an art. We hope that we have succeeded reasonably well in our efforts to inform and inspire both the practicing and the prospective elementary school teacher of arithmetic. In any event, we have become all the more conscious of the great debt of gratitude which all of us owe our teachers who in some remarkable and wondrous way succeeded in teaching us the difficult art of reckoning.

We express our thanks to the several instructors of in-service programs whose criticisms and suggestions have materially helped us. Mrs. R. B. McPherson, Miss Carole L. Sloan, and Miss Ardith C. Ericson with skill and efficiency transformed our handwritten copy into a legible and usable manuscript. We also sincerely appreciate the help and cooperation which the publishers have continually given us from the inception of this book to its completion.

S. G. H.

Pullman, Washington   W. E. B.

C. T. L.

CONTENTS

1. Early History and Development of Arithmetic

2. Some Intuitive Properties of the Natural Numbers

3. The Nature of Mathematical Systems

4. The Natural Numbers as a Mathematical System

FUNDAMENTAL
CONCEPTS
OF
ARITHMETIC

1

**EARLY
HISTORY
AND
DEVELOPMENT
OF
ARITHMETIC**

1.1 Babylonian Records

In the fertile valleys of the great rivers of the world, early man eventually came to find a way of life that provided some freedom from the ever present demands of mere survival. Within nomadic tribes or more permanent groups, such as villages centered around the raising of flocks or the growing of crops, a primitive culture gradually evolved. This culture concentrated at first on religious and linguistic matters. Subsequently a communicable kind of arithmetic was developed to meet the practical everyday necessities of counting and of measuring.

The oldest records which have come down to us are those of the ancient people who lived in Mesopotamia, the "land between the rivers" Tigris and Euphrates. It is a very small area in the country which is now called Iraq. At the north of this region the rivers flow from their widely separated origins through arid plateaus, and at the south they converge to flow into the Persian Gulf through rich alluvial plains. The ancient Babylonians, a Semitic people, lived in the fertile areas of the south. They inherited much of their culture from the Sumerians, a non-Semitic people, who lived in the rich delta of the confluent rivers at the head of the Persian Gulf. The Sumerian language is the oldest written language known; it came into existence about 3000 B.C. It is a language that makes no distinction between nouns and verbs, and in this and other respects is not related to any modern language. At about the same time, the Sumerians developed an arithmetic that, unlike their language, has had an effect on the arithmetics of other western peoples and even persists today in our choices of, for example, sixty minutes in an hour and 360 degrees in a circle. The Sumerian culture was eventually superseded by the Babylonian; we shall use the latter name and shall not distinguish between them.

The number symbols which these people used were wedge-shaped, or cuneiform, and were impressed with a stylus on small clay tablets which were later hardened in the sun. Many thousands of these tablets have been found. From these tablets we are led to credit these people with a well-developed system of reckoning as early as 6000 B.C. There is even evidence that a rudimentary number system had been devised by them as early as the twenty-eighth century B.C.

Addition and multiplication tables are found on many of these Babylonian tablets. Very common are tables of inverses which facilitate division, since to divide one number by another is to multiply the first by the inverse, or reciprocal, of the second. There are tablets containing tables of squares, square roots, and cube roots, and of course a great many dealing with the everyday problems of trade and commerce. Although Henry Creswicke Rawlinson had achieved the complete key to the translation of cuneiform tablets in 1847, it was not until 1854 that we obtained our first substantial knowledge of the arithmetic which the Babylonians had developed. In that year the British archæologist W. K. Loftus found two Babylonian tablets that provided this concrete evidence. This pair of tablets contains the squares of the numbers 1 through 60 and the cubes of the numbers 1 through 32. The tablets were written about 2100 B.C. during the reign of the great law-giver Hammurabi. In 1894 French archæologists found the remains of a schoolhouse of that same ancient time and uncovered numerous cuneiform tablets on which school children had done their arithmetic lessons.

1.2 Egyptian Records

It is usually difficult and often impossible to make reliable comparisons of the origins of ideas and methods among early peoples when we have only fragmentary evidence on which to reconstruct the run of history. The evidence that is available from Egypt for the period around 3000 B.C., for which the clay tablets from Babylonia are extant, has to be surmised from the great engineering accomplishments of the Egyptians. It was about this same time, for example, that the Great Pyramid of Gîza was built with a base covering more than thirteen acres and yet with a linear error of less than one part in 14,000 in the length of the sides and an almost negligible error in angle at the corners. Indeed, our lack of precise knowledge of the Egyptian arithmetic of that day results from the very thing which facilitated their work in the following centuries, namely the employment of papyrus for writing. The use of that remarkable plant as writing material was almost as significant for learning in the ancient world as was the invention of printing for medieval scholarship. Fortunately the very arid climate of Egypt made possible the desiccation and preservation of many papyrus manuscripts.

One of the oldest Egyptian works on arithmetic which has come down to us was written about 1700 B.C. It is on papyrus thirteen inches wide and eighteen feet in length. It was written by a scribe called Ahmes, who attributes the origin of the contents to an earlier work that is unknown to us but which apparently was written about 1800 B.C. This papyrus was found near Thebes by laborers in the area and was purchased from them by a Scottish antiquary named A. H. Rhind while on a visit to Egypt in 1858. This "Ahmes" or "Rhind" papyrus is now in the British Museum. An elaborate facsimile in color, together with a translation and commentary, was published in two volumes by the Mathematical Association of America in 1927-9.

The Rhind papyrus begins with a curious table of inverses, which as we have said were also a common concern of the Babylonians. This table expresses the fractions with the numerator 2 and denominators from 5 to 99 as the sums of unit fractions. For example, $\frac{2}{5}$ is written as the sum $\frac{1}{3} + \frac{1}{15}$; $\frac{2}{7}$ is $\frac{1}{4} + \frac{1}{28}$; and $\frac{2}{13}$ is $\frac{1}{8} + \frac{1}{52} + \frac{1}{104}$. We cannot say "and so on," for there is no real pattern. This representation in unit fractions is not unique, although only one such representation is given in each case in the Ahmes manuscript.

Far more interesting than this strange table is the collection of 84 miscellaneous problems and solutions that follow the table and are independent of it. Some of the problems deal with the apportionment of grain or bread or cattle. Twenty problems are concerned with the measurement of geometrical figures. Then there are problems which we might say today are of an "algebraic" kind, although no such generalization of method is given. On the contrary, the answers are found either directly by happy guesswork or by a succession of appropriate guesses which finally converge to yield the answer. Such a problem is Number 26 of the papyrus: "A quantity and its $\frac{1}{4}$ added together become 15. What is the answer?" It is not hard to guess the answer, but it is another matter to generalize the question and the method of its resolution. Although no such attempt is made in this ancient work, nevertheless in the series of problems there is some such attempt to be less specific. There is even an occasional bit of wise advice for a student, such as the directive in Problem 66: "Do the same thing in any problem like this." A student of any kind of mathematics who resolves to follow that instruction, constructing problems of his own choosing, will find himself well rewarded for his pains.

1.3 Records of the Orient

We know very little about the early history of arithmetic in the Orient. There are several reasons for this, but primarily it results from the general neglect by Oriental scholars of the history of the subject in their own antiquity. Even so, we know more about the early history of arithmetic in ancient China than in India. In the latter country the caste system has always hampered historical studies, and some Indian scholars have dated the origins of arithmetical ideas in India with such an overenthusiasm as to make them patently unreliable. There is in fact no authentic record of Indian science before the first Mohammedan invasion about the middle of the seventh century A.D. On the other hand, there is good evidence of a well-developed arithmetic in China as early as thirteen or fourteen thousand years B.C., but our more exact knowledge of Chinese mathematics does not go that far back.

There is, however, a Chinese book on arithmetic by an unknown author that was written sometime before the start of the first millenium B.C. Some scholars even date its origin as far back as 2000 or even 3000 B.C. It is called the *K'iu-ch'ang Suan-shu* or *Arithmetic in Nine*

Sections. Its nine chapters treat problems in percentage, square and cube roots, determinations of areas and volumes, linear equations, and even the so-called theorem of Pythagoras in geometry.

A second Chinese manuscript on arithmetic, which is called the *Chóu-peï*, was written about 1100 B.C. Its author too is unknown. It treats of methods in arithmetic and geometry with considerable emphasis on the calendar. It is, however, primarily an "arithmetic classic" and the words "Suan-king," which mean just that, are often affixed to its title.

1.4 Greek Mathematics and the Alexandrian School

We have spoken of the evidence that is available to us today of the surprising accomplishments in arithmetic in Babylonia and Egypt at a very early date. Our own rich heritage in arithmetic comes from the Greeks of a later period, who clearly learned some of their basic arithmetic from the Babylonian culture and were directly or indirectly associated, over a period of several centuries, with the great center of learning of the ancient world located in Alexandria, a city founded by Alexander the Great at the natural port just to the west of where the Nile now flows into the Mediterranean.

When Alexander died in 323 B.C., his empire fell into parts. The Egyptian area of his domain was given over to the control of one of his generals called Ptolemy Soter or "Ptolemy the Preserver"—not to be confused with the celebrated astronomer of that name who lived four centuries later. Ptolemy Soter, among other things, proceeded to establish a great library and to found a center of learning in Alexandria. The library was eventually burned in 642 A.D., a thousand years after its establishment. In the last four hundred years that preceded this tragedy, an ever deepening twilight gradually had settled over learning in the whole Mediterranean area, and with the final destruction of the library. the twilight turned to darkness.

Although there were other centers of learning in Greece and in the Greek-dominated Mediterranean areas, a majority of the mathematical scholars either studied or taught at Alexandria. Among the early ones were Aristotle, who was one of Alexander's own instructors, and Eudoxus (*c.* 400 B.C.), who like Aristotle was one of Plato's students. Aristotle's influence on science persisted until the time of Galileo and Newton in the seventeenth century. Eudoxus acquired much of the vast astronomical information that the Egyptians possessed and taught it to the theoretically-minded Greek mathematicians. Euclid (*c.* 300 B.C.) was an Alexandrian scholar, and so little is known about his life that no one knows whether he was Greek or Egyptian. Eratosthenes, who measured the circumference of the earth with remarkable accuracy; Apollonius of Perga, who enhanced the geometrical work of Euclid; and Archimedes, one of the truly dominant physicists and mathematicians of all time— all were at Alexandria near the beginning of the second century B.C. In the following centuries, on into the Christian era, there were many others. The last of the truly important scholars was Diophantus (*c.* 275 A.D.), the greatest arithmetician of antiquity.

The Greeks learned the use of papyrus for writing purposes as early as 650 B.C. As a result their work was transcribed, and a large share of it thereby became available to subsequent scholars. Although many of the mathematicians and philosophers under the early influence of Pythagoras (*c.* 550 B.C.) and of Plato (*c.* 400 B.C.) perfected the art of transmitting knowledge through conversation and strongly advocated this kind of instruction, the opportunity to write mathematics was significant and crucially important.

Our word *arithmetic* comes from the Greek word *arithmos* meaning *number*. The Greek mathematicians from the time of Thales of Miletus, some six hundred years B.C., to that of Diophantus of Alexandria, nearly a thousand years later, attached a deeper meaning to this word than we commonly do today. We use the word *arithmetic* in general as the equivalent of what is more accurately called *reckoning*, but to the Greeks *arithmos* suggested the intrinsic properties of number. It was in the sense of this much more significant meaning of the word that Pythagoras and Euclid, who are so commonly identified only with geometry, made essential and fundamental contributions to arithmetic. Certain aspects of these significant matters will be briefly considered later.

1.5 Contributions of the Mohammedans in the Dark Ages

For five and a half centuries following the destruction of the Alexandrian library, there was little or no development of mathematics except that which the Mohammedans stimulated. As they marched in conquest across northern Africa and into southern Spain, they transmitted to other people, mainly in the interests of trade, the mathematics that they themselves knew. They had learned this mathematics in Egypt and, what is of special significance to us as we shall see later, in India as a result of their invasions of that country and the commercial relations which followed.

In 820 A.D. a Mohammedan mathematician called al-Khowârizmî wrote a book on *al jebr* . . . meaning literally *the science* . . . . The full title was *The Science of Cancellation and Reduction*. It was essentially a book on arithmetic, but because of certain methods in the attack on such problems that this book strongly influenced, its title became the source of our word "algebra."

1.6 Arithmetic from the Middle Ages to the Seventeenth Century

It was not until six hundred years after the appearance of this book by al-Khowârizmî, indeed at the very beginning of the thirteenth century, that the first true arithmetician since Diophantus appeared. His name was Leonardo Fibonacci of Pisa. The great cities of northern Italy had now become important and active centers of commerce. And his first book, written in 1202, called *Liber Abaci*, was accordingly devoted to calculation and those same aspects of the subject which we ourselves now commonly mean when we use the word arithmetic. His other three books, principally his *Liber Quadratorium* and *Flos*, written a quarter of a century later, deal with those rich aspects of arithmetic in the transcendent sense in which the Greeks used the word *arithmos*.

Printing was invented in the fifteenth century, but its full effect on mathematics was not felt at first. In the sixteenth century several German writers—Adam Riese, Jokob Ködel, Michael Stifel, and Christoff Rudolf —and the Dutch mathematicians Gemma Frisius and Simon Stevin (whose book in 1585 was the first to treat decimal fractions) and the English mathematician Robert Recorde, all published books on computation and reckoning. Recorde was the first English mathematician to write in English. His book was published in London in 1557 with the flamboyant title, *The Whetstone of Witte*. In this book the equality sign appears in print for the first time. The work of the sixteenth century dealt primarily with the arithmetic of the market place. The work of Diophantus was translated into Latin and printed in 1575; ten years later Simon Stevin gave a Dutch translation, the first in a modern language.

The seventeenth century witnessed a renaissance of both the physical and mathematical sciences. It was a great age of scientific learning, very similar in this respect to the one in which we now live. Galileo, Napier, Descartes, Newton, Leibniz, and others helped change the course of history. Insofar as arithmetic is concerned, however, only one of these scientists was an arithmetician in the true sense. He was Pierre de Fermat (*c.* 1608-1665), an obscure French lawyer and office-holder in Toulouse, France, who started doing mathematics as an avocation after coming across a French translation of the works of Diophantus, which had appeared in 1621. As he found respite from the work by which he earned his living, he devoted himself to mathematical studies, primarily arithmetical ones, and corresponded constantly with distinguished scholars of his day. He never published anything and left only his letters and some miscellaneous notes. But this heritage was as significantly great as the one that Diophantus had left to him.

1.7 Inadequacy of Such Historical Accounts

In the preceding paragraphs we have briefly reviewed the history of arithmetic from ancient times through the seventeenth century. An adequate historical account of the development of mathematics, as of any science, should in fact be distinguished by being considerably more than a recitation of names, dates, and events. The important things in mathematics are ideas and concepts, and any true history of the subject deals with their origin and development, as well as with the methodology and techniques by which these ideas were realized. Clearly, such a history requires on the part of any student of the subject not only a dedication to historical accuracy, which is to be obtained primarily from the study of original materials, but also a particularly broad and precise knowledge of mathematics.

There is also a pre-historical development of mathematics. The origin of primitive concepts and the desperately slow realization of them can only be conjectured. Who first conceived these ideas, and how in turn the originators won other people to the adoption of their ideas and the use of their methods, must be forever unkown. As remarkable as these labored and persistent efforts at learning, has been the transmission of the results of this learning from one generation to the next. Neither this transmission nor the growth of knowledge has been a continuous and ever-increasing thing. Indeed, as has often been observed, the difficulties that the race encountered are experienced once again by the individual.

We turn now to some very primitive notions and see how we achieve an understanding and appreciative use of them.

1.8   The Notion of Counting and Its Representations

The most primitive of purely mathematical ideas is that of counting. To "count" the elements in any given set of discrete objects is to tally these off one-for-one against the elements of some particular standard set. When primitive man caught some fish, he counted his catch in a one-for-one tally against the fingers of his hands. Subsequently when he hit upon the idea of stringing beads on a string, he paired off the elements of any set of objects he wished to tally in one-to-one correspondence with the beads on the string. With increasing ability at abstraction, he made scratches in the sand, notches on sticks of wood, wedge-shaped cuts on clay tablets, or written marks on papyrus leaves.

Eventually he made the important mathematical abstraction that the counting process is independent of the concrete objects he either counts or counts with. The number concept is completely independent of the fish or the beads or the tablet scratches or the papyrus marks.

As man came to understand this abstraction he gradually abandoned concrete objects of reference against which to count—the fingers, the pebbles, the scratches—and he replaced them by an ordered set of objects of the imagination, which we call the *natural numbers*. These constructs of the mind were probably oral at first (such as the words "one," "two," ...) and later were written as symbols "|", "||", ... In some cases these written marks were devised in analogy with the fingers or even the whole hand like the Roman V, which probably originated from the appearance of the thumb and the four closed fingers. The tally mark || for two objects is also written $=$. Written hastily, the latter becomes Z. Likewise the tally ||| or $\equiv$ became $\exists$ or Υ. The latter is the symbol used in the Arabic countries today. Notice that when turned sidewise it strikingly resembles the symbol for "three" that we ourselves employ.

The Babylonians used simple wedges and quasi-circular symbols like our capitals O (for ten) and D (for sixty) with assorted arrangements of these: a vertical wedge with a horizontal wedge touching it on the right or a D with an intersecting O on the right represented 600. The Egyptians used a notation of specially shaped marks and elaborate drawings of men, birds, and animals that were eventually simplified, for everyday purposes, into an easily drawn script called hieratics. Later the Greeks used the alphabet α, β, ..., Γ, Δ, ..., for their number symbols, with slight modifications and conjunctions of letters. Subsequently the Romans did the same thing, employing for example I, ..., V, ..., X, ..., L, ..., C, ..., M, ... In the Orient, as in the West, the early peoples divised number symbols and many of these persist. Subsequently, in the Western Hemisphere the Mayas of Yucatan, for example, used both a simple dot and dash notation for everyday purposes and a more elaborate system of hieroglyphics for ceremonial purposes.

The particular details of these systems and of their manipulation need not concern us here. These are matters for the specialist who is engaged in the interpretation of an ancient culture.

The only system worthy of our attention now is the one that is universally employed today by everyone except for the few scattered primitive peoples whom civilization has not yet reached. It was devised by the Hindus and was learned from them by the Arabs, who taught it to the Western world.

Some scholars of antiquity have argued that the source of the Indian system is Babylonia or possibly Egypt or even China, but others of equal authority have claimed that the arithmetical ideas and methods were native to India. Probably we shall never really know which is true, especially since writing was not introduced in India until the fourth century B.C. and only oral traditions are available for earlier times.

The number symbols of India were learned by the Arabs, although just how or when has always remained a moot point among historians of the subject. Probably the most reliable and certainly the most attractive statement of the matter is the following by D. E. Smith and L. C. Karpinski in their book *The Hindu–Arabic Numerals:*

> It was in 622 A.D. that Mohammed fled from Mecca, and within a century from that time the crescent had replaced the cross in Christian Asia, in Northern Africa, and in a goodly portion of Spain. The Arab empire was an ellipse of learning with its foci at Bagdad and Cordova, and its rulers not infrequently took pride in demanding intellectual rather than commercial treasure as the result of conquest.
>
> It was under these influences, either pre-Mohammedan or later, that the Hindu numerals found their way to the North. If they were known before Mohammed's time, the proof of this fact is now lost. This much, however, is known, that in the eighth century they were taken to Bagdad. It was early in that century that the Mohammedans obtained the first foothold in northern India, thus foreshadowing an epoch of supremacy that endured with varied fortunes until after the golden age of Akbar the Great (1542–1605) and Shah Jehan. They also conquered Khorassan and Afghanistan, so that learning and the commercial customs of India at once found easy access to the newly

established schools and the bazaars of Mesopotamia and western Asia
. . . .

The Hindu–Arabic symbols 1, 2, 3, 4, 5, 6, 7, 8, 9, and 0 are the ones
we use today. Their particular form developed slowly, but by the middle
of the fourteenth century they had assumed an appearance that we would
easily recognize today.

The great German mathematician C. F. Gauss (1777–1855), one of
the very few men who ever possessed a universal knowledge of science
and who was, among other things, perhaps the greatest arithmetician
of all time, once remarked that in mathematics it "is not notations, but
notions which matter." So it is with the Hindu–Arabic numerals. As
symbols, they have important advantages in that they are distinct from
the alphabet and from each other, and are easily written and recognized.
But what really matters in the Hindu–Arabic system are the concepts
that underlie the use of the numerals. It is to this that we now turn our
attention in this chapter and thereby begin our study of arithmetical
concepts.

1.9 The Number Base

The Hindu–Arabic system employs the base ten. That is to say, the
counting is done in whole periods of ten, just as we do when we tally
on the digits of our hands, counting up to ten and then necessarily starting
over again. Ten is a base of a convenient size, neither too large nor too
small for the successful realization of the other important advantages
inherent in the Hindu–Arabic number system of which we shall subsequently speak.

Bases other than ten were used at various times and places. In earliest
times people counted in twos or threes. Some of the primitive tribes that
exist in the world today still do so. Thus, the African pygmies count
with sounds which we may transcribe as "a," "oa," "ua," "oa–oa,"
"oa–oa–a," "oa–oa–oa," . . . . The number count of many primitives
amounted only to the equivalents of "one," "two," "heap!" This sense
of a "heap" for three or more objects still persists in our language even
today. Thus, the English word "thrice" was used to mean "fully" or
"very much." Probably the base two was the first base used by most
people. But gradually other number bases evolved.

Having ten fingers, some men counted in tens as did the Egyptians,
the Greeks, and the Romans. Others, such as the Mayas and Aztecs,

counted in twenties, probably originally because of the availability of tallying with toes as well as fingers. The early English counted in twenties, and the Anglo-Saxon word "skar" means "scratch" or "tally." It also became the word for twenty, and today we have the etymological equivalents in our own language in the words "scar" and "score." In addition to counting in twenties, the Anglo-Saxons also employed the base twelve. Today we count twelve inches in a foot of length, and a dozen is the "unit of trade" in many commodities at the grocery or the bakery. The origin of the use of twelve has no apparently straghtforward explanation such as the bases ten or twenty do.

Another base of importance whose original choice is hard to fathom is the base sixty, which was employed by many early peoples. This base, for example, appears to have been introduced in China as early as 2700 B.C. It was the base that the Babylonians and Sumerians used. As we have said earlier, our division of an hour into 60 minutes and of a minute into 60 seconds is a result of the influence of this Sumerian base, which has been handed down to us through Greek and Roman culture.

Our choice of the division of the circle into 360 parts or degrees comes from the Sumerian partition of the circle into 6 times 60 parts, in which 60 is the base and the multiple 6 is used because it is an unusual number. The divisors of six that are smaller than 6 itself are 1, 2, and 3. It is a surprising fact that the sum of these divisors, $1 + 2 + 3$, is six. Such numbers are called "perfect," from an early and somewhat artificial use of the adjective. And one might ask whether there are any other perfect numbers. The next two perfect numbers are 28 and 496. We know a general theorem, found in Euclid, regarding the existence of perfect numbers. All such numbers that we know are even, and every even perfect number is of the form given by Euclid's formula, but we have as yet no idea whether any odd number can ever be perfect.

The Sumerian choice of the partition of the circle into 360 degrees is reflected in another way in our everyday life. In Euclidean plane geometry, if we are given any triangle we can circumscribe a circle about it so that the vertices of the triangle lie on the circumference. A theorem of Euclidean geometry states that each angle of such a triangle is measured by half the circular arc which it intercepts. Hence, the sum of the three angles of any plane triangle in this geometry is half of 360 degrees or 180 degrees. If we had divided a circle into, say, a thousand parts, then we would quote the sum of the angles of a Euclidean triangle to be five hundred of those parts.

1. Cite an example from literature where the word "thrice" is used in the sense of "very much" or "fully."

2. Using the quoted result regarding the measurement of the angles of a triangle inscribed in a circle, conclude that if one side of the triangle is a diameter of the circle, then the triangle is a right-angle triangle with that side as hypotenuse.

3. A prime number is one whose only divisors are itself and unity. Let p be any of the primes 2, 3, 5, and 7, and understand 2^p to be the product of p twos. Compute the four Euclid numbers $2^{p-1}(2^p - 1)$ corresponding to these four primes. Show that they are all perfect numbers. (Not every number given by this formula is a perfect number; when $p = 11$, for example, the number is not perfect, but the number for $p = 13$ is perfect. However, Euler proved that every even perfect number is of the form given by Euclid's formula.)

4. We shall see that if we are to employ the full advantages of the Hindu–Arabic number system with any integer N as the base, we need to employ $(N - 1)$ distinct symbols and a zero. Construct for the base ten the necessary number of symbols, avoiding the use of either known symbols or the alphabet. Discuss the relative advantages and disadvantages of your symbolism.

5. What are the disadvantages in symbolism, both oral and written, which occur for bases such as "twenty" or "sixty?"

1.10   The Two Fundamental Concepts of Zero and Place Value

The Hindu–Arabic system has a base of convenient size and one that has other divisors besides itself and unity, namely 2 and 5, a fact which facilitates the doing of certain parts of arithmetic. However, so does the base twelve. It is not the decimal base that primarily distinguishes the Hindu–Arabic system.

What really is fundamentally important in the Hindu–Arabic system is the full employment of the two fundamental concepts of zero and of place value. In its full realization, the latter depends on the zero concept. The race had a very difficult time with the notion of zero, that is to say with the idea of a set of elements which is "empty," entirely devoid of elements. Zero plays a strange role. It does not appear necessary for counting, and yet it is vital for the full exploitation of a successful system of reckoning.

Insofar as is known, the zero symbol first appeared in the ninth century A.D. The earliest use of zero in Indian arithmetic of which we have direct knowledge is 876 A.D., and an Arab manuscript of 873 A.D. also employs a symbol for zero. The Arabic word for the symbol was "as-sifr" and from it we derive our word "cipher" and the contraction "zero." Since the idea of zero is so abstract, the notion of zero and its employment were not readily adopted. Nevertheless, by the thirteenth century the zero symbol was being employed not only in the Western world, but in the Orient as well, where Chinese scholars made full use of it and of the notion of place value. This usage was one of the consequences of the lively exchange of merchandise and ideas by such travelers and traders as Genghis Khan (*c.* 1220) and Marco Polo (*c.* 1271).

1.11 Place Value

Given a convenient base, a symbol for zero, and a set of distinct, easily made, easily recognized, and readily distinguishable symbols such as we have in the Hindu–Arabic system, we can make full and efficient use of the notion of place value.

This notion may be used with any base that we employ. For convenience, let us refer to our base ten. We have the nine distinct symbols 1, 2, 3, 4, 5, 6, 7, 8, and 9, together with a zero symbol. We need no other symbols, for we write the number ten as 10, using the place on the right for units and the place on the left for tens. The next place on the left is for hundreds, the place to the left of that for thousands, and so on. Thus 7582 means 2 units, 8 tens, 5 ten-squared or hundreds, and 7 ten-cubeds or thousands. It is a very elegant idea.

We write the digits from right to left because that was the early way of writing, but we read them in order of magnitude from left to right because we ourselves customarily read in that order.

There was nothing resembling the notion of place value in Indian arithmetic until the sixth century A.D. Even then it was a place value of number words like our "tens," "hundreds," thousands," "millions," ..., and not of number symbols. There was no zero symbol at that time. This place-value wording was a clumsy system not much better than the one which earlier peoples labored under. But the use of words once again gave the hint of the idea for adaptation to symbols, and eventually Sanskrit symbols were invented for identification with the Sanskrit words.

In order to appreciate this idea of place value, think of the process of "carrying" which the child learns to do and which is also done by the mileage gauge on an automobile or the wheels on a desk calculator. For example, on the mileage indicator we have a series of mechanically interconnected disks, and each disk has inscribed on it only the ten symbols 0, 1, 2, ..., 9. Suppose your mileage indicator reads 03758. You drive another mile and it reads 03759. A mile after that, the last disk on the right has only 0 to turn to. It does so, and at the same time carries through the interlocking mechanism to the "tens" disk and changes the reading to 03760. Thirty-nine miles later the reading is 03799. Now the addition of another mile must turn the "units" disk on the far right to 0; carry one to the "tens" disk, giving a 0 there; and then turn the "hundreds" disk by one unit, giving 03800. One hundred ninety-nine miles later the reading is 03999. With the long cultivated interest and habit of counting in periods of ten, we watch the dials with a special interest as a new "record" is set. Once again the addition of a unit changes that disk to 0, a "ten" is carried to the next disk, a "hundred" is carried to the next, and "thousand" to the fourth disk from the right, to yield 04000. We take extremely good care of this remarkable car and eventually the mileage indicator reads 99999 as we start out one fine morning. Then shortly— but perhaps it is time to trade this car in for a new model.

The small child who is learning his "numbers" has no such convenient device at hand and he is faced with the addition problem

$$27$$
$$\underline{36}$$

He learns that he must first add the units, "6 plus 7." He could add 1 to 6 on his fingers, then add another 1, and so on, in mimicry of the dial on the car; but he is expected to be more than an automaton. By some magic his mind gives the answer "13." The idea that he must now learn to master is that of the proper utilization of the place-value concept by "carrying" the 1 in 13 to the tens place. At first he may get in the habit of reminding himself of this by writing

$$1$$
$$27$$
$$\underline{36}$$
$$3$$

and then, with that wonderful exhilaration of youth and excitement for all that is new, he adds the tens, 3 plus 2 plus 1, and writes his answer of 63.

Before long, he finds, to his exasperation, that to get "full marks" he must be able to do something a little more difficult, such as performing the addition

$$
\begin{array}{r}
976 \\
508 \\
765 \\
857 \\
\hline
\end{array}
$$

He adds the "units column," getting 26. He writes 6 in the units place on the far right and carries 2—that is, of course, 2 tens. He adds 2, 5, 6, 0, and 7, getting 20— that is 20 tens. He puts zero in the tens column and again carries 2, but this time 2 hundreds, to the third column, getting 2 plus 8 plus 7 plus 5 plus 9 with the sum 31. This is 31 hundreds. He puts 1 in the hundreds column and "carries" a 3 to the thousands column. And his final answer to the problem is 3106—that is, 3 thousands, 1 hundred, no tens, and 6 units.

But something more than this soon faces our young scholar. He must learn a multiplication table and acquire the facility of keeping this in his head along with the notion of carrying. Our young friend learns the multiplication table up to ten times ten and then, to exhibit a certain kind of erudition, up to twelve times twelve; but he soon realizes that all he really needs to know to do any multiplication is the table up to nine times nine and the fact that zero times any number is again zero. In later years he may turn to consideration of the effect of unity in multiplication and of zero in addition; but now he is expected to exhibit his ability by performing the following multiplication problem

$$
\begin{array}{r}
376 \\
297 \\
\hline
\end{array}
$$

He chooses 297 as the multiplier, although this is clearly some kind of convention that he has picked up by observing someone else at work. First he multiplies 376 by the 7 units and does the necessary carrying to obtain

$$2632$$

and he writes

$$
\begin{array}{r}
376 \\
297 \\
\hline
2632
\end{array}
$$

Then to multiply by the 9 tens he shifts one place to the left for tens and writes the product of 9 times 376, namely 3384, since the actual product is 90 times 376 or 33840

$$
\begin{array}{r}
376 \\
297 \\
\hline
2632 \\
3384
\end{array}
$$

Now he multiplies 376 by 2 hundreds and shifts once more, this time to the hundreds place, since he really has 200 times 376 or 75200

$$
\begin{array}{r}
376 \\
297 \\
\hline
2632 \\
3384 \\
752
\end{array}
$$

He is now finished with the job of actually multiplying and he has only to add up the results of the operations of multiplying and shifting. In doing the final addition he continues to keep track of place-value effects

$$
\begin{array}{r}
376 \\
297 \\
\hline
2632 \\
3384 \\
752 \\
\hline
111672
\end{array}
$$

As another example, let us illustrate the notion of place value with the two numbers 73528 and 27895 with the operations of addition, subtraction, and multiplication. Knowing the addition tables of $1 + 1$

through 9 + 9 and the fact that 0 plus any number is again that number, to add

$$
\begin{array}{r}
73528 \\
27895 \\
\hline
101423
\end{array}
$$

all we have to do is to keep the respective columns straight, adding in turns the units, writing 3 and carrying a ten, adding this ten to the 2 and 9 that are in the tens place, writing 2, carrying a hundred, adding this 1 to the 5 and 8 in the hundreds place, and so on.

Subtraction is the same story, where we merely have to borrow one from a higher place when necessary

$$
\begin{array}{r}
73528 \\
27895 \\
\hline
45633
\end{array}
$$

proceeding in a way that is marvelously simple, almost machine-like, but employing a notion that is not intuitive and that the race found difficult to achieve.

We leave it to the reader to recognize explicitly the employment of the place-value concept and the associated process of carrying in each step of the following multiplication

$$
\begin{array}{r}
73528 \\
27895 \\
\hline
367640 \\
661752 \\
588224 \\
514696 \\
147056 \\
\hline
2051063560
\end{array}
$$

The process of division employs the place-value concept and points up its use and importance. It is, however, the most difficult of the four operations of arithmetic, both for the boy in school and for the modern high-speed computer. We leave aside the matter of division for the moment and return to it after we have given a discussion of the uses of number bases other than ten.

EXERCISES

The employment of place value occurs in every arithmetical problem, but as the basis for general discussion cite its use in the addition, subtraction, and multiplication of the two numbers A and B where

1. $A = 3572$ and $B = 685$

2. $A = 1436$ and $B = 999$

3. $A = 8412$ and $B = 7512$

4. In Exercise 2, can you devise any shortcut?

1.12 The Abacus

The abacus is a device that employs a set of movable beads on a series of parallel wires. It was the first mechanical counting machine to be invented. It has been widely used, in one form or another, over many parts of the world for several centuries, and it is still in everyday use in the Orient by people in all walks of life. The modern Chinese abacus has been in continuous use since the twelfth century A.D., and the modern Japanese abacus, which differs somewhat in design from the Chinese, has been used since the sixteenth century.

The word "abacus" comes from the Greek word "abax." A very early device for counting involved fine sand spread on a flat surface (the "abax") in which number marks were made with a stylus. In Latin, a stylus is called a "talea" or "slender stick," and from it we get our word "tally." From such a tray of sand, like the abacus itself, mistakes can easily be erased, and the possibility of easy erasure of slips is essential, even in modern electronic computers.

The Japanese and Chinese use their abaci with great facility because they in fact learn their addition and multiplication tables in school as rules in the form of operations on the abacus. The schoolboy's question of "What do I do now?" means "Which bead do I move next?"

Both the Chinese and the Japanese abaci utilize the base ten. Parallel strings are fastened within a rigid rectangular framework with a partition across it that separates each string into a lower and a smaller upper section. On the lower section of each string there are four beads. Each bead represents a unit of its string value. In the Japanese abacus there is only one bead per string in the upper section, but in the Chinese abacus there are two, and in both cases each bead in the upper section is worth five beads on the lower section of the same string. The parallel strings represent in order, from right to left, the units, the tens, the hundreds, and so on. The operator tallies by moving the beads from a reserve position to another position on the string and by "carrying" from one string to the next using the notion of place value.

It is not difficult to construct a simple abacus, and the notion of place value is brought out by its use. On the other hand, it is difficult to learn to use the instrument with real facility, a fact which has a counterpart in the learning of a foreign language in adulthood, and which also parallels the small boy's difficulty in learning arithmetical ideas in school.

1.13   Addition, Subtraction, and Multiplication in Base Two

If one wishes to appreciate more fully the place-value concept, he has only to reckon in a base other than the familiar one of ten. We shall consider several different bases beginning with base two.

The base two is often called the "binary base." It is a primitive base, but it is not trivial. It plays a significant role in certain kinds of algebra. It is the base that is used in a majority of modern electronic computers; one feeds the machine his problem in base ten, the machine translates it to base two, does the necessary reckoning in that base, translates its base two results into base ten answers, and reports these back to the operator.

In the base two we need only two symbols, 1 and 0. This simple duality is one reason for the importance of using base two in electronic computers; an electrical switch that is open or a vacuum tube that is off can stand for 0, but when the switch is closed or the tube is on, the number 1 is represented.

Instead of the places for units, tens, hundreds in the base ten, our places are now for units, twos, "two-squareds" or fours, "two-cubeds" or eights, and so on. A unit of 1 is, of course, the zeroth power of 2.

The following table will help clarify the situation.

Number in base ten	Equivalent number expressed in base two
1	1 = one unit
2	10 = one "two" and no units (1 + 1 = 10)
3	11 = one "two" and one unit (10 + 1 = 11)
4	100 = one "four", no "two", no unit (11 + 1 = 100)
5	101 = one "four", no "two", one unit
6	110 = one "four", one "two", no unit
7	111 = one "four", one "two", one unit
8	1000 = one "eight", no "four", no "two", no unit
9	1001 ⎫
10	1010 ⎬ For these the reader may find it helpful to use the
11	1011 ⎱ foregoing language.
12	1100 ⎭

The addition and multiplication tables are simple. All one has to know is that

$$1 \times 1 = 1$$

and the two essential roles of 0 and 1, namely

$$1 + 0 = 0 + 1 = 1 \qquad 1 \times 0 = 0 \times 1 = 0$$

Given the expression for "eleven" in the base two, let us find the expression for "twelve." We are faced with the necessity of adding 1 to 1011

```
1  0  1  1
         1
_____
         0   and 1 to carry into the twos column
```

```
1  0  1  1
      1
_____
      0  0   and 1 to carry into the fours column
```

```
1  0  1  1
   1
_____
1  1  0  0   which is the answer: one "eight" and
             one "four"
```

As another example, add "seven," "ten," "eleven," and "twelve." In

the base ten the answer is 40. The sum in the binary base is found as
follows

```
        1  1  1
     1  0  1  0
     1  0  1  1
     1  1  0  0
   ─────────────
              0
```
and one "two" to carry into the twos
column

```
           (1)
        1  1  1
     1  0  1  0
     1  0  1  1
     1  1  0  0
   ─────────────
           0
```
getting 100, leaving a zero, and carry-
ing 0 to the fours column and 1 to the
eights column

```
   (1) (0)
        1  1  1
     1  0  1  0
     1  0  1  1
     1  1  0  0
   ─────────────
        0
```
and 1 to carry into the eights column

```
   (1)
   (1)
        1  1  1
     1  0  1  0
     1  0  1  1
     1  1  0  0
   ─────────────
     1
```
getting 101, leaving a 1, and carrying
0 to the sixteens column and 1 to the
thirty-twos column

```
   (1) (0)
        1  1  1
     1  0  1  0
     1  0  1  1
     1  1  0  0
   ─────────────
   1  0  1  0  0  0
```
(answer)

The answer 101000, reading from right to left, stands for no units, no twos, no fours, *one* eight, no sixteens, and *one* thirty-two in the base ten, and 32 plus 8, in the base ten, is our known result 40.

In the base two system, as stated previously, 1 added to 1 gives the sum 10. It follows that in the base two, 1 subtracted from 10 is 1. The following procedure shows how to subtract "five" from "ten" in the base two

$$
\begin{array}{cccc}
1 & 0 & 1 & 0 \\
  & 1 & 0 & 1 \\
\hline
\end{array}
$$

To take 1 from this 0 we borrow one "two" from the twos column

$$
\begin{array}{cccc}
1 & 0 & 0 & (10) \\
  & 1 & 0 & 1 \\
\hline
  &   &   & 1 \\
\end{array}
$$

The next step is clear

$$
\begin{array}{cccc}
1 & 0 & 0 & (10) \\
  & 1 & 0 & 1 \\
\hline
  &   & 0 & 1 \\
\end{array}
$$

And so also is the next

$$
\begin{array}{cccc}
(10) & 0 & (10) \\
     & 1 & 0 & 1 \\
\hline
     & 1 & 0 & 1 \\
\end{array}
$$

which is the answer, "five," the sum of one unit, no twos, and one four.

Consider the following problem in the base two. Newton was born in the year 11001101010 and he died in the year 11010111111. And so, clearly, he lived to be "eighty-five" years old

$$
\begin{array}{ll}
11010111111 & (1727, \text{ base } 10) \\
11001101010 & (1642, \text{ base } 10) \\
\hline
1010101 & (85, \text{ base } 10) \\
\end{array}
$$

The difference reading from right to left stands for the following sum in the base two: one unit, no twos, one four, no eights, one sixteen, no thirty-twos, and one sixty-four.

Conversion of a number in base ten to its equivalent in base two

By virtue of the meaning of place value it is straightforward to change a number in base two to its equivalent representation in base ten. Thus, for example

$$1010010$$

in base two means

$$(1 \times 2^6) + (0 + 2^5) + (1 \times 2^4) + (0 \times 2^3)$$
$$+ (0 \times 2^2) + (1 \times 2^1) + (0 \times 1)$$

or in the base ten

$$64 + 16 + 2 = 82$$

that is

$$(8 \times 10) + (2 \times 1)$$

But given 82 in the base ten, how may we convert it into the proper expression in base two? We must in fact first determine the highest power of two which it contains. Thus $2^7 = 128$ is too large, but $2^6 = 64$ is not.

$$\frac{82}{2^6} = \frac{82}{64} = 1 + \frac{18}{64}$$

In other words

$$82 = (1 \times 2^6) + 18$$

Clearly we have now to express 18 in the base two. Since $2^4 = 16$ is the largest power of two contained in 18, we have

$$18 = (1 \times 2^4) + 2$$

Hence

$$82 = (1 \times 2^6) + (1 \times 2^4) + (1 + 2^1)$$

or, in a detailed accounting for each power of two including the zeroth power of two, which is unity

$$82 = (1 \times 2^6) + (0 \times 2^5) + (1 \times 2^4)$$
$$+ (0 \times 2^3) + (0 \times 2^2) + (1 \times 2^1) + (0 \times 1)$$

In place-value notation in base two, this is our given number 1010010.

A convenient scheme for doing this is to divide 82 by 2 successively, keeping track of the remainders

	Remainder	*What power of two have we divided by at this stage?*

$$2 \,\big|\, \underline{82}$$
$$41 \qquad\qquad 0 \qquad\qquad\qquad 2^1$$

[That is, $82 = (41 \times 2) + $ a remainder of zero units]

$$2 \,\big|\, \underline{41}$$
$$20 \qquad\qquad 1 \qquad\qquad\qquad 2^2$$

[That is, $82 = (20 \times 2^2) + $ a remainder of one "two"]

$$2 \,\big|\, \underline{20}$$
$$10 \qquad\qquad 0 \qquad\qquad\qquad 2^3$$

[That is, $82 = (10 \times 2^3) + $ (a remainder of zero "fours" and of one "two" from above)]

$$2 \,\big|\, \underline{10}$$
$$5 \qquad\qquad 0 \qquad\qquad\qquad 2^4$$

[That is, $82 = (5 \times 2^4) + $ (a remainder of zero "eights" and of one "two" from above)]

$$2 \,\big|\, \underline{5}$$
$$2 \qquad\qquad 1 \qquad\qquad\qquad 2^5$$

[That is, $82 = (2 \times 2^5) + $ (a remainder of one "sixteen" and of one "two" from above)]

$$2 \,\big|\, \underline{2}$$
$$1 \qquad\qquad 0 \qquad\qquad\qquad 2^6$$

[That is, $82 = (1 \times 2^6) + $ (a remainder of zero "thirty-twos" and of one "sixteen" and of one "two" from above)]

We may summarize this in place-value notation by writing the last quotient (that is, the highest power of two that divides 82) and then following it with the remainders from the last obtained to the first one

1	0	1 0 0 1	0
(Last Quotient)	(Last Remainder)		(First Remainder)

A convenient abbreviation of the process is

$$2 \underline{|82}$$
$$2 \underline{|41} \ . \ . \ . \ . \ 0$$
$$2 \underline{|20} \ . \ . \ . \ . \ 1$$
$$2 \underline{|10} \ . \ . \ . \ . \ 0$$
$$2 \underline{|5} \ . \ . \ . \ . \ 0$$
$$2 \underline{|2} \ . \ . \ . \ . \ 1$$
$$1 \ . \ . \ . \ . \ 0$$

Let us illustrate with another example. Given the date of the discovery of America in the base ten, what is its equivalent in the base two?

$$2 \underline{|1492}$$
$$2 \underline{|746} \ . \ . \ . \ . \ 0$$
$$2 \underline{|373} \ . \ . \ . \ . \ 0$$
$$2 \underline{|186} \ . \ . \ . \ . \ 1$$
$$2 \underline{|93} \ . \ . \ . \ . \ 0$$
$$2 \underline{|46} \ . \ . \ . \ . \ 1$$
$$2 \underline{|23} \ . \ . \ . \ . \ 0$$
$$2 \underline{|11} \ . \ . \ . \ . \ 1$$
$$2 \underline{|5} \ . \ . \ . \ . \ 1$$
$$2 \underline{|2} \ . \ . \ . \ . \ 1$$
$$1 \ . \ . \ . \ . \ 0$$

Thus, in base two, Columbus discovered America in the year

$$10111010100$$

It pays to check the result. Thus, reading from right to left and writing in base ten, we have

$$4 + 16 + 64 + 128 + 256 + 1024 = 1492$$

EXERCISES

The following are numbers written in the base ten. Change each to base two and check the results.

1. 1066 (Battle of Hastings: Norman conquest of England)

2. 1076 (Capture of Jerusalem by the Turks)

3. 1095 (Crusades begun)

4. 1431 (Joan of Arc burned)

5. 1564 (Shakespeare born)

6. 1614 (Discovery of logarithms by Napier)

7. 1642 (Newton born)

8. 1707 (Euler born)

9. 1777 (Gauss born)

10. 1845 (Georg Cantor born)

Subtraction

An informative example of the role of place value is the subtraction of "seven" from "twelve"

$$
\begin{array}{cccc}
1 & 1 & 0 & 0 \\
  & 1 & 1 & 1 \\
\hline
\end{array}
$$

First one borrows from the fours place for use in the twos place

$$
\begin{array}{cccc}
1 & 0 & (10) & 0 \\
  & 1 & 1 & 1 \\
\hline
\end{array}
$$

and next from the twos place

$$
\begin{array}{r}
1 \quad 0 \quad 1 \ (10) \\
1 \quad 1 \quad 1 \\
\hline
0 \quad 1
\end{array}
$$

and next from the eights place

$$
\begin{array}{r}
(10) \ 1 \ (10) \\
1 \quad 1 \quad 1 \\
\hline
1 \quad 0 \quad 1
\end{array}
$$

and now a simple subtraction in each respective place gives the answer 101.

Now consider the following problem of subtraction

$$
\begin{array}{r}
1 \quad 0 \quad 1 \quad 0 \quad 1 \quad 0 \\
1 \quad 1 \quad 1 \quad 1 \quad 1 \\
\hline
\end{array}
$$

We may prepare this as follows

$$
\begin{array}{r}
1 \quad 0 \quad 1 \quad 0 \quad 0 \ (10) \\
1 \quad 1 \quad 1 \quad 1 \quad 1 \\
\hline
1
\end{array}
$$

$$
\begin{array}{r}
1 \quad 0 \quad 0 \ (10) \ 0 \ (10) \\
1 \quad 1 \quad 1 \quad 1 \quad 1 \\
\hline
1
\end{array}
$$

$$
\begin{array}{r}
1 \quad 0 \quad 0 \quad 1 \ (10)(10) \\
1 \quad 1 \quad 1 \quad 1 \quad 1 \\
\hline
0 \quad 1 \quad 1
\end{array}
$$

$$
\begin{array}{r}
(10) \ 0 \quad 1 \ (10)(10) \\
1 \quad 1 \quad 1 \quad 1 \quad 1 \\
\hline
0 \quad 1 \quad 1
\end{array}
$$

$$
\begin{array}{r}
1 \ (10) \ 1 \ (10)(10) \\
1 \quad 1 \quad 1 \quad 1 \quad 1 \\
\hline
1 \quad 0 \quad 1 \quad 1
\end{array}
$$

Subtraction in the respective places gives the answer 1011.

Clearly we have borrowed as necessary to obtain a 1 or a 10 in each successive place from which a 1 is to be subtracted. A little practice facilitates the doing of the work.

EXERCISES

The numbers in these exercises are expressed in base two. After performing the indicated operations check your results by changing to base ten.

Addition

1.
```
1 0 1 1
  1 0 1
```

2.
```
1 0 1 0 1 0
  1 1 0 1 1
```

3.
```
1 0 1 1 1 1
  1 1 1 1 1
```

4.
```
1 0 1 1
1 1 0 1
1 1 1 1
1 1 0
1 0 1
```

5.
```
1 1 0 1 1
1 0 1 0 1
1 1 1 1 1
1 1 0 0 1
  1 0 1 1
  1 1 1 1
```

6.
```
1 1 1 1 1
1 1 1 1 1
1 1 1 1 1
1 0 1 0 1
1 1 0 0 1
1 0 0 1 1
```

Subtraction

7.
```
1 0 1 1
  1 0 1
```

8.
```
1 1 0 1
  1 0 1
```

9.
```
1 0 0 0
    1 1
```

10.
```
1 0 1 0 1 0
  1 1 0 0 1
```

11.
```
1 1 1 0 0 0 0
    1 1 1 0 1
```

Multiplication

Multiplication is a simple matter in the base two. Only the "carrying" is apt to present any difficulty; and, once again, any trouble with this step may be attributed to mere lack of experience in using this base. Consider the following example of multiplication

$$
\begin{array}{r}
1111 \\
1011 \\
\hline
1111 \\
1111 \\
11110 \\
\hline
10100101
\end{array}
$$

Another example illustrating the carrying process in the realization of the concept of place value is the following

$$
\begin{array}{r}
1011101 \\
101101 \\
\hline
1011101 \\
10111010 \\
1011101 \\
10111010 \\
\hline
1000001011001
\end{array}
$$

1.14   Addition, Subtraction, and Multiplication in Certain Other Bases

In order to avoid confusion we shall distinguish the fact that a set of numerals is expressed in a particular base by putting them in parentheses and writing the base as a subscript on the right. We shall use T rather than 10 in this respect for the base ten. Of course this precaution against confusion often will not be necessary for the context will be clear. Thus, we write, for example

$$(2365)_T = (2 \times 10^3) + (3 \times 10^2) + (6 \times 10) + (5 \times 1)$$

$$(1011)_2 = (1 \times 2^3) + (0 \times 2^2) + (1 \times 2) + (1 \times 1)$$

$$(1021)_3 = (1 \times 3^3) + (0 \times 3^2) + (2 \times 3) + (1 \times 1)$$

In discussing the base two, we have so far ignored a problem of semantics or the use of language. We have spoken of binary numbers in terms of decimal numbers; for example, we have called the number $(100)_2$ "four," the number $(1000)_2$ "eight," and the number $(10000)_2$ "sixteen." The semantic difficulty is apparent in the use of the term "sixteen" for the number $(10000)_2$, since the "teen" obviously refers to the base ten numeration. If we were to adopt the base two for everyday use, we should properly revise the names of our arithmetical symbols. This, of course, becomes all the more apparent when we discuss numbers in other bases as well. However, nothing would be gained for our present purposes in the use of some *ad hoc* terminology, and so we shall continue to ignore here this otherwise important problem of language.

In a strict sense we should also adopt number symbols different from our familiar base-ten symbols for use with other bases. Clearly this is not essential provided that the base is smaller than ten. When the base is larger than ten, such as twelve or twenty or sixty, and we continue to use the place-value concept, we are forced to invent additional symbols which preferably have the easy legibility and distinctive individuality that characterize the Hindu–Arabic symbols. This is a very difficult thing to achieve.

In the following paragraphs, we shall discuss rather briefly some other bases that are smaller than ten.

Base three

Clearly, one of the disadvantages of the base two is that a number which has only a relatively few places in its base-ten representation becomes a series of ones and zeros in the base two. These ones and zeros are hard to keep track of and the ready identification of numbers is difficult.

The situation with base three is similar in this regard. In base three, we employ the symbols 1, 2, and 0, and use the places in a digit of several units to represent, respectively, writing from right to left: 1, 3^1, 3^2, 3^3, 3^4, and so on. Thus, we have, for example

Number in base ten	1	2	3	4	5	6	7	8	9	10
Number in base three	1	2	10	11	12	20	21	22	100	101

A number in base three is readily converted to base ten. Thus

$$(12102)_3 = [(1 \times 3^4) + (2 \times 3^3) + (1 \times 3^2) + (0 \times 3^1) + (2 \times 1)]_T$$
$$= [81 + 18 + 9 + 2]_T = (110)_T$$

The change in the expression of a number in base ten to its equivalent in base three is obtained by the same process used in the case of base two and with the corresponding justifications. For example, we change $(1776)_T$ into base three as follows

$$3\,\underline{|\,1776}$$
$$3\,\underline{|\,592} \,\ldots\, 0$$
$$3\,\underline{|\,197} \,\ldots\, 1$$
$$3\,\underline{|\,65} \,\ldots\, 2$$
$$3\,\underline{|\,21} \,\ldots\, 2$$
$$3\,\underline{|\,7} \,\ldots\, 0$$
$$2 \,\ldots\, 1$$

and thus find that

$$(1776)_T = (2102210)_3$$

a result which we verify by

$$(2102210)_3 = [(2 \times 729) + (1 \times 243) + (0 \times 81)$$
$$+ (2 \times 27) + (2 \times 9) + (1 \times 3) + (0 \times 1)]_T$$

EXERCISES

The following numbers are written in base ten. Express them in base three and verify your results

1. 6561   2. 6588   3. 1492

4. 1900   5. 186,000   6. 240,000

For computation in base three, we employ the following addition and multiplication tables, which are extended beyond the actually necessary information for convenience in use.

ADDITION TABLE, BASE THREE

+	0	1	2	10
0	0	1	2	10
1	1	2	10	11
2	2	10	11	12
10	10	11	12	20

MULTIPLICATION TABLE, BASE THREE

×	0	1	2	10
0	0	0	0	0
1	0	1	2	10
2	0	2	11	20
10	0	10	20	100

Let us exhibit an addition problem in base three which will again illustrate the place value concept and the process of "carrying." We add $(210121)_3$ and $(222222)_3$

$$
\begin{array}{ccccccc}
(1)&(1)&(1)&(1)&(1)& & \\
2&1&0&1&2&1 \\
2&2&2&2&2&2 \\
\hline
1&2&1&0&1&2&0
\end{array}
$$

A simple example in subtraction is $(210)_3$ *minus* $(121)_3$

$$
\begin{array}{ccc}
2&1&0 \\
1&2&1 \\
\hline
&1&2
\end{array}
$$

Here it has first been necessary to borrow a three from the threes place in 210 for use as three "ones" in the units column

$$
\begin{array}{ccc}
2&0&(10) \\
1&2&1 \\
\hline
& &2
\end{array}
$$

and then a nine from the 2 in the nines column for use as three "threes" in the threes column

$$
\begin{array}{ccc}
1 & (10) & (10) \\
1 & 2 & 1 \\
\hline
 & 1 & 2
\end{array}
$$

Another example in subtraction is $(21011)_3$ *minus* $(2222)_3$

$$
\begin{array}{ccccc}
2 & 1 & 0 & 1 & 1 \\
 & 2 & 2 & 2 & 2 \\
\hline
\end{array}
$$

We may proceed with the "borrowing" as follows

$$
\begin{array}{ccccc}
2 & 1 & 0 & 0 & (11) \\
 & 2 & 2 & 2 & 2 \\
\hline
 & & & & 2
\end{array}
$$

and next

$$
\begin{array}{ccccc}
2 & 0 & (10) & 0 & (11) \\
 & 2 & 2 & 2 & 2 \\
\hline
 & & & & 2
\end{array}
$$

and next

$$
\begin{array}{ccccc}
2 & 0 & 2 & (10) & (11) \\
 & 2 & 2 & 2 & 2 \\
\hline
 & & 0 & 1 & 2
\end{array}
$$

and finally

$$
\begin{array}{ccccc}
1 & (10) & 2 & (10) & (11) \\
 & 2 & 2 & 2 & 2 \\
\hline
1 & 1 & 0 & 1 & 2
\end{array}
$$

Multiplication is illustrated by the following example

$$
\begin{array}{cccc}
 & 2 & 1 & 2 \\
 & & & 2 \\
\hline
1 & 2 & 0 & 1
\end{array}
$$

since, from right to left, $2 \times 2 = 11$, that is 1 unit and 1 to carry, and $2 \times 1 = 2$, which, with the carried 1, is 10, leaving 0 and 1 to carry, which, with $2 \times 2 = 11$, leaves 12.

Next consider the product

```
              2  1  2
              2  0  2
           1  2  0  1
        1  2  0  1  0
        ─────────────
        1  2  2  0  0  1
```

or the product

```
              2  1  2  2
              1  2  1  2
           ───────────────
           1  2  0  2  1
           2  1  2  2
        1  2  0  2  1
        2  1  2  2
     ──────────────────────
     1  1  2  1  2  1  1  1
```

To appreciate fully the processes involved, and to do the reckoning with proper dispatch, one should carefully avoid any intermediate translations back to the base ten. This can be avoided only by memorizing the base three addition and multiplication tables.

One way in which to appreciate this need is by transforming a number written in base three directly into its base two representation without going through the base ten. We shall illustrate this, but first remind the reader that in base three

$$\frac{10}{2} = 1 + \frac{1}{2}, \qquad \frac{11}{2} = 2, \qquad \frac{12}{2} = 2 + \frac{1}{2}$$

Now consider the problem of expressing $(2121)_3$ directly in the base two

```
2 | 2121
2 | 1022 . . . . 0
2 | 122 . . . . 1
2 | 22 . . . . 1
2 | 11 . . . . 0
2 | 2 . . . . 0
    1 . . . . 0
```

The answer is therefore

$$(2121)_3 = (1000110)_2$$

EXERCISES

Add the following numbers which are in base three

1. 2 2 2
    2 2 1
    ———

2. 2 1 1 1
    2 2 2 1
    ———

3. 2 2 2 1 0
    2 1 2 0 1
    2 0 1 2 2
    1 2 2 1 2
    ———

4. 2 2 2 2 2 2
    2 1 1 1 1 1
    2 0 1 0 2 1
    1 2 2 2 1 0
    1 1 1 0 1 2
    ———

Subtract the following numbers in base three

5. 2 0 2 1
    1 2 1 2
    ———

6. 2 2 0 1 2 1
    1 2 2 2 1 2
    ———

7. 2 1 1 0 1 1
      2 2 1 2 2
    ———

8. 1 0 0 0 0 0
      2 1 1 0 1
    ———

Multiply the following numbers in base three

9. 2 1 2 2
      1 2 2
    ———

10. 2 0 1 2 1
      2 1 2 2
    ———

11. 2 2 2 1 2
    2 1 2 1 2
    ———

12. 2 2 1 2 0 1 1
      2 2 2 1 1 2
    ———

Express the following in base three

13. $(101101)_2$

14. The square of $(1011)_2$

15. Construct the addition table for base four.

16. Construct the multiplication table for base four.

Base five

Since there are five digits on one hand, it would have been as natural to select five as a base as it was to choose ten.

We shall present only the addition and multiplication tables for base five and then cite some exercises, which the reader may wish to consider, in the same spirit as our previous ones.

The digits to be used in base five are 0, 1, 2, 3, and 4. "Five" is written 10. As we have done before, we extend the addition and multiplication tables to include 0 and 10 merely for easy reference by the reader.

ADDITION TABLE, BASE FIVE

+	0	1	2	3	4	10
0	0	1	2	3	4	10
1	1	2	3	4	10	11
2	2	3	4	10	11	12
3	3	4	10	11	12	13
4	4	10	11	12	13	14
10	10	11	12	13	14	20

MULTIPLICATION TABLE, BASE FIVE

×	0	1	2	3	4	10
0	0	0	0	0	0	0
1	0	1	2	3	4	10
2	0	2	4	11	13	20
3	0	3	11	14	22	30
4	0	4	13	22	31	40
10	0	10	20	30	40	100

Merely checking these tables in various ways will prove instructive.

EXERCISES

Add the following numbers which are represented in base five

1. 3 1 4
   2 4 1

2. 1 4 2 3 4
   3 4 1 2 0
   1 1 2 3 4

Subtract the following numbers which are represented in base five

3. 4 1 3 2 1
   2 3 4 2

4. 2 4 4 3 2 1
   1 3 4 4 3 2

Multiply the following numbers which are represented in base five

5. 4 1 2
    2 3
   ―――

6. 2 4 3 1
     4 3 2
    ――――

7. Change $(41243)_5$ into its equivalent in base ten.

8. Change $(89327)_T$ into its equivalent in base five.

9. Without employing the base ten change $(21342)_5$ into its equivalent in base two.

10. Express $(21342)_5$ in base three.

Some other bases

Since six attracted so much attention among early peoples and because of its intrinsic interest, six might have been a very likely candidate for the base of a number system. The digits would be 0, 1, 2, 3, 4 and 5. The following would be the addition and multiplication tables, extended to exhibit entries for 0 and 10.

ADDITION TABLE, BASE SIX

+	0	1	2	3	4	5	10
0	0	1	2	3	4	5	10
1	1	2	3	4	5	10	11
2	2	3	4	5	10	11	12
3	3	4	5	10	11	12	13
4	4	5	10	11	12	13	14
5	5	10	11	12	13	14	15
10	10	11	12	13	14	15	20

MULTIPLICATION TABLE, BASE SIX

×	0	1	2	3	4	5	10
0	0	0	0	0	0	0	0
1	0	1	2	3	4	5	10
2	0	2	4	10	12	14	20
3	0	3	10	13	20	23	30
4	0	4	12	20	24	32	40
5	0	5	14	23	32	41	50
10	0	10	20	30	40	50	100

The number seven has attracted special interest from earliest times, perhaps because it is the number following six. The number seven has no special intrinsic interest. In fact, either six or eight would make a more suitable base than seven in the following sense. It turns out in fractional representations that the more divisors a base has, the more convenient the representation.

The old Anglo-Saxon base of twelve has some advantages over ten. Since we do use the base ten, it is regrettable that twelve creeps into so many of the common measures that we employ. If the base were twelve and our units of linear measure remained the same, we would have 100 square inches to the square foot and 1000 cubic inches to the cubic foot.

On the other hand, the base twenty, used by so many early people, has the disadvantage of requiring nineteen distinct symbols and a zero, and it is essential for its completely satisfactory use to remember the multiplication from "one times one" to "nineteen times nineteen," involving combinations for all these nineteen different symbols. The reader will find it instructive to compare these difficulties with those that are involved in addition.

Clearly, the base sixty is even worse in this regard. Whereas the base two is too small, in the sense of requiring so many ones and zeros to represent a number of some size, the base sixty is too large.

EXERCISES

1. Represent the base ten numbers one through twenty in every base that we have mentioned in this chapter.

2. Construct the addition and multiplication tables for bases four, seven, eight, and twelve. In the latter, use $*$ for "eleven" and read it "star," and use $†$ for "twelve" and read it "dagger."

3. In each of the bases mentioned in the foregoing problem, solve the equivalents of the following problems

   a. Add each pair and all four of the numbers: the pair $(357)_T$, $(2981)_T$; and the pair $(3725)_T$, $(9999)_T$.

   b. Subtract the pairs

   $$(7831)_T \qquad (834716)_T$$
   $$\underline{(6513)_T} \qquad \underline{(259357)_T}$$

   Multiply the pairs

   $$(283)_T \qquad (5164)_T$$
   $$\underline{(75)_T} \qquad \underline{(296)_T}$$

1.15 Division and "Decimal Point" Representation

The fundamental principle involved in the operation of division is the *division transformation*. This means that if we are given two non-zero numbers (in any base), say A and B, where B is smaller than A, then the division of A by B yields a quotient Q and a remainder R

$$\frac{A}{B} = Q + \frac{R}{B}$$

where R *is smaller than* B. If $R = 0$, then B is called a divisor of A. We shall examine the meaning and deeper implications of division in a later chapter. Here we are concerned only with aspects of reckoning.

When we divide the two numbers A and B in practice, we in fact subtract B a total of Q times from A. Let us illustrate with the problem of 8316 ÷ 1573, keeping count of the number of subtractions

$$
\begin{array}{r}
8316 \\
1573 \quad . \ . \ . \ (1) \\
\hline
6743 \\
1573 \quad . \ . \ . \ (2) \\
\hline
5170 \\
1573 \quad . \ . \ . \ (3) \\
\hline
3597 \\
1573 \quad . \ . \ . \ (4) \\
\hline
2024 \\
1573 \quad . \ . \ . \ (5) \\
\hline
451
\end{array}
$$

The last figure is the remainder after subtracting 1573 *five* times from 8316; thus

$$8316 = (1573 \times 5) + 451$$

Dividing this statement through by 1573 we have

$$\frac{8316}{1573} = 5 + \frac{451}{1573}$$

Instead of showing explicitly the series of subtractions, we commonly organize the work in the following schematic way

$$\frac{Q}{1573\overline{\smash{)}8316}}$$

and ask what is the largest possible number Q such that ($Q \times 1573$) *does not exceed* 8316. By essentially going through our multiplication tables, we find that $Q = 5$, as shown here

$$
\begin{array}{r}
5 \\
1573\overline{\smash{)}8316} \\
7865 \\
\hline
451
\end{array}
$$

This is all very well known, but let us exhibit the role of place value in somewhat more detail. Consider the division of 8316 by 43. We could subtract 43 a series of times from 8316, keeping count of the number of subtractions, but we do not find this to be the most practicable way of proceeding. It is likewise awkward and difficult to write

$$\frac{Q}{43\overline{\smash{)}8316}}$$

and ask immediately for the integer Q. What we need is a way to ascertain Q by a direct *method* of operation. We can do this by using the place-value aspects of the notation. The problem is first to find the digit (A), from 1 to 9, in

$$
\begin{array}{r}
(A)\ .\ . \\
43\overline{\smash{)}8\ \ 3\ \ 1\ \ 6}
\end{array}
$$

which tells how many 43's are in 8316. We have

$$
\begin{array}{r}
1\ .\ . \\
43\overline{\smash{)}8316} \\
43 \\
\hline
40
\end{array}
$$

This "partial quotient" is not unity, but 100, since the 1 appears in the hundreds place of the dividend 8316, and the remainder is 4016. Now we seek the specific digit from 0 to 9 which is to occupy the tens place of the quotient. This part of the problem is equivalent to

$$
\begin{array}{r}
9. \\
43 \overline{\smash{)}\ 4016} \\
387 \\
\hline
14
\end{array}
$$

which represents a partial quotient of 90 and a remainder of 146. Then we find the specific digit, 0 to 9, which is to be in the units place of the quotient, as follows

$$
\begin{array}{r}
3 \\
43 \overline{\smash{)}\ 146} \\
129 \\
\hline
17
\end{array}
$$

The entire work is therefore shown by

$$
\begin{array}{r}
193 \\
43 \overline{\smash{)}\ 8316} \\
43 \\
\hline
401 \\
387 \\
\hline
146 \\
129 \\
\hline
17
\end{array}
$$

We can illustrate the problem of place value in division by choosing numbers in other bases. Let us illustrate with the following example in the base two

$$
\begin{array}{r}
1.. \\
1011 \overline{\smash{)}\ 111011} \\
1011 \\
\hline
11
\end{array}
$$

This partial quotient is in the fours place. Bringing down 1 from the twos place in the dividend we have the indicated division

$$\frac{0}{1011 \overline{)\ 111}}$$

where 1011 is clearly, place-wise, greater than 111; and our next partial quotient is 0 in order to properly fill the twos place, for this is the role of zero in any symbolism which involves place value. The next step is to bring 1 down from the units place in the dividend

$$
\begin{array}{r}
01 \\
1011 \overline{)\ 1111} \\
1011 \\
\hline
100
\end{array}
$$

Put together in neater form we have

$$
\begin{array}{r}
101 \\
1011 \overline{)\ 111011} \\
1011 \\
\hline
1111 \\
1011 \\
\hline
100
\end{array}
$$

Hence we are saying that

$$\frac{(111011)_2}{(1011)_2} = (101)_2 + \frac{(100)_2}{(1011)_2}$$

As another example, consider the problem that follows, where the numbers are all expressed in the base six

$$
\begin{array}{r}
(A).\ . \\
53 \overline{)\ 5\ 2\ 3\ 4\ 2}
\end{array}
$$

Clearly the digit (A), from 0 to 5, is in the 6^2 place. If we know the addition table but do not know the multiplication table sufficiently well to recall (A) immediately, we can resort to a series of subtractions of the divisor 53 from the partial dividend 523.. as follows, using the digits in the 6^2, 6^3, and 6^4 places

$$
\begin{array}{r}
523 \\
\underline{53} \quad \text{. . . (1)} \\
430 \\
\underline{53} \quad \text{. . . (2)} \\
333 \\
\underline{53} \quad \text{. . . (3)} \\
240 \\
\underline{53} \quad \text{. . . (4)} \\
143 \\
\underline{53} \quad \text{. . . (5)} \\
50
\end{array}
$$

Hence, (A) is the digit 5 and our work on the problem proceeds by shifting one place to the right

$$
\begin{array}{r}
\overline{ (B) } \\
53 \,)\, 5\ 0\ 4\ 2
\end{array}
$$

where (B) is the digit in the sixes place of the quotient. We perform the following subtractions to ascertain (B); that is, the quotient in 504/53

$$
\begin{array}{r}
504 \\
\underline{53} \quad \text{. . . (1)} \\
411 \\
\underline{53} \quad \text{. . . (2)} \\
314 \\
\underline{53} \quad \text{. . . (3)} \\
221 \\
\underline{53} \quad \text{. . . (4)} \\
124 \\
\underline{53} \quad \text{. . . (5)} \\
31
\end{array}
$$

Hence, the digit (B) is 5. Finally, we have to find the units place of our quotient, say (C)

$$\begin{array}{r} (C) \\ \hline 53 \overline{)\,3\ 1\ 2} \end{array}$$

and again using successive subtractions we have

$$\begin{array}{r} 312 \\ 53 \quad \ldots \ (1) \\ \hline 215 \\ 53 \quad \ldots \ (2) \\ \hline 122 \\ 53 \quad \ldots \ (3) \\ \hline 25 \end{array}$$

and, hence, (C) is 3. The final remainder is 25. Our result is then

$$\frac{(52342)_6}{(53)_6} = (553)_6 + \frac{(25)_6}{(53)_6}$$

Of course, had we known the multiplication table well, we would have observed, since 52 in the dividend is smaller than the divisor 53, the products

$$\begin{array}{cccc} 52 & 53 & 53 & 53 \\ 2 & 3 & 4 & 5 \\ \hline 150 & 243 & 340 & 433 \end{array}$$

and we would have written

$$\begin{array}{r} 553 \\ \hline 53 \overline{)\,52342} \\ 433 \\ \hline 504 \\ 433 \\ \hline 312 \\ 243 \\ \hline 25 \end{array}$$

In the elementary schools, the student learns to "do decimals" in the course of his studies of division. This means that he learns the extension of the place-value system to the representation of numbers between 0 and 1. The first place to the left of the "decimal point" is for units, the second for a number base B is the B's position, and so on. To the right of the "decimal point" is the place for "1 over Bths," the second for "1 over B-squareds," the third for "1 over B-cubeds," and so on. In the base ten we properly call these *decimals*: tenths, tenths-squared or hundredths, tenths-cubed or thousandths, ... But in the base six these places would be for sixths, sixths-squared, sixths-cubed, and so on. In base seven they would be sevenths, sevenths-squared, ... In base twelve they would be for twelfths, twelfths-squared, ... Nevertheless, whatever the base, say B, we would have, in that base, $B = 10$ and, thus

$$\frac{1}{B} = \frac{1}{10} \qquad \frac{1}{B^2} = \frac{1}{100} \qquad \frac{1}{B^3} = \frac{1}{1000} \qquad \cdots$$

although of course 10 is not "ten" except in the decimal base itself.

The particular symbolism of long division and the decimal point itself, which we take so much for granted, actually first appeared at about the time that Columbus discovered America, and both originated in Italy. A Florentine scholar named Calandi published, in 1491, a book which gave the first printed example of long division written in the form we employ today. In 1492, F. Pellos published, in Turin, a book on arithmetic where the decimal point was used for the first time.

There is no reason for disappointment in a young student if he shows a certain obtuseness in continuing with speed, accuracy, and lively enthusiasm the problem in base ten

$$
\begin{array}{r}
2.635\ldots\ldots \\
27895 \overline{\smash{\big)}\ 73528.000\ldots\ldots} \\
\underline{55790} \\
177380 \\
\underline{167370} \\
100100 \\
\underline{83685} \\
164150\ldots\ldots
\end{array}
$$

We ourselves shall stop here because, for good reason, we profess to have been interested in the result to *two* decimal places, having checked the third place to assure that there is no need for rounding off (involving say 5, 6, 7, 8, 9).

Let us examine the situation for the divisions involving the base two and the base six which we had a few paragraphs earlier. Continuing the problem in base two

$$
\begin{array}{r}
101. \\
1011 \overline{)\ 111011.0} \\
1011 \\
\hline
1111 \\
1011 \\
\hline
100
\end{array}
$$

we proceed to the "decimal" representation of the remainder 100/1011 out to a final or previously agreed upon place. Carrying the zero in the halves place which has been appended to the right of the point in the dividend, and regarding the remainder 100 now as 1000/1011 halves, we are satisfied that the first place in the quotient after the point is a zero

$$
\begin{array}{r}
101.0 \\
1011 \overline{)\ 111011.00} \\
1011 \\
\hline
1111 \\
1011 \\
\hline
1000
\end{array}
$$

Now it is a question of putting this remainder in the fourths place and finding 10000/1011 fourths. However, in the base two we have a choice only between 0 and 1. Thus, we must have a one in the second place to the right of the point of the quotient

$$
\begin{array}{r}
101.01 \\
1011 \overline{\smash{)}\ 111011.00} \\
1011 \\
\hline
1111 \\
1011 \\
\hline
100\ 00 \\
10\ 11 \\
\hline
1\ 01
\end{array}
$$

This result is readily checked by addition. Continuing, we find the following succession of digits in the "decimal" representation of the quotient

$$
\begin{array}{r}
101.010111 \\
1011 \overline{\smash{)}\ 111011.000000} \\
1011 \\
\hline
1111 \\
1011 \\
10000 \\
1011 \\
\hline
10100 \\
1011 \\
\hline
10010 \\
1011 \\
\hline
10010 \\
1011 \\
\hline
1110 \\
1011 \\
\hline
11
\end{array}
$$

To this place, a corresponding fractional representation of the quotient in base *ten* would be

$$
4 + 1 + \frac{1}{4} + \frac{1}{16} + \frac{1}{32} + \frac{1}{64}
$$

Similarly, our example in base six proceeds to the "decimal" point representation as follows

$$
\begin{array}{r}
553.303134\ldots \\
53\,)\,\overline{52342.000000\ldots} \\
\underline{433} \\
504 \\
\underline{433} \\
312 \\
243 \\
\underline{250} \\
243 \\
\underline{300} \\
243 \\
\underline{130} \\
53 \\
\underline{330} \\
243 \\
\underline{430} \\
340 \\
\underline{50}
\end{array}
$$

The reader may continue to practice if he wishes. Here, once again, the problem solver may hope for the problem to end after a finite number of places, with a zero remainder, or become clearly repetitious so that the chore of performing the division is at last over from the computational viewpoint. A deeper question is the meaning to be attached to a finite or infinite repeating decimal as contrasted with an infinite non-repeating decimal. That is a question of importance to which we shall give attention later.

EXERCISES

Perform the indicated divisions to the second "decimal" place.

1. $(10111)_2 \div (1011)_2$

2. $(1212)_3 \div (22)_3$

3. $(4123)_5 \div (423)_5$

4. $(3525)_6 \div (25)_6$

5. $(6124)_7 \div (336)_7$

6. $(4756)_8 \div (57)_8$

7. $(9 * 5\dagger)_{\text{Twelve}} \div (3 *)_{\text{Twelve}}$

8. In financial circles in this country, the prices of U. S. Government securities are quoted as follows: 100 for a $1000 bond "at par"; 99 when the bond price is "discounted" to $990; 101 for a bond selling at a "premium" price of $1010; 102 for a bond at $1020; and so on. But fractional prices are quoted in 32nds. Thus a quotation of 100.1 means 100 and $\frac{1}{32}$, and a quotation of 102.20 means 102 and $\frac{20}{32}$, and one pays $1035 for a bond quoted at 103.16. What would you pay for "discount" bonds quoted at 98.16 and at 99.3, and for "premium" bonds quoted at 100.28 and at 105.17? If a bond is quoted at 101.30 and the price rises $\frac{15}{32}$, what will the quotation be? If the bond is quoted at 100 and the price drops $\frac{12}{32}$, what will the new quotation be? Criticize the several various aspects of this "decimal" representation of bond price quotations.

9. In the stock market, fractional prices are quoted in eighths. A stock selling at $47.125 is quoted at $47\frac{1}{8}$. If the price is $47.75, the quotation is $47\frac{3}{4}$. Thus the stock of a company may sell at $47\frac{1}{8}$, $47\frac{3}{8}$, $47\frac{1}{2}$, $47\frac{7}{8}$, as prices rise in the course of a day's trading. Usually the fractional notation is used; but occasionally one will see these prices reported as 47.1, 47.3, 47.5, 47.7. Criticize this "decimal" representation, and compare your criticisms in this case with those of the representation of the quotations for government securities.

1.16   The Roman System as a Counter Example

As one of the consequences of the very great influence which the Romans had on almost every aspect of western civilization, their number system persists even today in a variety of uses; for example, as chapter numbers in some books and dates on some corner stones.

The persistence in the employment of the Roman numerals is surprising, for the system suffers in every one of those significant respects which distinguish the Hindu–Arabic system. Leaving aside such æsthetic but nonetheless important matters as the employment of the alphabet for number symbols, the Roman system suffers from the absence of the zero symbol and of the place-value concept.

There is, to be sure, a naive attempt at a place-value idea. In the sequence of the first eleven integers, for example

$$I, \quad II, \quad III, \quad IV, \quad V, \quad VI, \quad VII, \quad VIII, \quad IX, \quad X, \quad XI$$

one sees an unsophisticated attempt at place value in writing a I to the left or right of certain other symbols in order to indicate essentially a subtraction or an addition. This idea of juxtaposition on the left of another symbol for subtraction and on the right for addition is commonly used in the Roman notation, but its use is not only unsystematic but often ambiguous.

Reminiscent of the earliest primitive use of a number language involving the idea of place value before the concept in number symbols was fully realized, there is the Roman use of ten (X), fifty (L), hundred (C), and thousand (M). To write a "thousand thousand" one has either to devise a new literal symbol for the product of "M times M," or to write a thousand adjacent M's. By no such simple, almost automatic, operation of the kind which the notion of place value permits can we calculate $50 + 40 = 90$

$$L + XL = XC$$

The capability of counting is present in the Roman system, however, and Caesar could order his legions to "count off" while his personnel officers devised new literal symbols and combinations of these as required.

Any reader who has not already suffered a disenchantment or even an exasperation with Roman numerals has only to set for himself the simplest of problems involving the four fundamental operations of reckoning. The Roman system serves to point up the remarkable advantages of the Hindu–Arabic system or of any corresponding system that employs the fundamental concepts of zero and place value.

1. Compare the development of literature and art with that of mathematics from earliest times to the beginning of the seventeenth century. Arrange your work chronologically.

2. Prepare a talk from appropriate selections of your choosing from the *Encyclopaedia Britannica* or from one or more of the following references.

REFERENCES

Cajori, F., *A History of Elementary Mathematics*. New York: The Macmillan Company, 1924.

———, *A History of Mathematical Notations*, Vol. 1. Chicago: Open Court Publishing Co., 1928.

Chace, A. B., *et al. The Rhind Mathematical Papyrus*, 2 vols. Oberlin, Ohio: Mathematical Association of America, 1927–1929.

Eves, H., *An Introduction to the History of Mathematics*. New York: Holt, Rinehart & Winston, Inc., 1953.

Fine, H. B., *The Number-System of Algebra*. Boston: Leach, Shewell and Sanborn, 1890.

Heath, T. L., *History of Greek Mathematics*, Vol. 1. New York: Oxford University Press, Inc., 1921.

Karpinski, L. C., *The History of Arithmetic*. Chicago: Rand McNally & Co., 1925.

Neugebauer, O., *The Exact Sciences in Antiquity*. Princeton, N. J.: Princeton University Press, 1952.

Newman, J. R., *The World of Mathematics*. New York: Simon and Schuster, Inc., 1956.

Ore, O., *Number Theory and its History*, pp. 1–100. New York: McGraw-Hill Book Company, Inc., 1948.

Rouse-Ball, W. W., *A Short Account of the History of Mathematics*. London: Macmillan & Co., Ltd., 1940.

Smith, D. E., *History of Mathematics*, Vols. 1 and 2. Boston: Ginn & Company, 1923.

——— and L. C. Karpinski, *The Hindu–Arabic Numerals*. Boston: Ginn & Company, 1911.

2

SOME
INTUITIVE
PROPERTIES
OF THE
NATURAL
NUMBERS

2.1 Introduction

In Chapter 1 we have presented an historical account of the development of the natural numbers and of various schemes used for the representation of numbers. It is most important that the reader observe that these remarkable ideas are the products of man's fertile imagination, that man invented numbers in response to his need for a means of counting, and that the properties of numbers were determined by man and were chosen so that the resulting system would do the desired job.

We continue this line of reasoning in the present chapter, examining various aspects of the problem of counting in an effort to discover basic facts relative to the addition and multiplication of natural numbers. Our attitude will be much like that of an experimental scientist as we study a series of specific number situations in an effort to discover arithmetical laws. The reader should be aware, however, that the discussions leading up to the statement of the different laws are not offered in proof of the correctness of the laws. Rather, they are offered in an attempt to show that these laws must be required to hold if the system is to be useful in counting situations. In the sequel we will show how this basic process of invention continues as the number system is extended to include more and more numbers to meet the demands of still more complex situations.

There are many rules concerning the addition and multiplication of natural numbers which will not be considered at the present time. The twelve laws to be discussed, however, are basic to the structure of the natural number system, and all other such laws can be deduced as logical consequences of these twelve. The point is that the system of natural numbers is completely characterized by the laws to be considered, so that one understands the natural numbers only in so far as he understands these laws or their logical equivalents.

2.2 Mathematical Symbolism

Before proceeding to discussion of the laws concerning the addition and multiplication of natural numbers, it may be helpful to consider briefly the mathematical language and symbolism which will be used in their statement. Mathematical language, of course, is just ordinary language, but used in a very precise way. Thus, it behooves the writer of mathematics to say exactly what he means, neither more nor less, and it behooves the reader to understand neither more nor less than was written. For example, if one reads the statement "let a and b be any two natural numbers," he should understand only that the symbols "a" and "b" are being used to denote natural numbers; nothing more is intended. Possible values for a and b are 3 and 5, 6 and 87, or even 8 and 8. Nothing is said which implies that a and b are different, that one is smaller than the other, that they are even numbers or odd numbers, or anything else. If the writer had wanted a and b necessarily to be different, then he should have written "let a and b be two distinct natural numbers." And if he had wanted to specify that a was larger than b, he should have written something like "let a and b be any two natural numbers with a greater than b."

Another characteristic of mathematical language, which is already apparent in the preceding examples, is that it makes extensive use of various signs and symbols. To the beginner this may seem somewhat unnecessary and confusing; but if he will take the time to write out the "plain English" equivalents of only a few of the mathematical laws to be stated in the sequel, he will very soon discover that the use of the signs and symbols not only makes for a greater economy but for increased clarity as well. To give but a single example, consider the following involved sentence. "The result of multiplying a natural number by the sum of two other natural numbers is the same as the result obtained by adding the product of the first number and the first number in the sum and the product of the first number and the second number in the sum." This is really quite a simple matter when one finally sorts out just what is being said, but the English sentence with no use of signs and symbols is not well suited to the expression of ideas of this sort. The insertion of a few well chosen signs and symbols, however, with a proper understanding of their meaning, can serve to make the sentence both concise and clear.

Since the statement we desire to make has to do with three natural numbers one might use specific numbers like 4, 5, and 7 and say that 4 times the sum of 5 and 7 is equal to 4 times 5 plus 4 times 7. Although this effects a certain improvement over the earlier wording of the statement, the usage of 4, 5, and 7 seems to imply that the result is true only for these three numbers, whereas we want to say that it is true for *any* three natural numbers. We can accomplish this end, however, and still gain the economy of the usage of symbols if, instead of 4, 5, and 7, we use a, b, and c, to represent *any* three natural numbers. As noted earlier, a, b, and c may represent 4, 5, and 7; but they may also represent 6, 7, and 59, or 2, 2, and 5, or any three natural numbers whatsoever. The point is that by using a, b, and c we can make the statement we desire to make, in all generality and with greater clarity and economy of expression than the use of words alone would allow. Thus, we might now say that, if a, b, and c represent any three natural numbers, then a times the sum of b and c is equal to a times b plus a times c.

While this last statement is an obvious improvement over the first, an even better version can be obtained by using the familiar symbols of "$+$," "$\times$," and "$=$" respectively in place of "plus," "times," and "is equal to." It is also convenient to use parentheses to indicate that the quantity enclosed is to be considered as a single number. Thus, for example, we write $4 \times (5 + 7)$ to indicate the product of 4 and the number which is the sum of 5 and 7. We might now couch our assertion in the following shorter and more understandable way: "If a, b, and c are any three natural numbers, then $a \times (b + c) = (a \times b) + (a \times c)$."

An even more concise version of this assertion is possible if we adopt certain other conventions. In the first place, multiplication is often indicated with a dot or, when there is no danger of confusion, with no symbol at all. Thus, the product of a and b can be written as $a \times b$, $a \cdot b$, or simply as ab. Also, in an expression such as $ab + ac$, involving both addition and multiplication with no grouping specified, it is agreed that the multiplication shall be carried out before the addition. Thus, $ab + ac$ properly means $(ab) + (ac)$, and so denotes the sum of the two indicated products. Using these refinements, the assertion may finally be written in the following concise and easily understood form: "If a, b, and c are any three natural numbers, then $a(b + c) = ab + ac$."

By way of a brief review of these ideas, the reader should note that the last statement in the preceding paragraph implies that $2(3 + 4) = 6 + 8$, that $3(3 + 5) = 9 + 15$, and that $4(4 + 4) = 16 + 16$. Also, if u, v, and w are three natural numbers, it implies that $u(v + w) = uv + uw$, that $3(u + v) = 3u + 3v$, and that $2(5 + w) = 10 + 2w$. Finally, it implies that $b(a + c) = ba + bc$, that $b(b + a) = bb + ba$, and that $a(a + a) = aa + aa$. Of course, the products bb and aa are usually written b^2 and a^2, so that the last two equations could have been written $b(b + a) = b^2 + ba$, and $a(a + a) = a^2 + a^2 = 2a^2$.

2.3   Addition of Natural Numbers

As everyone knows, the sum of any two natural numbers can be found by the simple device of counting. Thus, to find the sum of 3 and 8, it suffices to count out one set of 3 objects and another set of 8 objects, and then to obtain the total count of both sets by counting the items in the first set and continuing on to count those in the second set. Indeed, the problem of finding the total count of a set of objects (sheep, oxen, arrows, etc.), formed by combining two sets whose counts were already known, undoubtedly originally led man to *invent* the idea of addition and to devise rules by which formal addition of numbers might be carried out. We understand addition, therefore, in terms of counting; and with this in mind, a number of laws for addition immediately become apparent.

2.4 The Law of Closure for Addition

In the first place, it is clear that the result of adding any two natural numbers must again be a natural number, since it is simply the result of counting some set of objects as described above. This is often expressed by saying that the set of natural numbers is *closed* under the operation of addition. For easy reference this property is given the following formal statement.

P1. *Closure Law for Addition.* If a and b are any two natural numbers then $a + b$ is also a natural number.

A better appreciation of the preceding law may be obtained if we consider the idea of closure in more detail. In general, a set of elements is said to be closed under an operation if, whenever that operation is applied to elements of the set in question, elements of the same set are obtained as a result. For example, the set of even numbers is closed under the operation of addition, since the result of adding any two even numbers is to obtain another even number. But, the set of odd numbers is *not* closed under addition, since the result of adding two odd numbers is to obtain an even number rather than an odd number.

EXERCISES

Answer the following questions on the basis of your present knowledge of arithmetic. If you assert that a proposition is not generally true, give an example showing at least one case where the proposition fails.

1. Which of the following sets are closed under the operation indicated?

   (a) The set of even natural numbers under multiplication.

   (b) The set of odd natural numbers under multiplication.

   (c) The set of natural numbers under subtraction.

   (d) The set of natural numbers under division.

   (e) The set of natural numbers which are multiplies of 3 under addition. NOTE: This set includes the numbers 3, 6, 9, 12, ...; i.e., the numbers of the form $3k$ where k is a natural number.

   (f) The set of natural numbers which leave a remainder of 1 when divided by 3 under the operation of multiplication. NOTE: This set includes the numbers 1, 4, 7, 10, 13, ...; i.e., the numbers of the form $(3k + 1)$ where k is a natural number.

(g) The set of natural numbers which leave a remainder of 1 when divided by 3 under the operation of addition.

(h) The set of natural numbers which leave a remainder of 2 when divided by 3 under the operation of addition. NOTE: This set includes the numbers 2, 5, 8, 11, ... ; i.e., the numbers of the form $(3k + 2)$ where k is a natural number.

(i) The set of natural numbers which leave a remainder of 2 when divided by 3 under the operation of multiplication.

2. Let $*$ denote the operation of averaging; i.e., $a * b = (a + b)/2$. For example, $2 * 4 = 3$ and $5 * 7 = 6$.

(a) Compute $8 * 20$, $15 * 21$, $7 * 10$, and $5 * 27$.

(b) Under what conditions is $a * b$ a natural number given that a and b are natural numbers?

(c) Is the set of natural numbers closed under the operation $*$?

3. Let $S = \{1, 2, 3, 4, 5, 6, 7\}$ be the set of natural numbers from 1 to 7 inclusive. Is S closed with respect to addition?

4. Let $T = \{1\}$; i.e., T contains only the number 1.

(a) Is T closed with respect to multiplication?

(b) Is T closed with respect to addition?

(c) Is T closed with respect to the operation $*$ of Exercise 2?

(d) Is T closed with respect to division?

(e) Is T closed with respect to subtraction?

2.5 The Commutative Property for Addition

A second aspect of addition of natural numbers, which becomes apparent if we think of addition in terms of counting, is that the result of adding two natural numbers is independent of the order in which we consider the numbers involved. For example, in the addition of 3 and 8 as discussed above, it is immaterial whether one first counts the set of 3 objects and then the set of 8 objects, or first counts the 8 objects and then the 3. In either case, the result is the same, and one has $3 + 8 = 8 + 3$. This situation is usually expressed by saying that the natural numbers are *commutative* with respect to addition. Formally, this property is stated as follows.

P2. *Commutative Law for Addition.* If a and b are any two natural numbers, then $a + b = b + a$.

It is easy to find situations where the commutative law does not hold, and it is instructive to consider some examples. Since 6 divided by 2 is not equal to 2 divided by 6, it is clear that the natural numbers are not commutative with respect to the operation of division. Also, if we were to define an operation ■, called "box," by the equation a ■ $b = b$, then we would have that 2 ■ 3 = 3, while 3 ■ 2 = 2. Thus, 3 ■ 2 is not equal to 2 ■ 3, and the natural numbers are not commutative under the "box" operation. An example of a humorous nature is provided by noting that the actions of taking off one's clothes and taking a shower are certainly not commutative under the operation "followed by." Another situation that is not subject to the commutative law comes from the field of chemistry. The experiment of pouring concentrated sulfuric acid into water is a harmless way of obtaining a dilute solution of the acid. But the very similar experiment of pouring water into concentrated sulfuric results in a particularly violent and dangerous explosion.

EXERCISES

As before, the following questions are to be answered on the basis of your present knowledge of arithmetic. If you assert that a proposition is not generally true, you should give an example of at least one case where the proposition fails.

1. Are the natural numbers commutative with respect to subtraction? Why or why not?

2. As before, let $*$ denote the operation of averaging so that $a * b = \frac{1}{2}(a + b)$. Are the natural numbers commutative with respect to this operation?

3. Cite five pairs of actions from ordinary life which are commutative under the operation "followed by," and cite five pairs of actions which are not commutative under this operation. Which situations are more common, the commutative or the noncommutative?

4. Define the operation $\bigcirc$ over the set of natural numbers by the equation $a \bigcirc b = 2a + b$. Thus, $3 \bigcirc 2 = 8$, and $5 \bigcirc 7 = 17$.

    (a) Find $7 \bigcirc 6$; $11 \bigcirc 5$; and $6 \bigcirc 7$.

    (b) Are the natural numbers closed under this operation?

    (c) Are the natural numbers commutative with respect to this operation?

    (d) Under what condition is $a \bigcirc b = b \bigcirc a$, where a and b are natural numbers?

2.6   The Associative Law for Addition

A third rule of fundamental importance for the addition of natural numbers has to do with the sum of three numbers. Technically, addition is an operation which involves just two numbers, and as such is called a *binary operation*. Thus, without a rule, it would not be clear how addition should be extended to include sums of more than two numbers.

If a person were asked to combine 10, 6, and 3 by the operation of addition, he might proceed by adding 10 to the sum of 6 and 3; or alternatively, he might add the sum of 10 and 6 to 3. Thus, instead of thinking of $10 + 6 + 3$, he unconsciously thinks of $10 + (6 + 3)$ or $(10 + 6) + 3$, where the numbers are grouped so that the addition can be carried out by adding just two numbers at each step. Of course, in terms of counting, this is precisely what ought to be done, for we can think of the problem as that of finding the total count of a set of objects formed by combining three sets of 10, 6, and 3 objects respectively into a single set. Clearly the result is the same for any of the possible orders of counting the sets so that we ought to have $(10 + 6) + 3 = 10 + (6 + 3) = 19$. This property is stated as follows.

P3. *Associative Law for Addition.* If a, b, and c are any three natural numbers, then $(a + b) + c = a + (b + c)$.

For later work it may help the reader to restate the associative law in "plain English" even though it becomes less concise in the restatement. In words, the associative law for the addition of natural numbers says that, if one is given any three natural numbers (not necessarily distinct), the result of adding the sum of the first two to the third is the same as the result of adding the first to the sum of the last two. Among other things, this implies that $(2 + 3) + 7 = 2 + (3 + 7)$; that $(2 + a) + b = 2 + (a + b)$; that $(a + a) + b = a + (a + b)$; and that $(u + v) + w = u + (v + w)$ if a, b, u, v, and w represent natural numbers.

That the associative law is necessary is easily seen by considering the operation of subtraction. Like addition, subtraction is a binary operation, but examination of just a single case will show that the natural numbers are *not* associative under this operation. For example, $(10 - 6) - 3 = 4 - 3 = 1$, whereas $10 - (6 - 3) = 10 - 3 = 7$; therefore, $(10 - 6) - 3$ is not equal to $10 - (6 - 3)$. Thus, it is clear that, in subtraction, the numbers may not be freely associated and that an expression like $10 - 6 - 3$ is meaningless unless some sort of grouping is specified or understood.

On the other hand, it follows from the associative law of addition together with the commutative law that all of the twelve expressions that can be obtained from the sum $a + b + c$ by ordering and grouping the numbers in all possibles ways are equal. Thus, $a + b + c$ is understood to represent any of these expressions, and the signs of grouping are frequently omitted.

To illustrate how the results of the preceding paragraph follow from the associative and commutative laws for addition, we show that $a + (b + c) = (a + c) + b$. The other equalities would be derived in a similar way. First we note that $(a + c) + b = a + (c + b)$ by the associative law. Secondly, $a + (c + b) = a + (b + c)$, since $c + b = b + c$ by the commutative law. Thus, $(a + c) + b = a + (b + c)$ as desired, since both are equal to $a + (c + b)$.

It is important to note that the associative law guarantees that more complicated sums of natural numbers may also be obtained by associating the numbers involved in any way. For example, consider the equality

$$[(a + b) + c] + d = (a + b) + (c + d)$$

which indicates that the sum of four natural numbers a, b, c, and d may be obtained by adding c to the sum of a and b and then adding d to the result, or by adding the sum of a and b to the sum of c and d. This equality may be obtained from the preceding laws in the following way. By the closure law for addition, there exists some natural number e such that $a + b = e$. Therefore, proving the desired equality will be equivalent to showing that $(e + c) + d = e + (c + d)$. But this is true by the associative law for addition, and so the desired equality is true as claimed. In view of the fact that such sums may be obtained by associating the numbers in any way, it is frequently the case that no grouping is indicated. Thus, in the preceding example, one might simply write $a + b + c + d$ without designating how the addition should be carried out.

EXERCISES

1. Compute each of the following:

(a) $(4 + 7) + 5$ (b) $4 + (7 + 5)$

(c) $(4 + 5) + 7$ (d) $(5 + 4) + 7$

(e) $7 + (4 + 5)$ (f) $(7 + 5) + 4$

2. There are six possibilities for ordering and grouping the sum $4 + 5 + 7$ in addition to those listed in Exercise 1. Write out the other six possibilities.

3. Consider $(24 \div 6) \div 2$ and $24 \div (6 \div 2)$, where the division is to be carried out in the order indicated. Are the natural numbers associative with respect to division?

4. Could you find natural numbers a, b, and c such that $(a \div b) \div c = a \div (b \div c)$? What must be the case in order that this be so?

5. Define the operation $*$ by $a * b = (a + b)/2$. Are the natural numbers associative with respect to $*$?

6. Let the operation $\bigcirc$ be defined by $a \bigcirc b = 2a + b$. Are the natural numbers associative with respect to $\bigcirc$?

7. Without changing the order in which the numbers appear, in how many ways can we group the sum $7 + 5 + 4 + 8$ for addition so that only two numbers will be added at each step? Compute the result for each possible grouping.

2.7 The Law of Trichotomy

Another law concerning addition of natural numbers which is made clear by the counting process is the law of trichotomy. The word "trichotomy" refers to a situation in which the various possibilities are grouped into three mutually exclusive and exhaustive classes. That is to say, each possibility must fall into one and only one of three categories. The reader is probably more familiar with the word "dichotomy," which describes a situation in which the various possibilities fall into two mutually exclusive classes. For example, the fact that any metal is either pure gold or not pure gold is a dichotomy. Any metal must fall into one classification or the other, and cannot be in both. Similarly, the fact that any natural number leaves a remainder of 0, 1, or 2 when divided by 3 is an example of a trichotomy. The particular trichotomy which concerns us here can be stated in the following way.

P4. *Law of Trichotomy.* If a and b are any two natural numbers, then precisely one of the three following possibilities holds: either $a = b$; or there exists a natural number r such that $a = b + r$; or there exists a natural number s such that $a + s = b$

This law simply says that two natural numbers are equal, or the first is larger than the second, or the second is larger than the first, and that no two of these possibilities occur simultaneously. In terms of the counting of sets of objects, this assertion corresponds to the simultaneous counting one-for-one of the items in two sets of objects. Clearly, three situations are possible, and they correspond exactly to the three possibilities admitted in the law of trichotomy. Either both sets are exhausted at the same time, or elements of the first set remain uncounted after the second set has been exhausted, or elements of the second set remain uncounted after the first set has been exhausted.

EXERCISES

1. Using the physical measures of length, speed, and temperature, cite examples of both a dichotomy and a trichotomy involving each.

2. Let $S = \{1, 2, 3, 4, 5, 6, 7\}$. Does the law of trichotomy hold for S? That is, if a and b are any two elements of S, does just *one* of the following possibilities hold? Either $a = b$; or there is an element r in S such that $a + r = b$; or there is an element s in S such that $a = b + s$.

3. Consider the "arithmetic" A defined by the following "addition" table, where $a \oplus b$ is found at the intersection of the ath row and bth column.

$\oplus$	1	2	3	4
1	2	4	3	1
2	4	3	1	2
3	3	1	2	3
4	1	2	3.	4

(a) Compute $2 \oplus 3$; $3 \oplus 2$; $(3 \oplus 2) \oplus 4$; and $3 \oplus (2 \oplus 4)$.

(b) Is A closed with respect to $\oplus$?

(c) Is A commutative with respect to $\oplus$?

(d) Is $(2 \oplus 3) \oplus 1 = 2 \oplus (3 \oplus 1)$?

(e) Does the law of trichotomy hold for A? That is, if a and b are any two elements of A, does just *one* of the following possibilities hold? Either $a = b$; or there exists an element r in A such that $a \oplus r = b$; or there exists an element s in A such that $a = b \oplus s$.

2.8 The Cancellation Law

A final rule for the addition of natural numbers may be seen in the following way. Suppose one counts out a set of n objects by first counting out a objects and then counting out b objects so that $a + b = n$. Now if the n objects are again counted out by first counting out the a objects and then counting out c more objects so that $a + c = n$, it follows from the counting process that $b = c$. This situation is formalized in the following statement.

P5. *Cancellation Law for Addition.* If a, b, and c are any three natural numbers such that $a + b = a + c$, then $b = c$.

   This law is of such importance that we state it as a separate property, but it is interesting to note that it can be derived as a consequence of the law of trichotomy as follows. By the law of trichotomy, $b = c$; or there is a natural number r such that $b = c + r$; or there is a natural number s such that $b + s = c$. Thus, in deriving the cancellation law from the law of trichotomy, our strategy will be to show that if $a + b = a + c$, then neither of the last two possibilities of the law of trichotomy can hold. Then, it must be the case that $b = c$ as desired. Let a, b, and c be natural numbers with $a + b = a + c$. If there exists a natural number r such that $b = c + r$, then $a + b = a + (c + r)$. Also, $a + (c + r) = (a + c) + r$ by P3, the associative law for addition. Thus, it follows that $a + b = (a + c) + r$. But then, by the law of trichotomy, it is impossible that $a + b = a + c$, and this violates the given condition. Therefore no such r exists. In exactly the same way, we could show that there is no s such that $c = b + s$. Thus, since $b = c + r$ and $b + s = c$ are both impossible, it follows from the law of trichotomy that $b = c$ as claimed in the cancellation law.

EXERCISES

1. Does the cancellation law for subtraction hold for the set of natural numbers? That is, if $a - b = a - c$, does it follow that $b = c$?

2. Define the operation $*$ by $a * b = (a + b)/2$ for every pair of natural numbers a and b. Does the cancellation law for $*$ hold for the set of natural numbers?

3. Define the operation $\bigcirc$ by $a \bigcirc b = 2a + b$ for every pair of natural numbers a and b. Does the cancellation law for $\bigcirc$ hold for the set of natural numbers?

4. Consider the "arithmetic" A of Exercise 3 of the preceding section. Does the cancellation law for $\oplus$ hold for this "arithmetic?"

5. The cancellation law for addition is frequently useful in solving equations. For example, suppose we desire to find a natural number x such that $5 + x = 12$. If we rewrite the equation in the form $5 + x = 5 + 7$, then

it is apparent from the cancellation law that $x = 7$. Moreover, it is easy to see that this value of x makes the original equation a true statement. Use this idea to solve the following equations. In each case, check to see that your answer is correct.

(a) $6 + x = 13$ (b) $17 + x = 43$

(c) $x + 7 = 21$ (d) $x + 105 = 231$

6. Applying the cancellation law for addition involves more than physically striking out the same number from both sides of an equation. In each of the following, decide which "cancellations" are justified and which are not.

(a) If $2a + 4 = 2a + b$, then $\cancel{2a} + 4 = \cancel{2a} + b$ and $4 = b$.

(b) If $2(a + 4) = a + c$, then $2(\cancel{a} + 4) = \cancel{a} + c$ and $2 \cdot 4 = c$.

(c) If $x + 7 = 7 + 14$, then $x + \cancel{7} = \cancel{7} + 14$ and $x = 14$.

(d) If $5x + 7 = 5y + 6$, then $\cancel{5x} + 7 = \cancel{5y} + 6$ and $x + 7 = y + 6$.

2.9 Multiplication of Natural Numbers

Just as addition of numbers is a natural outgrowth of the counting process, multiplication arises as a natural extension of addition. Indeed, the problem of finding sums of equal numbers undoubtedly originally led man to *invent* the idea of multiplication and to devise rules by which formal multiplication of numbers might be carried out. We understand multiplication, therefore, in terms of repeated addition; and, with this in mind, it is not difficult to discover the fundamental rules governing multiplication of natural numbers. For example, consider the problem of finding the number of squares in the array shown in Fig. 2.1. How would you solve the problem? Certainly very few would take the time to count each individual square, since the total can be found more easily by counting the number of squares per row and then adding over the number of rows, or by finding the number of squares per column and then adding over the number of columns. Thus, we easily find the answer of 56 as the sum of seven eights or the sum of eight sevens, and Fig. 2.1 provides a natural geometrical representation of the product of 7 and 8.

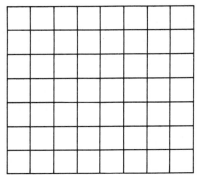

Figure 2.1 A geometrical representation of the product 7 · 8.

With this understanding of multiplication, it is apparent that the value of a product should be independent of the order in which the numbers involved are considered. This situation is formalized in the statement of the following properties which are clearly analogous to the corresponding properties for addition. As mentioned earlier, we denote the product of a and b by writing either $a \cdot b$ or ab.

P6. *Closure Law for Multiplication.* If a and b are any two natural numbers, then ab is a natural number.

P7. *Commutative Law for Multiplication.* If a and b are any two natural numbers, then $ab = ba$.

2.10 Associative Law for Multiplication

Like addition, multiplication is a binary operation, and so it is necessary to have a rule specifying how the product of more than two numbers should be found. Suppose, for example, that we want the product of 3, 4, and 5. If we interpret this to mean $3 \cdot (4 \cdot 5)$, so that we take 3 times the product of 4 and 5, then we are essentially taking the sum of three of the products $4 \cdot 5$. The product $4 \cdot 5$ can be geometrically interpreted in the sense of Fig. 2.1 as a rectangular array of squares with 4 rows and 5 columns. Or, if one adds a third dimension, one might interpret the product as a rectangular array of cubes with 4 rows and 5 columns, as in Fig. 2.2. Since $3 \cdot (4 \cdot 5)$ can be conceived as the sum of three of the products $4 \cdot 5$, we might now obtain a geometrical representation of the entire product by placing three of the arrays of Fig. 2.2 together to form a solid array of boxes measuring 3 units by 4 units by 5 units, as shown in Fig. 2.3

If the product $(3 \cdot 4) \cdot 5$ is treated in the same way, essentially the same solid array of boxes will result; and it is easy to see that we should have $3 \cdot (4 \cdot 5) = (3 \cdot 4) \cdot 5$. This result is formalized in the statement of the associative law for multiplication, which is completely analogous to the corresponding law for addition.

P8. *Associative Law for Multiplication.* If a, b, and c are any three natural numbers, then $(ab)c = a(bc)$.

As before, this law makes it possible to associate numbers in more complicated products in any way whatever, so that it is customary to

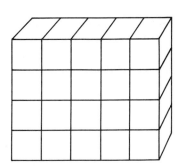

Figure 2.2 A geometrical representation of the product 4 · 5.

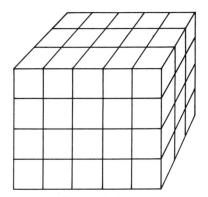

Figure 2.3 A geometrical representation of the product 3 · (4 · 5).

omit any grouping symbols. Thus, for example, one would simply write *abcd* rather than $[(ab)c]d$ or $(ab)(cd)$ or any of the other possible groupings.

2.11 Cancellation Law for Multiplication

Another property of multiplication which is exactly analogous to its additive counterpart is the cancellation law for multiplication.

P9. *Cancellation Law for Multiplication.* If *a*, *b*, and *c* are any three natural numbers such that $ab = ac$, then $b = c$.

To see that this is so, we consider two rectangular arrays of boxes, one with *b* columns and *a* boxes per column representing the product *ab*, and the other with *c* columns and *a* boxes per column representing *ac*. If we are further given that both arrays involve the same number of boxes, then it is clear that the number of columns must be the same in each case, so that $b = c$. For, if *b* were not equal to *c*, then by the law of trichotomy either *b* is greater than *c* or *c* is greater than *b*. Therefore, if we were to count off the boxes in each array one for one by columns (since all of the columns contain *a* boxes), it is clear that one array would be exhausted before the other so that the number of boxes in the two arrays could not be the same. Thus, if *ab* is equal to *ac*, it must be the case that $b = c$.

1. Draw a single diagonal in each of the small squares in Fig. 2.1 and explain how you can then conclude that there are 112 triangles in all.

2. A famous and very old (*c.* 1730) puzzle reads as follows:

   > *As I was going to St. Ives,*
   > *I met a man with seven wives,*
   > *Each wife had seven sacks,*
   > *Each sack had seven cats,*
   > *Each cat had seven kits:*
   > *Kits, cats, sacks, and wives,*
   > *How many were going to St. Ives?*

3. Of course, the correct answer to Exercise 2 is 1 since, according to the poem, the man with the wives is coming from, not going to, St. Ives. On the other hand, the number of kits, cats, sacks, and wives coming from St. Ives is quite large. Compute this number and show how the associative laws for multiplication and addition are involved in making the computation.

4. The cancellation law for multiplication is frequently useful in solving equations of the form $ax = b$. For example, suppose we desire to find a natural number x such that $3x = 21$. If we rewrite the equation in the form $3x = 3 \cdot 7$, then it follows from the cancellation law for multiplication that $x = 7$. Moreover, it is easy to see that this value of x checks in the original equation. Use this idea to solve and check the following equations.

   (a) $5x = 95$ (b) $11x = 451$

   (c) $x \cdot 7 = 1001$ (d) $13x = 1001$

5. The following is a solution of the equation $7 + 3x = 28$. We begin by assuming that x is a natural number for which the equation is true. State a property which justifies each step of the solution left unjustified.

$$7 + 3x = 28 \qquad \text{Given}$$
$$7 + 3x = 7 + 21 \qquad \text{Since } 7 + 21 = 28$$
$$3x = 21 \qquad \text{Why?}$$
$$3x = 3 \cdot 7 \qquad \text{Since } 3 \cdot 7 = 21$$
$$x = 7 \qquad \text{Why?}$$

To check our solution we note that, if $x = 7$, then $7 + 3x = 7 + 3 \cdot 7 = 7 + 21 = 28$ as required.

6. The following is a solution of $3x + 7 = 22$. Give a reason justifying each step of the solution left unjustified. We begin by assuming that x is a natural number such that $3x + 7 = 22$.

$3x$ is a natural number	Why?
$3x + 7 = 7 + 3x$	Why?
$7 + 3x = 22$	Since $3x + 7 = 7 + 3x$, and $3x + 7 = 22$
$7 + 3x = 7 + 15$	Since $7 + 15 = 22$
$3x = 15$	Why?
$3x = 3 \cdot 5$	Since $3 \cdot 5 = 15$
$x = 5$	Why?

Check that the solution is correct.

7. Solve the following equations and check your answers.

    (a) $7x + 14 = 35$ (b) $11x + 9 = 130$ (c) $7x + 6 = 34$

2.12 The Multiplicative Identity

A final rule concerning multiplication formalizes a rather obvious property of the number 1. If we continue to think of multiplication in terms of repeated addition, then the product $1 \cdot a$ should be regarded as a sum involving a single a whose value, therefore, is simply a. A geometrical representation of the product $1 \cdot 8$, for example, consists simply of eight squares in a rectangular array, as shown in Fig. 2.4, with 1 row and 8 columns. A formal statement of this property is contained in the following statement.

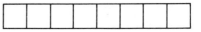

Figure 2.4 A geometrical representation of the product $1 \cdot 8$.

P10. *Existence of a Multiplicative Identity.* There exists a natural number, designated by the symbol "1," having the property that $1 \cdot a = a$ for every natural number a.

Of course, because of the commutative law for multiplication, $1 \cdot a = a \cdot 1$, so that $a \cdot 1 = a$ also.

The existence of a unit element or *multiplicative identity* is an important property of the natural number system which is not always shared by other systems of numbers. To be quite explicit, if we have a set S of elements and an operation $*$ defined for all pairs of elements in S, an element e of S is said to be an *identity with respect to the operation* $*$ in case $e * a = a * e = a$ for every a in S. For example, we note that 1 is the multiplicative identity for the set of odd numbers, and that there is no multiplicative identity in the set of even numbers. We also note that there is no *additive* identity in the set of natural numbers since there is no *natural number* e such that $e + a = a + e = a$ for every natural number a. Of course, we know that $0 + a = a + 0 = a$ for any number a, so that the set including 0 and the natural numbers does have an additive identity.

EXERCISES

1. Does the set of natural numbers which are multiples of 3 possess a multiplicative identity?

2. Does the set of natural numbers which leave a remainder of 1 when divided by 3 possess a multiplicative identity?

3. If the operation $*$ is defined by $a * b = (a + b)/2$ for every pair of natural numbers, does the set of natural numbers possess an identity with respect to $*$? That is, is there a single natural number e such that $e * a = a * e = a$ for every natural number a?

4. Let the operation $\bigcirc$ be defined by $a \bigcirc b = 2a + b$.

   (a) Does the set of natural numbers possess an identity with respect to $\bigcirc$?

   (b) Does the set comprising the natural numbers and zero possess an identity with respect to $\bigcirc$?

5. Let $S = \{1, 2, 3, 4, 5, 6, 7\}$.

   (a) Is S closed with respect to multiplication?

   (b) Is there an additive identity in S?

   (c) Is there a multiplicative identity in S?

6. Let A denote the arithmetic defined by the "addition" table shown. Does A possess an identity with respect to the operation $\oplus$?

$\oplus$	1	2	3	4
1	2	4	3	1
2	4	3	1	2
3	3	1	2	3
4	1	2	3	4

7. Since there is no natural number e such that $e \div a = a$ for every natural number a, the natural numbers do not possess an identity with respect to division. On the other hand, there is a natural number, namely 1, such that $a \div 1 = a$ for every natural number a. Unlike multiplication, the situation here is not symmetric; and this is because the natural numbers are not commutative with respect to division. In this case, we say that the natural numbers possess a *right identity* with respect to division but not a *left identity*. Does the set comprising the natural numbers and zero possess an identity for subtraction? a right identity? a left identity?

2.13 The Distributive Law

Up to this point we have considered properties concerned separately with addition and multiplication of natural numbers. One of the most important properties of the natural numbers, however, involves a combination of these two notions. For example, the product of 3 and 8 can be thought of as the product of 3 and $(3 + 5)$ or as the sum of the products $3 \cdot 3$ and $3 \cdot 5$. Geometrically, this corresponds to separating an array of boxes with 3 rows and 8 columns into two arrays, one with 3 rows and 3 columns, and the other with 3 rows and 5 columns, as shown in Fig. 2.5. It is apparent that $3(3 + 5) = 3 \cdot 3 + 3 \cdot 5$ and we have the following general rule.

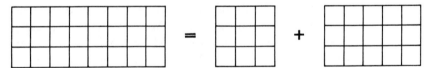

Figure 2.5   A geometrical interpretation of the distributive law.

P11. *Distributive Law.* If a, b, and c, are any three natural numbers then $a(b + c) = ab + ac$.

This property, which is often quite useful, is the basis for a standard trick in mental computation. For example, the product $23 \cdot 32$ is more easily handled mentally by thinking of the product $23 \cdot (30 + 2)$. This quite easily gives the answer of $690 + 46$, or 736, without the use of pencil and paper. Incidentally, the same trick also works with regard to subtraction since, as we will show later, $a(b - c) = ab - ac$. With this in mind, one might mentally compute the product $23 \cdot 29$ by thinking of $23 \cdot (30 - 1) = 690 - 23 = 667$ instead of $23(20 + 9) = 460 + 207 = 667$.

EXERCISES

1. Compute the following pairs of expressions.

   (a) $3(7 + 6)$ and $3 \cdot 7 + 3 \cdot 6$

   (b) $11(8 + 5)$ and $11 \cdot 8 + 11 \cdot 5$

   (c) $48(20 + 1)$ and $48 \cdot 20 + 48 \cdot 1$

   (d) $63(20 - 1)$ and $63 \cdot 20 - 63 \cdot 1$

2. Use the distributive law and mental arithmetic to find the following products.

   (a) $33 \cdot 21$ (b) $54 \cdot 201$

   (c) $45 \cdot 19$ (d) $35 \cdot 198$

2.14 The Inductive Property

The last property of the natural numbers to be considered in this chapter might very well have been first since it is so intimately associated with the notion of counting and the origin of the set of natural numbers. As we have pointed out, the natural numbers are abstractions created for the enumeration of finite sets of objects, one natural number corresponding to all sets of a given size and conversely. Moreover, it is clear that a finite set of any desired size can be constructed by starting with a single element and introducing additional elements one at a time until the desired number of elements is obtained. Numerically, this is to say that any natural number can be obtained by starting with 1 and adding 1 successively until the desired number is reached. Differently put, this statement says that, starting with 1 and adding 1 successively *ad infinitum*, one can generate the entire set of natural numbers. Thus, the sequence

$$1, \quad 1 + 1 = 2, \quad 2 + 1 = 3, \quad 3 + 1 = 4, \quad \ldots$$

contains all natural numbers. This property is given the following formal statement.

P12. *The Inductive Property.* Any set of natural numbers that contains the natural number 1 and contains $(k + 1)$ whenever it contains k, contains *all* natural numbers.

Note that the second part of P12 states that, if the set of numbers in question contains any particular natural number, then it also contains the next natural number. Thus, since the first part of the statement guarantees that 1 is in the set, it follows that 2 must be in the set. But again, if 2 is in the set, then 3 must be in the set; and if 3 is in the set, then so is 4; and so on. Since P12 then says that the set must contain all natural numbers, we are assured that all natural numbers can be generated in this way.

It may be helpful to compare P12 to a situation where a person is to climb an endless ladder. If it is guaranteed that he can climb to the first step, and that from any particular step he can climb to the next step, then there is no doubt about his ability to climb the ladder. Similarly, the inductive property of the natural numbers guarantees that the entire set of natural numbers is generated by the process of successively adding one to itself as described above.

EXERCISES

1. The principle of mathematical induction can be compared to the childhood pastime of setting up dominoes in a line in such a way that they all fall down when the first one in line is pushed over. Two things are necessary in order that all of the dominoes fall down: first, the dominoes must be set up in such a way that if any domino falls it will knock down its neighbor; and second, the first domino must be pushed down.

   (a) Suppose that the dominoes are correctly situated as in the diagram and that the third one is pushed over as shown. What will be the result?

   (b) What can be said about a set of natural numbers that contains the number 3 and contains $(k + 1)$ whenever it contains the number k?

2.15 Clock Arithmetic

In order to provide a brief review of the matters discussed in this chapter, we turn to the study of clock arithmetic. This is a system similar to and yet significantly different from the system of natural numbers. We begin by considering the face of an ordinary clock and asking what type of arithmetic is involved. That is, we have a system consisting of the numbers 1, 2, 3, ..., 12, and we ask what addition and multiplication of these numbers in this situation should mean and what rules of computation should prevail.

Immediately we note that if addition and multiplication were to have their usual meaning, then our system would *not* be closed under either operation. For example, $7 + 8 = 15$ and 15 is not a member of the system, and $7 \cdot 8 = 56$ and 56 is not a member of the system. However, if we again think of addition in terms of counting *in this system*, and if we also think of multiplication as repeated addition, we will arrive at modified notions of these concepts more consistent with the reckoning of time. As noted earlier, the sum of 7 and 8 can be found by counting out sets of seven objects and eight objects respectively, and then combining the sets and finding the total count of the resulting set of objects. Any sets of objects can be used, but a particularly useful counting set consists of a numbered set of points on a stick or line as indicated in

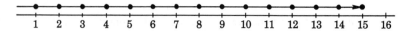

Figure 2.6   *Addition of 7 and 8 by counting on a numbered line.*

Fig. 2.6. Here, to add 7 and 8, one might proceed by counting the first seven points and then continuing on to count the next eight points, for

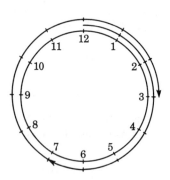

Figure 2.7   Addition of 7 and 8 on the clock.

a total of 15 as indicated in the figure. If this operation were performed on the face of a clock, as illustrated in Fig. 2.7, one would start at 1, count up to 7, count 8 more, and stop at 3. Thus, in this system, one might reasonably say that the "sum" of 7 and 8 is 3.

Since addition on the clock is not our ordinary notion of addition, we will not indicate it with an ordinary plus sign. Instead, the clock sum will be indicated by the symbol $+_{12}$ so that, for example, $7 +_{12} 8 = 3$. Similarly, we would write $5 +_{12} 9 = 2$; $11 +_{12} 6 = 5$; $11 +_{12} 11 = 10$; and so on.

Of course, one can easily obtain the entire addition table for this finite arithmetic. The result is shown in Fig. 2.8 with the clock sum of a and b at the intersection of the ath row and bth column.

$+_{12}$	1	2	3	4	5	6	7	8	9	10	11	12
1	2	3	4	5	6	7	8	9	10	11	12	1
2	3	4	5	6	7	8	9	10	11	12	1	2
3	4	5	6	7	8	9	10	11	12	1	2	3
4	5	6	7	8	9	10	11	12	1	2	3	4
5	6	7	8	9	10	11	12	1	2	3	4	5
6	7	8	9	10	11	12	1	2	3	4	5	6
7	8	9	10	11	12	1	2	3	4	5	6	7
8	9	10	11	12	1	2	3	4	5	6	7	8
9	10	11	12	1	2	3	4	5	6	7	8	9
10	11	12	1	2	3	4	5	6	7	8	9	10
11	12	1	2	3	4	5	6	7	8	9	10	11
12	1	2	3	4	5	6	7	8	9	10	11	12

Figure 2.8 Table for addition on the clock.

Just as ordinary multiplication can be understood in terms of repeated addition, one might define multiplication on the clock in terms of repeated clock addition. Of course, the results will be different from those of ordinary multiplication and so we indicate clock multiplication with the symbol $\times_{12}$. For example, we easily obtain $2 \times_{12} 7 = 7 +_{12} 7 = 2$; $3 \times_{12} 5 = 5 +_{12} 5 +_{12} 5 = 3$; $5 \times_{12} 7 = 11$; and so on. Again we can construct a complete multiplication table, and the result is shown in Fig. 2.9.

$\times_{12}$	1	2	3	4	5	6	7	8	9	10	11	12
1	1	2	3	4	5	6	7	8	9	10	11	12
2	2	4	6	8	10	12	2	4	6	8	10	12
3	3	6	9	12	3	6	9	12	3	6	9	12
4	4	8	12	4	8	12	4	8	12	4	8	12
5	5	10	3	8	1	6	11	4	9	2	7	12
6	6	12	6	12	6	12	6	12	6	12	6	12
7	7	2	9	4	11	6	1	8	3	10	5	12
8	8	4	12	8	4	12	8	4	12	8	4	12
9	9	6	3	12	9	6	3	12	9	6	3	12
10	10	8	6	4	2	12	10	8	6	4	2	12
11	11	10	9	8	7	6	5	4	3	2	1	12
12	12	12	12	12	12	12	12	12	12	12	12	12

Figure 2.9 Table for multiplication on the clock.

The arithmetical properties of clock arithmetic are, in fact, completely determined by the two tables we have just constructed. Let us see if we can determine what these properties are.

In the first place, we note that, with the modified interpretations, we now have closure for both addition and multiplication on the clock. To check the commutative laws, we must determine whether

$$a \mathbin{+_{12}} b = b \mathbin{+_{12}} a \quad \text{and} \quad a \mathbin{\times_{12}} b = b \mathbin{\times_{12}} a$$

for all numbers a and b in the system. This is easy to see from the addition and multiplication tables, since both tables are symmetrical about a line drawn diagonally from the upper left hand corner to the lower right-hand corner, and $a \mathbin{+_{12}} b$ and $b \mathbin{+_{12}} a$, and $a \mathbin{\times_{12}} b$ and $b \mathbin{\times_{12}} a$ are symmetrically placed in the tables with respect to this diagonal as shown in Fig. 2.10. The reader should check this for specific values of a and b in both Fig. 2.8 and 2.9.

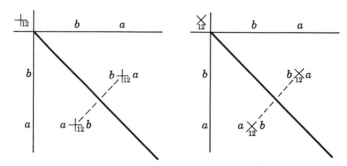

Figure 2.10   Symmetric character of the addition and multiplication tables.

The associative and distributive laws are easily checked for particular values. For example, from the tables

$$(3 \mathbin{+_{12}} 7) \mathbin{+_{12}} 5 = 3 \mathbin{+_{12}} (7 \mathbin{+_{12}} 5)$$

and

$$4 \mathbin{\times_{12}} (6 \mathbin{+_{12}} 8) = (4 \mathbin{\times_{12}} 6) \mathbin{+_{12}} (4 \mathbin{\times_{12}} 8).$$

It is usually very difficult, given only addition and multiplication tables, to show that these laws hold in general in a given system since it is necessary to check each different triple of numbers in the system individually. In the present case, this would involve $(12)^3 = 1728$ individual computations for each table, and the work is prohibitive. Arithmetic on the clock, however, is closely related to ordinary arithmetic; and it is not too difficult to argue that these laws hold in clock arithmetic in view of the fact that they hold for the system of natural numbers.

A moment's reflection will show that the clock sum or product of any two numbers can be obtained from the oridinary sum or product in the following way. If the result of the usual computation is a multiple of 12, the result in clock arithmetic is 12. If the result in ordinary arithmetic is not a multiple of 12, then the result in clock arithmetic is the *remainder* when the result in ordinary arithmetic is divided by 12. For example, in ordinary arithmetic $3(2 + 6) = 24$, and in clock arithmetic $3 \underset{12}{\times} (2 \underset{12}{+} 6) = 12$. Also, in ordinary arithmetic $(5 + 8) + 6 = 19$; in clock arithmetic $(5 \underset{12}{+} 8) \underset{12}{+} 6 = 7$, and 7 is the remainder when 19 is divided by 12. Now in ordinary arithmetic

$$(a + b) + c = a + (b + c), \quad (ab)c = a(bc), \quad \text{and} \quad a(b + c) = ab + ac.$$

Therefore, if these results are interpreted in clock arithmetic according to the preceding rules, we still have

$$(a \underset{12}{+} b) \underset{12}{+} c = a \underset{12}{+} (b \underset{12}{+} c)$$

$$(a \underset{12}{\times} b) \underset{12}{\times} c = a \underset{12}{\times} (b \underset{12}{\times} c)$$

and

$$a \underset{12}{\times} (b \underset{12}{+} c) = (a \underset{12}{\times} b) \underset{12}{+} (a \underset{12}{\times} c).$$

Thus, the associative and distributive laws hold in clock arithmetic as well as in ordinary arithmetic.

It is interesting to note that the law of trichotomy does *not* hold in arithmetic on the clock. Recall that the law of trichotomy for the natural numbers states that, given any two natural numbers a and b, precisely one of the three following situations prevails: either $a = b$; or there exists a natural number r such that $a = b + r$; or there exists a natural number s such that $a + s = b$. To see that this is not always true in clock arithmetic, it suffices to show a single instance which violates the stated conditions. In particular we note that $2 = 10 \underset{12}{+} 4$ *and* $2 \underset{12}{+} 8 = 10$. Thus, if $a = 2$ and $b = 10$, we can find *both* r and s such that $a = b \underset{12}{+} r$ and $a \underset{12}{+} s = b$ in violation of the restriction that *precisely one* of the three stated conditions hold. Therefore, the law of trichotomy does not hold in clock arithmetic.

To show that the cancellation law for addition holds in clock arithmetic, it is necessary to show that it is impossible to find three numbers a, b, and c in the system with $b \neq c$ such that $a +_{12} b = a +_{12} c$. Since this simply involves checking to see that no entry appears twice in any row of the addition table, it is clear that the law holds for clock arithmetic. On the other hand, a glance at the multiplication table shows that the cancellation law for multiplication does *not* hold. In particular, for example, we have $3 \times_{12} 4 = 3 \times_{12} 8$, but $4 \neq 8$.

Since $1 \times_{12} a = a \times_{12} 1 = a$ for any a in the clock arithmetic, it is clear that this system possesses a unity or multiplicative identity. In this connection it is interesting to note that, unlike the system of natural numbers, clock arithmetic also contains an additive identity or zero element. That is, there is an element e in clock arithmetic such that $e +_{12} a = a +_{12} e = a$ for every a in the system. As seen from the addition table, $e = 12$ has this property. As mentioned earlier, the number 0 is the additive identity in ordinary arithmetic, but 0 is usually not classified as a natural number.

It may also be of interest to note that 12 plays the same multiplicative role in clock arithmetic as 0 does in ordinary arithmetic. Thus, we note that $0 \cdot a = 0$ for any natural number a, and that $12 \times_{12} a = 12$ for any a in clock arithmetic. On the other hand, the equation $ab = 0$ is impossible if a and b are natural numbers; whereas, in clock arithmetic, we have expressions like $3 \times_{12} 8 = 12$ and $4 \times_{12} 6 = 12$, with neither 3, 4, 6, nor 8 equal to 12. In such cases, where a product of two numbers is the additive identity or zero of a system though neither is itself the zero, the numbers are said to be *divisors of zero*, and the system is said to contain divisors of zero. Thus, in clock arithmetic, 2, 3, 4, 6, 8, 9, and 10 are all divisors of zero. One might make the correspondence between 0 in ordinary arithmetic and 12 in clock arithmetic even more clear by replacing the 12 by the 0 in each instance in the latter case. This would not change clock arithmetic in any way since it is simply renaming one of the elements, but it would make more apparent such statements as "2 is a divisor of zero in clock arithmetic" and "there is an additive identity in clock arithmetic."

Finally, it is clear from the addition table that the inductive property holds for clock arithmetic. Indeed, the reader can easily check that any set of numbers in clock arithmetic that contains 5, and that contains $k +_{12} 5$ whenever it contains k, contains all numbers in the clock arithmetic. Thus, the inductive property holds in clock arithmetic with 5 substituted in place of 1. Moreover, 7 and 11 can also be used as generators in place of 1. This situation is, of course, quite contrary to that with the system of natural numbers.

To summarize, we note that the closure laws, commutative laws, associative laws, the cancellation law for addition, and the inductive property all hold in clock arithmetic, and that there is a multiplicative identity. However, unlike the system of natural numbers, the law of trichotomy and the cancellation law for multiplication fail to hold, and clock arithmetic has both an additive identity, or zero, and divisors of zero. In the sequel we will note still other similarities and differences between arithmetic on the clock and the ordinary arithmetic familiar to us all.

EXERCISES

1. Compute the following mentally and check your answers by looking at Figs. 2.8 and 2.9:

   (a) $11 +_{12} 7$ (b) $6 +_{12} 2$ (c) $6 +_{12} 8$

   (d) $9 +_{12} 9$ (e) $4 \times_{12} 5$ (f) $3 \times_{12} 7$

   (g) $6 \times_{12} 8$ (h) $11 \times_{12} 7$

2. Compute the following pairs of sums and products:

   (a) $(6 +_{12} 7) +_{12} 5$ and $6 +_{12} (7 +_{12} 5)$

   (b) $(8 +_{12} 4) +_{12} 7$ and $8 +_{12} (4 +_{12} 7)$

   (c) $(6 \times_{12} 7) \times_{12} 5$ and $6 \times_{12} (7 \times_{12} 5)$

   (d) $(8 \times_{12} 4) \times_{12} 7$ and $8 \times_{12} (4 \times_{12} 7)$

   (e) $6 \times_{12} (7 +_{12} 5)$ and $(6 \times_{12} 7) +_{12} (6 \times_{12} 5)$

   (f) $8 \times_{12} (4 +_{12} 7)$ and $(8 \times_{12} 4) +_{12} (8 \times_{12} 7)$

3. Compute the following pairs of sums and products:

   (a) $3 +_{12} (4 \times_{12} 6)$ and $(3 +_{12} 4) \times_{12} (3 +_{12} 6)$

   (b) $7 +_{12} (1 \times_{12} 5)$ and $(7 +_{12} 1) \times_{12} (7 +_{12} 5)$

   (c) $4 +_{12} (2 \times_{12} 7)$ and $(4 +_{12} 2) \times_{12} (4 +_{12} 7)$

   (d) Does it follow from these examples that

   $$a +_{12} (b \times_{12} c) = (a +_{12} b) \times_{12} (a +_{12} c)$$

   for every triple a, b, c, of numbers in clock arithmetic?

   (e) Check your answer to part (d) by constructing another example.

4. Construct three examples that show that the law of trichotomy does not hold in clock arithmetic.

5. We have noted that the cancellation law for multiplication does not hold in clock arithmetic. However, for certain values of a in clock arithmetic, it is true that if $a \overset{\times}{_{12}} b = a \overset{\times}{_{12}} c$, then $b = c$. For what values of a is this true? Is it true if a is a divisor of zero?

6. It is clear from Fig. 2.8 that the principle of mathematical induction holds for clock arithmetic; i.e., all of the numbers in clock arithmetic can be generated by starting with 1 and adding 1 successively. Show that the numbers in clock arithmetic can also be generated by starting with 5 and adding 5 successively.

7. Solve and check the following equations in clock arithmetic:

   (a) $x \overset{+}{_{12}} 4 = 2$

   (b) $(5 \overset{\times}{_{12}} x) \overset{+}{_{12}} 1 = 2$

   (c) $(11 \overset{\times}{_{12}} x) \overset{+}{_{12}} 12 = 4$

   (d) $5 \overset{\times}{_{12}} (x \overset{+}{_{12}} 7) = 1$

8. Suppose the clock were divided into 7 equal "hours" instead of 12. Construct the addition and multiplication tables for the arithmetic on this clock, using $\overset{+}{_{7}}$ and $\overset{\times}{_{7}}$ to denote addition and multiplication respectively for this arithmetic.

9. Answer the following questions concerning the clock arithmetic of Exercise 8. Explain each of your answers.

   (a) Are the closure laws satisfied?

   (b) Are the commutative laws satisfied?

   (c) Are the associative laws satisfied?

   (d) Is the distributive law satisfied?

   (e) Is the law of trichotomy satisfied?

   (f) Do the cancellation laws hold?

   (g) For which values of a is it true that if $a \overset{\times}{_{7}} b = a \overset{\times}{_{7}} c$, then $b = c$?

   (h) Does the inductive property hold?

   (i) Would the inductive property hold with some other number replacing 1? If so, which numbers?

   (j) Is there a multiplicative identity?

   (k) Is there an additive identity or zero?

   (l) Are there any divisors of zero?

10. Repeat Exercises 8 and 9 for a clock divided into four equal "hours," using $+_4$ and $\times_4$ to denote addition and multiplication for this clock arithmetic.

11. Review the results of Exercises 8, 9, and 10, as well as the arithmetic for the 12-hour clock, and answer the following questions. It may help to work out the addition and multiplication tables for clocks with 3 hours, 5 hours, and 9 hours so that you will have more experimental data.

   (a) Can you guess for which clocks the corresponding arithmetics will fail to have divisors of zero?

   (b) For any given clock with n hours, can you guess for which values of a it is true that if $a \times b = a \times c$, then $b = c$?

   (c) Can you guess for which values of n it is true that if $a \times b = a \times c$, and $a \neq n$, then $b = c$?

   (d) For any given clock arithmetic, can you guess which numbers can serve as "generators" in connection with the inductive property?

12. Consider the set S of elements α, β, γ, δ, with the operation $\odot$ defined by the following table where, for example, $\beta \odot \delta$ is found at the intersection of the second row and fourth column.

$\odot$	α	β	γ	δ
α	β	γ	α	α
β	γ	γ	β	β
γ	α	β	α	γ
δ	α	β	γ	δ

   (a) Is S closed with respect to $\odot$?

   (b) Is S cummutative with respect to $\odot$?

   (c) Does the cancellation law for $\odot$ hold in S?

   (d) Is there an identity element for $\odot$ in S?

   (e) Consider the expressions $(\beta \odot \beta) \odot \alpha$ and $\beta \odot (\beta \odot \alpha)$. Does the associative law for $\odot$ hold in S?

13. Repeat Exercise 12 and its parts for the set $T = \{a, b, c, d, e\}$ and the operation X defined by the following table. For part e, consider $(a\ X\ c)\ X\ d$ and $a\ X\ (c\ X\ d)$

X	a	b	c	d	e
a	b	c	a	d	e
b	c	a	b	d	e
c	a	b	c	e	d
d	e	e	d	e	d
e	d	d	e	d	e

3

**THE
NATURE
OF
MATHEMATICAL
SYSTEMS**

3.1 Introduction

We have been considering arithmetic as an intuitive system, arising out of the need to count and in this way to compare two sets of things so as to determine whether one or the other has more elements, or to describe how many elements there are in some given set. From this intuitive notion of number we have obtained, also in an intuitive manner, a set of rules for the manipulation of the numbers, or more precisely for the manipulation of the numerals which represent the numbers in some system of notation.

Geometry also originated in much the same way, as an intuitive and empirical set of rules for describing shapes and their properties, comparing sizes, and so forth. Indeed, it is difficult to imagine that these subjects could have originated in any other way. One must have considerable experience with those abstractions that we call quantity and shape before these concepts can be thought about. Then there must follow a period of discovering patterns of relationship before one can organize his thoughts about these things into a form in which they can be systematically studied.

But even as early as the time of the Greeks, the idea occurred to some students of geometry that perhaps the subject could be transformed from a collection of related observations into a system wherein most of the results were deduced logically from comparatively few basic principles. Thus, while one still needed to determine which geometric properties were in some sense basic, the greater part of the development of the subject become deduction rather than discovery. Of course, the deductions were still largely guided by the previously developed intuitive sense of what seemed to be true. Once a basic property was selected, it was distinguished by the title of *axiom* or *postulate*, meaning that which was to be assumed without question in the ensuing discussion.

If one is going to have postulates or axioms, they clearly must be about something, whether numbers, points, or whatever. This raises the problem of definition of terms. Just what does one mean by the number two, or by a point? If we approach the problem of defining terms by giving definitions like those in a dictionary, we soon encounter *circularity*. That is, in a dictionary a given word is defined in terms of a second, the second in terms of a third, and so on until one encounters a word whose definition involves the initial word. This form of definition is fine if one already knows the meaning of some word in the circular chain, but certainly will not do for defining terms *ab initio*. Thus it does us no good to say that a triangle is a plane figure formed by three line segments joined at their extremities in pairs, and then later to say that such a figure is a triangle.

If we try to give definitions of terms and yet avoid the trap of circularity, we encounter the difficulty of *infinite regression*. That is, no matter how long a chain of definitions we produce, the terms at the end of the chain still are undefined, and we are essentially no better off than we were at the beginning.

The only way out of the apparent dilemma is simply to adopt certain terms as being undefined and start from there. We then give meaning to these terms by postulating certain properties which they are to possess. Of course, we may have rather clear intuitive notions of what the terms are to mean. However, we must agree that no properties of these terms will be admissible in our arguments except those specifically stated in the postulates or deduced therefrom.

The development of this deductive approach to geometry made possible a great unification and extension of the subject, and it is somewhat surprising therefore that no such development occurred in arithmetic for about two thousand years. As contributing factors to this seeming neglect of arithmetic, one might mention the lack of a suitable notation system (until the introduction of the Hindu–Arabic notation which we still use) as well as the low opinion which scholars held for many years of the world of commerce, the principal user of arithmetic. In any case, the deductive method was not systematically applied to arithmetic until comparatively modern times, and it remained largely a collection of rules of experience.

In the first half of the nineteenth century, a mathematical revolution occurred, both in geometry and in arithmetic, of perhaps even greater import than the introduction of the deductive method by the Greeks. Until that time, less than a century and a half ago, both geometry and arithmetic had been generally considered to be descriptions of reality which had been discovered over the centuries. Thus a mathematical result was considered to be true or false depending on whether or not it checked with observations of the physical world. If a result deduced from postulates failed to check, then the trouble had to be in the postulates, some of which must be wrong.

In the early part of the nineteenth century Carl Friedrich Gauss (1777–1855), a German mathematician; John Bolyai (1802–1860), a Hungarian; and Nicholas Lobachevski (1793–1856), a Russian, independently developed systems of geometry in which not all the properties of Euclidean geometry are valid. One such property, the famous theorem of Pythagoras (Fig. 3.1), states that in any plane right triangle the square of the length of the hypoteneuse (the side opposite the right angle) is equal to the sum of the squares of the lengths of the other two sides.

On the surface of a sphere (which the earth's surface approximates) this theorem does not hold. To see this we must first say what we mean by a triangle, and in particular a right triangle, on this surface. It can be shown that the shortest distance between two points on a spherical surface is along an arc of a *great circle*; that is, a circle whose center is at the center of the sphere and which passes through the two points in question. For example, the equator and the circles of longitude are great circles on the earth's surface, whereas the parallels of latitude other than the equator are not great circles. Thus in a direct flight from Los Angeles to Tokyo, which are about the same latitude, an airplane would not follow a parallel of latitude since it could save considerable distance by

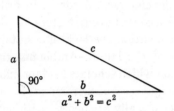

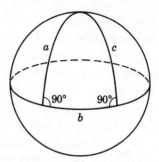

Figure 3.1   The theorem of
Pythagoras.

Figure 3.2   A right spherical
triangle.

flying along a great circle. (This may easily be checked with a globe
and a piece of string.) Since great circles, or arcs thereof, form the shortest
paths between points on a spherical surface, they play a role in this
geometry similar to that of straight lines in a plane.

By a spherical triangle we then mean the figure formed by joining
arcs of three great circles on a sphere. A right spherical triangle is one in
which two of the sides meet at a right angle; i.e. an angle of 90°. Consider
then the right spherical triangle of Fig. 3.2. Here we have the triangle
formed by arcs of two different circles of longitude and an arc of the
equator. Since $a = c$, it is clear that we do not have $a^2 + b^2 = c^2$ as
the theorem of Pythagoras would require. We also note that while
the sum of the angles in any plane triangle is always 180°, the spherical
triangle of Fig. 3.2 has more than 180° in its three angles.

Thus we have a perfectly sound and indeed very useful two-dimensional geometry which is quite different from two-dimensional Euclidean
geometry.

During the same period in which the development of non-Euclidean
geometries began, similar events were taking place in arithmetic, or
algebra. In seeking to develop an algebra that would describe certain
physical relationships in which he was interested, Sir William R. Hamilton
(1805–1865), an Irish mathematician and physicist, invented what he
called the algebra of quaternions. This algebra is quite different from
the algebra of ordinary numbers. In particular the commutative law of
multiplication is not true for quaternions. That is, the product xy need
not be the same as the product yx. At about the same time, Hermann
G. Grassman, a German, also formulated a very general type of algebra
that obeyed laws quite different from those of ordinary arithmetic.

The development of more and more such systems by a number of different mathematicians soon followed. The term "algebra" then came to mean any of a multitude of systems in each of which one was able to calculate the effect of combining elements of the system under whatever set of rules, or postulates, the inventor of the system had laid down. While many of these algebras were motivated by the needs of physics and other studies, some were deliberately designed to be more general in scope than was needed by any known application.

With these developments in the two principal mathematical streams of algebra and geometry, the way was clear at last for mathematics to be *invented* rather than *discovered*. Mathematics was no longer restricted to the description of what was believed to be the case in the real world, but could investigate the properties of all sorts of systems resulting from various sets of postulates. It has turned out to be the case that a great number of these mathematical systems have already had important applications in many other areas of study. Indeed, the development of the presently wide and varied assortment of mathematical systems has played an essential role in the application of mathematics to fields thought to be quite non-mathematical only a few years ago.

3.2 Formal Mathematical Systems

Before attempting to formulate the arithmetic of the natural numbers in the style of modern postulational mathematics, we wish to consider briefly just what is meant by a mathematical system in this modern sense, and also to see some examples of such systems.

In formulating a particular mathematical system, we begin with a set of undefined terms, some of which we call "elements," others "relations among the elements," and still others "operations on the elements." For example, in the system of the natural numbers, the numbers themselves are the elements of the system, the relations are those of equality and greater (or less) than, and the operations are addition and multiplication. Next we have a series of statements about these undefined terms. These postulates, or axioms, serve to define the essential characteristics of the elements, relations, and operations, and in this way give meaning to these otherwise undefined terms. We must always remember that even if the terms used are ones to which we have already attached intuitive or other meanings, in the arguments of the system only those properties contained in or derived from the postulates may be used.

Finally, we must have a system of logic, or rules of deduction, to use in obtaining further properties which we call theorems to distinguish them from the assumed properties.

This use of postulates to characterize our undefined terms is quite similar to that employed by a physicist in defining an electron or a meson. In defining an electron, the physicist initially describes it by saying how it is related to other physical entities, how and with what result it may be operated on, and so forth. It is only later that such properties as mass and electrical charge are derived as consequences of the earlier definition. Thus here the initially undefined elements also receive their essential descriptions by means of certain assumed relations and operations.

While there is this strong similarity between the definitions of physical entities and the postulates of a mathematical system, there is also an important difference. Whereas the physicist describes the behavior of an electron in terms of supposedly known physical concepts, in defining a mathematical system we start by assuming that nothing is known and that our elements, relations, and operations are defined by the interelationships given in the postulates. Of course, in defining any of the elementary mathematical systems, such as the arithmetic of the natural numbers or the Euclidean geometry of the plane, we have a pretty good idea of the characteristics which we wish to obtain for our system, but nonetheless we are not permitted to make use of any properties not explicitly assumed in the postulates as we seek to develop these properties as consequences.

Having adopted a set of undefined terms and a set of postulates characterizing them, we then proceed to deduce other statements, called theorems, which are necessary consequences of our assumptions. Also, we frequently have occasion to introduce new terms into the system for the sake of simplifying our language. These definitions of new terms are always given in terms of the initial set of undefined terms or earlier definitions. Theoretically, we could avoid this introduction of more and more new terminology, and state everything in our system by using only the original set of terms. But to attempt to do so would be to lose ourselves in a forest of verbiage. As already noted in Chapter 2, if one does not allow the use of any algebraic symbolism whatever, it then becomes quite difficult to give clear statements of the basic properties of the natural numbers. Just as in any other area of learning, as the ideas which we wish to express become more extensive both in number and complexity, we are forced to introduce new terminology in order to keep the sheer bulk of language in a discussion from concealing the point of the discussion. We emphasize, however, that in mathematics definitions of new terms are much more precise than in general discourse. They must be so if we are to avoid confusion such as that now prevailing in the world as to the meaning of terms like democracy, freedom, etc.

There are two general types of definitions which we shall encounter. First are those definitions that are made once and for all and introduce a new name for some expression involving only the original undefined terms and other terms already permanently defined in terms of them. For example, if a and b are two natural numbers, then we define "a is greater than b" (written $a > b$) to mean that "there is some natural number c such that $a = b + c$." Having made such a definition, we may then replace either of the equivalent expressions by the other whenever such replacement is convenient.

We shall also have frequent occasions to use temporary definitions, which are to hold only for the purposes of a single argument or discussion. For instance, in the course of a discussion, we might find it convenient to say "let $a = b + c$," and then go on with our discussion. This would mean that through the rest of that particular discussion a and $b + c$ would always have exactly the same meaning. However, in subsequent discussions we would be free to assign new meanings to a, b, and c if we so desired.

The principal rule of deduction which we shall use is that if we have established that condition p implies condition q, and also that condition p is true in our system, then we may conclude that condition q is true in our system. This is of course the essential meaning of the phrase "p implies q," or "if p, then q." As a nonmathematical example, suppose we have established that "stepping off a cliff implies falling" or "if someone steps off a cliff, then he will fall." Then if we are told "Joe stepped off a cliff yesterday," we are justified in concluding that "Joe fell."

We spend much of our lives in obtaining a long list of such established implications, some learned by experience, others by less arduous means, in order that we may draw conclusions in hypothetical situations. Formal mathematics is thus not so different from ordinary life as it might appear. Of course, in mathematical deduction we are very particular that we do not "jump to conlusions," but insist that each conclusion must be carefully reasoned from the assumptions originally agreed upon.

In a formal mathematical system, the postulates provide us with some initial conditions which are true, and from these we deduce other conditions as consequences. Thus, in a formal mathematical system, there is no reference to what is or is not true in the real world. In order to distinguish between mathematical truth and real-world truth, we often prefer to use the term *validity* rather than truth in referring to mathematical results. The idea here is that our mathematical results are valid as consequences of the assumed postulates.

Sometimes we shall wish to show that a possible statement is not true in a particular system. As an illustration, in the natural numbers $(a + b)^2 = a^2 + b^2$ *is not true* for general natural numbers a and b. To establish that this is not generally true; that is, is not a law of the system, it suffices to give a single example to the contrary. In this case, $(2 + 3)^2 = 5^2 = 25$ whereas $2^2 + 3^2 = 4 + 9 = 13$, serves as an entirely satisfactory counterexample, or example proving that the possible general result is in fact not true.

3.3 Application of Formal Mathematics

In formal mathematics we are not concerned at all with "truth" in the sense of what is the case in the real world, whatever that may be, but only in validity, that is, in whether or not a particular statement about our terms is a logical consequence of our assumed axioms or postulates. "If such and such is the case, then so and so must also be the case" is the typical statement of formal mathematics.

This is not to say that mathematics is not concerned with the application of its formal systems to concrete situations. On the contrary, from the very beginning and continuing throughout its history, applications have been the principal inspiration and justification for the study of mathematics. In applying mathematical systems, the main problem is to determine whether a given concrete system is such that if the terms of some mathematical system are interpreted in a definite way in the language of the concrete system, the postulates of the system are then true. If such is the case, then the entire body of theorems can also be translated into the language of the concrete system with assurance that they will also hold true. If, on the other hand, the given concrete and mathematical systems do not match, then one has the problem of searching through the list of available mathematical systems to find a system which does match the concrete situation in which one is interested, or perhaps the task of trying to devise a new mathematical system.

It might be thought that it would be far easier to deal with the concrete situation from the beginning, where we could be guided by our intuition and previous experience. In a sense this is certainly the case, as witness the fact that mathematics initially developed in just this way. But one can also be misguided by intuition, and experience has shown that in unfamiliar situations this happens all too often. Subtle points in an argument can easily be overlooked if the language of the argument is too familiar. The use of formal systems offers very worthwhile safeguards at these points. But, of even greater importance, the formulation and study of formal systems offers great economy of effort in that many apparently different concrete situations turn out to be formally the same. Also, when we clear away the preconceptions of intuition and experience to some degree by using formal mathematics, we often find that new and very important relationships become apparent which formerly were obscured.

3.4 The Algebra of Subsets of a Set

In order to make the foregoing ideas somewhat clearer, let us consider some simple examples of formal mathematical systems, and some interpretations of these formal systems.

As in the case of the natural numbers, we shall first examine an intuitive system. We shall then reformulate the intuitive system as a formal system, and finally look for other apparently quite different interpretations of the formal system.

We begin by considering the algebra of subsets of some given set U. By a set we mean any collection of things, called members of the set U. For instance, one may wish to consider the set whose members are all people in the United States, or the set whose members are all ideas discussed by Aristotle, or the set whose members are all books in the Library of Congress. In the last instance we would have, among many others, the subset A of all books with green covers, or the subset B of all books printed before 1800, or the subset C of all books on witchcraft, or the subset D of all books written in Chinese, or the subset E of all books with over 300 pages, etc. It is also convenient to consider the entire set U as a subset of itself, and also to consider the empty set; i.e., the set having no members at all, as a subset of any set. We will denote the empty set by the letter Z. Our reasons for wishing to include both U and Z as subsets of U will become evident when we start combining subsets; that is, when we define operations in this algebra of subsets.

For any subsets A and B of U, we may consider the *intersection* of A and B, which we write as $A \cap B$. $A \cap B$ is that subset of U consisting of all members of U common to both A and B. In our example of the set of all books in the Library of Congress, the intersection of subsets C and D would consist of all books on witchcraft written in Chinese. It is at least conceivable that there might be no such books in the Library of Congress. Since we wish our algebra to be closed under the operation of intersection, that is since we wish the intersection of subsets to be always a subset, we see that we must include the empty set Z as a subset of U.

A second method of combining subsets is that of forming their *union*. By the union of subsets A and B, written $A \cup B$, we mean that subset of U consisting of all things which are in A or in B or in both A and B. If U is the set of all people in the United States, A is the subset of all absent-minded people, and P is the subset of all professors, then $A \cup P$ contains absent-minded waitresses, professors with perfect memories, and of course the famous absent-minded professor.

A third operation on the subsets of U is *complementation*. Whereas intersection and union each operate on a pair of subsets to produce a single subset, complementation operates on a single subset to produce a single subset. The *complement* of A, written $\bar{A}$, consists of all those members of U which are not members of A. Thus, the complement of the subset of all books in the Library of Congress written in Chinese is the subset of all books written in all other languages. Clearly the union of A and $\bar{A}$ is U, $A \cup \bar{A} = U$, since very member of U is in either A or $\bar{A}$. Hence we must include U as a subset of itself if we wish the set of all subsets of U to be closed under the operation of union.

A very useful device for visualizing the relationships involved in this "algebra of subsets of the set U," is that of so-called Venn diagrams. In this visualization device we imagine U to consist of all points within some region of a plane surface, say a rectangle, such as a page of a book or a blackboard. We then think of arbitrary subsets A, B, and so forth as being all points within certain circles or other simple geometric figures. Since obviously such simple figures do not exhaust the many possibilities, Venn diagrams may not in general be used to prove theorems, but may well suggest how a proof may be given.

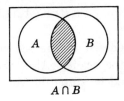

$A \cap B$

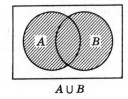

$A \cup B$

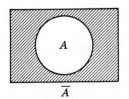

$\bar{A}$

Figure 3.3

As sample Venn diagrams, let us suppose U to be all the points in a rectangle, and indicate the meaning of $A \cap B$, $A \cup B$, and $\bar{A}$. In Fig. 3.3 we have shaded the appropriate regions to represent $A \cap B$, $A \cup B$, and $\bar{A}$ respectively.

We now list some of the basic properties of this "algebra" S of subsets of U. It is quite evident that both intersection and union are closed, commutative, and associative operations on the subsets of S; that is, for all A, B, and C in S we have

B1. $A \cap B$ is in S, and $A \cup B$ is in S.

B2. $A \cap B = B \cap A$, and $A \cup B = B \cup A$.

B3. $A \cap (B \cap C) = (A \cap B) \cap C$, and $A \cup (B \cup C) = (A \cup B) \cup C$.

Not so evident are the two distributive properties

B4. $A \cap (B \cup C) = (A \cap B) \cup (A \cap C)$ and

$A \cup (B \cap C) = (A \cup B) \cap (A \cup C)$.

The first of these says that a member of U is in both A and (B or C) if and only if it is in (both A and B) or (both A and C). This may be illustrated in Venn diagrams as in Fig. 3.4, where the shaded region in (a)

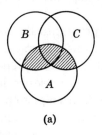

(a)

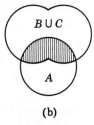

(b)

$A \cap B$ ▨
$A \cap C$ ▨

(c)

Figure 3.4

can be expressed either by $A \cap (B \cup C)$ as in (b), or by $(A \cap B) \cup (A \cap C)$ as in (c).

Similar diagrams may be used to convince oneself of the second distributive property, an exercise we leave to the reader. Also, the meaning of this second distributive property should be stated in words to make clear its validity.

The reader may have noted that properties B1, B2, and B3 are respectively very like properties P1 and P6, P2 and P7, and P3 and P8, of the natural numbers (Chapter 2). However property B4 contains two distributive laws as compared to the single distributive law of the natural numbers. The other possible distributive property in the natural numbers would read $a + (bc) = (a + b)(a + c)$, which is not true as may be seen by trying specific numbers for a, b, and c. For example, if we try 2, 3, and 4 for a, b, and c, we obtain $a + (bc) = 2 + (3 \cdot 4) = 2 + 12 = 14$, whereas $(a + b)(a + c) = (2 + 3)(2 + 4) = 5 \cdot 6 = 30$. We thus have a counterexample, concluding that $a + (bc) = (a + b)(a + c)$ is not a general law of the natural numbers.

The particular subsets U and Z have very interesting properties, namely

B5. $A \cap U = A$ and $A \cup Z = A$ for every A in $\mathcal{S}$.

These elements U and Z are thus identity elements for the respective operations of intersection and union. This is entirely similar to the property that the number 1 possesses of being an identity element for the operation of multiplication in the natural numbers.

Thus far we have not taken into account the operation of complementation. The most obvious properties of this operation are that

B6. $A \cap \bar{A} = Z$ and $A \cup \bar{A} = U$ for every A in $\mathcal{S}$.

That is, no members of U are in both A and the complement $\bar{A}$ of A, while every member of U is either in A or in $\bar{A}$.

With the possible exception of the distributive properties B4, all of the properties we have listed are quite apparent in this algebra of the subsets of U. It may therefore seem surprising that any other property we might discover can be derived as a consequence of those we have just given; but such is the case, although we shall not attempt to prove it here. When we say "any other property," we mean "any other property that is true provided that U is taken to be a perfectly arbitrary set to start with." Of course, if U were taken as some specific set, such as the set of all books in a particular library, then we could obtain properties of this particular set which would not be valid in general, hence not derivable from properties B1 through B6.

For convenience we shall repeat this description of properties of the algebra of subsets of an arbitrary set U.

The algebra $\mathcal{S}$ of all subsets $A, B, C, \ldots$ of the given set U has three operations, intersection (written $A \cap B$), union (written $A \cup B$), and complementation (written $\bar{A}$), such that for any A, B, and C in $\mathcal{S}$:

B1. $A \cap B$ and $A \cup B$ are unique elements of $\mathcal{S}$.

B2. $A \cap B = B \cap A$ and $A \cup B = B \cup A$.

B3. $A \cap (B \cap C) = (A \cap B) \cap C$ and $A \cup (B \cup C) = (A \cup B) \cup C$.

B4. $A \cap (B \cup C) = (A \cap B) \cup (A \cap C)$ and

$A \cup (B \cap C) = (A \cup B) \cap (A \cup C)$.

B5. There are elements U and Z of $\mathcal{S}$ such that

$A \cap U = A$ and $A \cup Z = A$ for every A of $\mathcal{S}$.

B6. There is an element $\bar{A}$ of $\mathcal{S}$ such that

$A \cap \bar{A} = Z$ and $A \cup \bar{A} = U$.

If one examines this list of properties, he is soon struck by their parallel nature. That is, if we interchange $\cap$ and $\cup$, and simultaneously interchange U and Z, throughout, we get back exactly the same set of properties. If we accept the fact that these properties do characterize this algebra of subsets, we then see that the duality of the characterizing properties means that whenever we obtain one result in this algebra we may automatically obtain its *dual*, namely that result obtained from the first by performing throughout the above interchanges. Thus for example, if we establish that

$$\overline{(A \cup B)} = \bar{A} \cap \bar{B}$$

then

$$\overline{(A \cap B)} = \bar{A} \cup \bar{B}$$

follows at once by this principle of duality. The reader should convince himself of the validity of these two properties, known as *DeMorgan's laws* after the English logician and mathematician, Augustus DeMorgan (1806–1871), both by an analysis of the members of the various sets involved as well as by the use of Venn diagrams.

Besides the relation of equality, or identity of elements of s (i.e., of subsets of U), we often wish to speak of a relation of inclusion. We say that subset A is included in subset B, and write $A \subset B$, if every member of A is also a member of B. This relation may be illustrated by a Venn diagram of the form given in Fig. 3.5.

If we wish, we may define this relation in terms of the notions of union and equality by: $A \subset B$ means $A \cup B = B$. Alternatively, we could define inclusion in terms of intersection and equality by: $A \subset B$ means $A \cap B = A$. In the first case, we are saying that if one joins to B the members of A, the result is B, or everything in A is already in B. In the second case, we are saying that the members common to A and B are precisely those of A, or, again, everything in A is also in B.

At the other extreme from the situation where $A \subset B$, or all members of A are also members of B, is that in which $A \cap B = Z$, or no members of A are also members of B. We may indicate this diagrammatically as shown in Fig. 3.6. Here it is clear from the Venn diagram that no

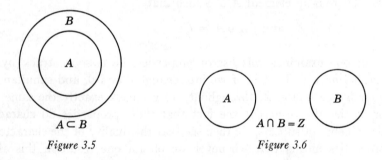

Figure 3.5   *Figure 3.6*

member of U can be in both A and B. Note that, by virtue of the commutative property of intersection, $A \cap B = Z$ is equivalent to $B \cap A = Z$, an equivalence also apparent from Fig. 3.6. Thus, to say "no members of A are members of B," is equivalent to saying "no members of B are members of A."

At times we may also wish to make a statement such as "some of this class are sophomores," or "some members of C are also members of S." We may write this symbolically as $C \cap S \neq Z$, or equally well as

$S \cap C \neq Z$ since intersection is a commutative operation. (The symbol $\neq$ means "is not equal to.") Here the question may arise as to how many we mean by "some." Although we may have different intuitive notions of how many this should be, we will agree that "some" means "at least one." Thus "some flowers are red" is to mean "there is at least one thing which is both a flower and red." Diagrammatically we will indicate this situation by drawing a dotted line just within the region in which we assert something exists, in this case the region $S \cap C$ in Fig. 3.7.

As a further illustration, let us suppose we are given three subsets A, B, and C, and are told that $A \cap B \neq Z$. We obtain the accompanying diagram (Fig. 3.8). Notice that we can not conclude from the given

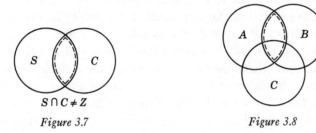

Figure 3.7   Figure 3.8

statement whether there is anything in $A \cap B \cap C$ or not, nor whether there is anything in $A \cap B \cap \bar{C}$ or not. There *must* be something in at least one of these regions, and it *might* be the case that there is something in each of them, but we are unable to decide this latter question from the information at hand.

Let us now draw a Venn diagram for a more complicated set of statements. Suppose we are told that the following statements are all true.

1. All paintings are interesting.

2. All toads are ugly.

3. Some paintings are expensive.

4. No interesting things are ugly.

5. No toads are expensive.

We will let P be the set of paintings, I the set of interesting things, T the set of toads, G the set of ugly things, and E the set of expensive things. In terms of these our statements become:

1. $P \subset I$.

2. $T \subset G$.

3. $P \cap E \neq Z$.

4. $I \cap G = Z$.

5. $T \cap E = Z$.

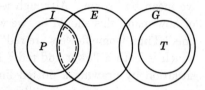

Figure 3.9

For this set of statements we obtain the Venn diagram of Fig. 3.9. A few comments on the construction of this diagram may be helpful. We start with statement 1, $P \subset I$, and hence draw the P circle inside the I circle. Next we look for any other statement(s) involving P, and notice statement 3, $P \cap E \neq Z$. We therefore draw the E circle cutting the P circle, and put dots just inside the boundary of $P \cap E$. Note that we must not draw the E circle entirely within the I circle, since we are not told that E is contained in I. Next we look for additional statements involving I, the other set in the first statement, and find, in statement 4, $I \cap G = Z$. So we now draw the G circle, not cutting the I circle. However, since we are not told that the intersection of G and E is empty, we must draw the G circle cutting the E circle to allow for the possibility that there may be expensive ugly things. We have left the statements 2, $T \subset G$, and 5, $T \cap E = Z$. Taken together these tell us to draw the T circle entirely within the G circle and not cutting the E circle, thus completing the diagram. From this diagram, we may now draw many conclusions as consequences of the statements 1, 2, 3, 4, and 5. For example, it is evident that $I \cap \bar{T} \neq Z$, that is, there are interesting things which are not toads. Note, however, that from the given statements we can say nothing about whether there are toads or not, or whether there are or are not any ugly things.

From this example we may note some general principles concerning the construction of Venn diagrams for a set of statements about sets of things. We must always be careful that our drawings allow for all possibilities that are not specifically ruled out by the given conditions. We also observe that it is easiest to diagram the statements by following first one set, and then another, through all the statements, not necessarily in the order they are given. In this manner we have all the information about a particular set available "at our fingertips" when we draw the corresponding circle.

EXERCISES

1. Suppose U is the set consisting of the numbers 1, 2 and 3; that is, $U = \{1, 2, 3\}$. List all the subsets of U.

2. How many subsets of U are there if U contains exactly 1 element? If U contains exactly 2 elements? Exactly 3 elements? Exactly 4 elements? How many subsets would you expect there to be if U contains exactly 7 elements?

3. Give Venn diagrams to illustrate the second of the distributive properties:

$$A \cup (B \cap C) = (A \cup B) \cap (A \cup C).$$

4. Give Venn diagrams to illustrate the two associative properties of the algebra of subsets; i.e., the properties B3.

5. Suppose U is the set of all people, A the subset of adults, B the subset of busy people, and C the subset of college students. Give verbal statements of the distributive properties B4 in this particular case.

6. Use Venn diagrams to illustrate the DeMorgan laws.

7. Give verbal statements of the DeMorgan laws in the case of the sets B and C of Exercice 5.

8. Is it the case that $A \cup (B \cap A) = A$ for arbitrary subsets A and B of some universe set U?

9. Illustrate separately each of the following by Venn diagrams:
   (a) $\bar{A} \cap B = Z$.
   (b) $A \cap B \cap C \neq Z$. (Why are no parentheses needed here?)
   (c) $\bar{A} \cup B \neq Z$.
   (d) $A \cap (B \cup \bar{C}) \neq Z$.
   (e) $(A \cap B) \cap \bar{C} = Z$.
   (f) $(A \cap B) \cap \bar{C} \neq Z$.

10. What is the simplest possible description of the set:

$$[A \cap (\bar{B} \cup \bar{C})] \cup [A \cap (B \cup C)]$$

11. Find the simplest possible description of the set $(\bar{A} \cap B) \cup \overline{(A \cup B)}$.

12. Give symbolic statements for the following:
   (a) No worthwhile activities involve no effort.
   (b) Some worthwhile activities are lots of fun.

13. Give a Venn diagram illustrating the simultaneous assumption of both statements in Exercise 12.

14. Suppose it is true that the following three statements are all true:

(a) If any food is sweet, it must have sugar in it.

(b) All honey has sugar in it.

(c) Some cookies are made without sugar.

Which of the following (if any) must then also be true?

(d) Some cookies are not sweet.

(e) All honey is sweet.

(f) Not all cookies are made with honey.

(g) All sweet cookies contain sugar.

15. What conclusions can you draw from the Venn diagram of Fig. 3.9? In particular, give a conclusion involving only two of the sets I, P, E, G, and T (and possibly the empty set Z) which you could not draw if any of the five assumptions leading to Fig. 3.9 were deleted.

3.5 Boolean Algebra and Some Interpretations

Let us now change our approach, and instead of looking for properties of the algebra of subsets of a given set, give a postulational definition of a formal mathematicical system.

A Boolean algebra (named for George Boole, 1815–1864, another English mathematician and logician) is a set S of elements denoted by A, B, C, ..., together with two operations on ordered pairs of elements of S denoted by "∩" and "∪" and called "cap" and "cup" respectively, an operation on single elements of S denoted by "‾" and called "bar," and a relation of equality (or identity) denoted by " =," such that each of the following postulates holds:

B1. For any A and B of S, both $A \cap B$ and $A \cup B$ are elements of S.

B2. For any A and B of S, both $A \cap B = B \cap A$ and $A \cup B = B \cup A$.

B3. For any A, B, and C of S, both $A \cap (B \cap C) = (A \cap B) \cap C$ and $A \cup (B \cup C) = (A \cup B) \cup C$.

B4. For any A, B, and C of $\mathcal{S}$, both $A \cap (B \cup C) = (A \cap B) \cup (A \cap C)$
and $A \cup (B \cap C) = (A \cup B) \cap (A \cup C)$.

B5. There are fixed elements U and Z of $\mathcal{S}$ such that both $A \cap U = A$
and $A \cup Z = A$ for every A of $\mathcal{S}$.

B6. For each A of $\mathcal{S}$, there is an element $\bar{A}$ of $\mathcal{S}$ such that both $A \cap \bar{A} = Z$
and $A \cup \bar{A} = U$.

Except for the "names" used, this is nothing but our algebra of subsets
of the set U. But why should we have bothered to introduce this formal
system whose elements and operations are meaningless except for the
properties specified by the postulates? Would it not be simpler to stick
to the familiar names of subsets, intersection, union, and complement?
We propose to answer these questions by giving two alternative interpretations or realizations of formal Boolean algebra.

For our first interpretation we let the elements A, B, C, and so forth
of $\mathcal{S}$ be combinations of simple electrical switches which are either closed
or open. The operation "cap" or "$\cap$" applied to switches A and B means
"connected in series with." (See Fig. 3.10.) The operation "cup" or

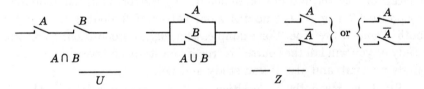

$$\overline{U} \qquad\qquad \overline{Z}$$

Figure 3.10

"$\cup$" means "connected in parallel with," while $\bar{A}$ is to represent a switch
so controlled as to be always opposite to A; i.e., when A is open, $\bar{A}$ is
closed, and vice versa. Finally, by U we mean a switch permanently
closed, and by Z a switch permanently open.

By equality we shall mean electrical equivalence; i.e., two networks
of switches are equal if they have the same property of conducting or
not conducting for all conditions of their component switches.

That B1, B2, and B3 are valid in this system is almost obvious.
For example, $A \cap (B \cap C) = (A \cap B) \cap C$ simply means that if A, B,
and C are all connected in series it makes no difference whether we
write "A in series with (B in series with C)" or "(A in series with B)
in series with C," since in either case the combination conducts only
when all three of A, B, and C are closed.

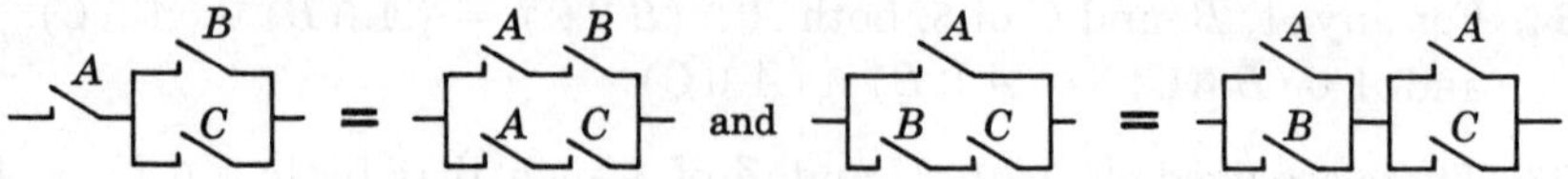

Figure 3.11

In the case of B4 we have the networks of Fig. 3.11, from which the electrical equivalences are clear. The postulates B5 and B6 also clearly hold, and we see that this is indeed a possible realization of Boolean algebra.

As a second interpretation, we let S be the set of logical propositions. By a proposition we mean a statement which must be either true or false, but never both, in any given universe. Thus "the moon is made of green cheese" is certainly true or false but not both, regardless of whether we know what the moon is made of or not.

The operation "cap" is now the connective "and," while "cup" is to be the connective "or." We emphasize that this logical "or" is not the "or" of ordinary discourse. In ordinary discourse, "or" is usually used in the sense of either one or the other but not both, whereas the logical "or" has the meaning often denoted by and/or. Thus the compound proposition "A or B" is true if A alone is true, if B alone is true, and if both A and B are true. For example, as a logical proposition, "You will study or you will fail the course" is true if you study and pass, if you don't study and fail, and also if you study and fail.

By $\bar{A}$ we mean the proposition "not A," or "A is false." Thus if A is "it is cold," then $\bar{A}$ is "it is not cold." By equality we mean logical equivalence: the propositions A and B are equal if they are jointly true and jointly false; or, if either is true, then so is the other, and if either is false, then so is the other.

By U we mean any (hence every) proposition which is necessarily always true regardless of the actual state of affairs; for example, "it is raining or it is not raining" is true regardless of the weather conditions. Such a proposition we call a *tautology*. Similarly, Z is any (hence every) proposition which is necessarily always false, such as "it is raining and it is not raining." A Z-type proposition is called a *self-contradiction*. A proposition which is neither a tautology nor a self-contradiction is called a *conditional proposition*.

That postulates B1 to B6 are true for this algebra of propositions is rather easy to verify with the possible exception of B4. In the case of B4, the only difficulty is that the statement of the postulate in terms of propositions is sufficiently involved that we may experience difficulty in realizing just what it really says. Moreover, we can readily construct possible statements in this algebra; for instance

$$\overline{(\bar{A} \cup B) \cap (\bar{B} \cup C)} \cup (\bar{A} \cup C) = U$$

and wish some means of determining whether or not they are always true, that is, are theorems in the algebra.

Fortunately, a device to determine the answer to such questions is available. This device is known as the truth table. The basic idea of a truth table is simply to tabulate the truth or falsity of a given compound proposition for all possible combinations of truth or falsity of its constituent propositions.

As an example, let us construct such a table for the compound proposition $A \cap B$, that is, A and B. We shall use "$+$" to indicate truth and "$-$" to indicate falsity.

A	B	$A \cap B$
$+$	$+$	$+$
$+$	$-$	$-$
$-$	$+$	$-$
$-$	$-$	$-$

Figure 3.12

In Fig. 3.12 we have listed to the left of the double line all possible combinations of truth or falsity of the constituent propositions A and B. Then in each row we list under the "$\cap$" sign the resulting truth or falsity of the compound proposition $A \cap B$.

Similarly, we may construct the truth table for $A \cup B$, shown in Fig. 3.13. This table merely summarizes in convenient form what we said

A	B	$A \cup B$
$+$	$+$	$+$
$+$	$-$	$+$
$-$	$+$	$+$
$-$	$-$	$-$

Figure 3.13

in defining the meaning of the logical "or." That is, $A \cup B$ is true if both A and B are true, if A is true and B is false, or if A is false and B is true; but $A \cup B$ is false if both A and B are false.

As another example, let us check the truth of $\overline{(A \cap B)} = \bar{A} \cup \bar{B}$; i.e., not (both A and B) = (not A) or (not B). We obtain the truth table of Fig. 3.14. Here the bar indicating the negation of $(A \cap B)$ is extended

A	B	$\overline{(A \cap B)} = \bar{A} \cup \bar{B}$
+	+	− + + − − −
+	−	+ − + − + +
−	+	+ − + + + −
−	−	+ − + + + +

Figure 3.14

slightly to the left so that the truth or falsity of $\overline{(A \cap B)}$ may be indicated by placing the appropriate symbol, $+$ or $-$, under this extension. The truth or falsity of $\bar{A}$ and of $\bar{B}$ have been listed, these being of course precisely opposite to the truth or falsity of A and of B respectively. Then beneath the "∪" symbol the resulting truth values of $\bar{A} \cup \bar{B}$ are listed. Finally, comparing the truth values of $\overline{(A \cap B)}$ and of $\bar{A} \cup \bar{B}$ in the table, we see that they are exactly the same in each of the four cases; hence we place a "$+$" under the "$=$" symbol in each case. From this truth table, we may conclude that, since for all possible combinations of truth and falsity of A and of B we have $\overline{(A \cap B)} = \bar{A} \cup \bar{B}$ is true, this latter statement is always true; that is, it is a law of the algebra of propositions.

We now turn to a truth table, Fig. 3.15, for the first half of postulate

A	B	C	$A \cap (B \cup C) = (A \cap B) \cup (A \cap C)$
+	+	+	+ + + + + +
+	+	−	+ + + + + −
+	−	+	+ + + − + +
+	−	−	− − + − − −
−	+	+	− + + − − −
−	+	−	− + + − − −
−	−	+	− + + − − −
−	−	−	− − + − − −

Figure 3.15

B4, $A \cap (B \cup C) = (A \cap B) \cup (A \cap C)$. In this case, there are eight possible combinations of truth and falsity of A, B, and C to list to the left of the double line. In the first column to the right of the double line, we have the resulting truth values of $A \cap (B \cup C)$, and in the next to last column those of $(A \cap B) \cup (A \cap C)$. Since these columns are identical, the over-all statement, $A \cap (B \cup C) = (A \cap B) \cup (A \cap C)$, is true in every possible case. Thus we have verified that the first part of postulate B4 is indeed a law of the algebra of propositions. The second part of B4 may be verified in a similar manner.

Thus far we have not considered what $A \subset B$ is to mean when A and B are propositions. We recall that, in the algebra of sets, $A \subset B$ has the same meaning as either of $A \cup B = B$, or $A \cap B = A$. Let us therefore construct a truth table, as in Fig. 3.16, for $A \cup B = B$. We

A	B	$A \cup B = B$	
+	+	+	+
+	−	+	−
−	+	+	+
−	−	−	+

Figure 3.16

see that $A \cup B = B$, hence also $A \subset B$, is true in all cases except when A is true and B is false. Thus, for $A \subset B$ to be true, it must not be possible for A to be true and B false. But this is what it means to say that "A implies B"; that is, whenever A is true, B must also be true, or alternatively, either B is true or else A must be false. We shall therefore read "$A \subset B$" as "A implies B," or "If A, then B." Also, to conform with symbolism commonly used for this compound proposition, we shall write "$A \subset B$" as "$A \to B$." The truth table for $A \to B$, A implies B, is shown in Fig. 3.17.

A	B	$A \to B$
+	+	+
+	−	−
−	+	+
−	−	+

Figure 3.17

In Section 3.2 we noted that one of our main tools in deducing theorems in any mathematical system would be to establish that condition P implies condition Q and that condition P is true, from which we could conclude that Q must be true. In terms of our present symbolism, this means that $[P \cap (P \to Q)] \to Q$ is always true. Let us check this with a truth table, Fig. 3.18.

P	Q	$[P \cap (P \to Q)] \to Q$		
+	+	+	+	+
+	−	−	−	+
−	+	−	+	+
−	−	−	+	+

Figure 3.18

It is easy to fill in the values of $P \to Q$ in Fig. 3.18, and then of $P \cap (P \to Q)$. To make filling in the final column easier, we note that we may at this stage replace $P \cap (P \to Q)$ mentally by a single symbol, say A. We then need to determine truth values for $A \to Q$ where we are given the truth values of A and of Q. We remember that $A \to Q$ is false only when A is true and Q is false. Now, observing that this never occurs, the values of A being in the first column to the right of the double line, we conclude that $A \to Q$, or $[P \cap (P \to Q)] \to Q$ is true in every possible case. Thus it is indeed a law, and our rule of deduction is established.

We note that in each of the three interpretations or realizations of Boolean algebra which we have considered, namely subsets of a given set, networks of electrical switches, and logical propositions, we have had available a graphic method to assist our reasoning. Venn diagrams, drawings of a network of switches, and truth tables are of great assistance in the respective instances. Truth tables are, however, a much more powerful tool than Venn diagrams. While a Venn diagram can illustrate an idea or theorem, it cannot provide a proof of the theorem. But the method of truth tables not only assists us in handling a complicated compound proposition; it even provides a definite procedure for proving whether or not the compound proposition is always true and hence a correct theorem.

Thus we see that in the algebra of propositions there is a way to decide whether or not a given compound proposition is always true and hence is a theorem. Actually, we have more than this, if we will accept the provable fact that all three of our interpretations have precisely the same formal structure as has Boolean algebra. For it then follows that Boolean algebra, and also any interpretation thereof, has this same decidability property; that is, we can decide whether a given statement is always true and, hence, is a theorem.

Once one knows that our three interpretations all have the same formal structure as Boolean algebra, we may then freely "translate" from one "language" into another. Thus it is sufficient to establish a given result in any one of the "languages" in order to be justified in using it in all. This is both a saving of effort and a great means of assisting one's limited ability in the sense that one may be able to guess a theorem much more readily in one "language," prove it in a second, and finally apply it by means of a third.

It is also owing to this "convertibility" that one can do such things as decide logical questions on an electronic computer (whose computing units are really just a huge array of switches), or apply the relatively large theory of sets in designing a switching network for transcontinental dialing of telephone numbers. Or again, in dealing with the problems of propositional algebra, it is very helpful to be able to "draw pictures," that is, translate into the language of sets and then use Venn diagrams, as an aid to one's thought. The reader will likely think of still other uses to which this formal equivalence of structure may be applied.

As an aid in this translating from one system to another, as well as a useful exercise in fixing many of the notions of our three interpretations, the reader should construct a short "tri-lingual dictionary." For example, the set relation "$A \subset B$" or "A is contained in B" becomes "B conducts whenever A conducts" in switch language, and "proposition A implies proposition B" or "if A, then B" in propositional language.

EXERCISES

1. Give sketches similar to Fig. 3.11 to indicate the validity of postulates B2, B3, B5, and B6 in the algebra of networks of switches.

2. Give examples contrasting the use of "or" in logic and in ordinary discourse.

3. Give examples of (a) a tautology, and (b) a self-contradiction, not involving the use of "and" or "or."

4. Demonstrate the validity of postulates B2–B6 by the method of truth tables.

For each of the following set theoretic statements, translate into a switch statement, then into a propositional statement, and check the validity by a truth table.

5. For any A in S, $A \cup U = U$, and $A \cap Z = Z$.

6. For any A and B in S, $A \cup (B \cap A) = A$.

7. For any A and B in S, $\overline{(A \cup B)} = \bar{A} \cap \bar{B}$.

8. For any A, B, and C in S, if $A \subset B$ and $B \subset C$, then $A \subset C$.

9. Translate each of the following into a statement concerning sets, and draw Venn diagrams to determine what, if any, conclusions can be drawn by jointly assuming a, b, and c.

   (a) All automobiles are expensive.

   (b) All paintings are expensive.

   (c) No expensive things are necessary.

10. Do similarly for the following:

   (a) All fools are liars.

   (b) No teachers are liars.

   (c) All liars are rich.

11. Classify the following as tautologies, self-contradictions, or conditional propositions:

   (a) $P \rightarrow (P \cup Q)$.

   (b) $P \rightarrow P$.

   (c) $(P \cup Q) \rightarrow Q$.

   (d) $\overline{(P \cup \bar{P})}$.

   (e) $P \rightarrow (\bar{P} \cup Q)$.

   (f) $(P \cap \bar{P}) \rightarrow Q$.

   (g) $(P \cup \bar{P}) \rightarrow Q$.

12. Give a verbal proposition to illustrate each of the propositions in Exercise 11. (For example, an illustration of $P \rightarrow P$ could be "If it is raining, then it is raining.")

13. Show that $(P \rightarrow Q) = (\bar{P} \cup Q)$, and $(P \rightarrow Q) = \overline{(P \cap \bar{Q})}$, are tautologies.

14. Find expressions logically equivalent to $P \cap Q$ involving
   (a) only $P, Q, \rightarrow$, and $^-$.   (b) only $P, Q, \cup$, and $^-$.

15. Find expressions logically equivalent to $P \cup Q$ involving
   (a) only $P, Q, \rightarrow$, and $^-$.   (b) only $P, Q, \cap$, and $^-$.

16. Classify the following as tautologies, self-contradictions, or conditional propositions:

(a) $(P \rightarrow Q) \rightarrow (Q \rightarrow P)$.

(b) $[P \cap (\bar{P} \cup Q)] \cap \bar{Q}$.

(c) $[(P \rightarrow Q) \cap \bar{P}] \rightarrow \bar{Q}$.

(d) $[(P \rightarrow Q) \cap (Q \rightarrow R)] \rightarrow (P \rightarrow R)$.

(e) $[(P \cap Q) \cup \bar{P}] \rightarrow R$.

(f) $[P \rightarrow (Q \rightarrow R)] \rightarrow [(P \rightarrow Q) \rightarrow (P \rightarrow R)]$.

3.6 Another Formal Mathematical System with Interpretations

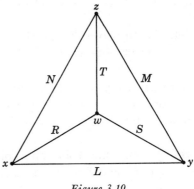

Figure 3.19

Let us consider Fig. 3.19, composed of the four points x, y, z, w, and the six lines (more precisely line segments) L, M, N, R, S, T. This is a "miniature geometry," and we now wish to investigate its basic properties. As before, we shall then use these properties to define a formal system and shall seek further interpretations of the formal system.

Before listing properties of this miniature geometry, we should say a word about the language we shall use to describe such properties. The terminology "x lies on L" is familiar; but the phrase "L lies on x" may not be. However, we shall use this latter language as well as the former, since we wish to consider "lies on" as a relation among elements of our two sets of things, four points and six lines.

We may then observe, among others, the following properties of our miniature geometry G.

G is composed of two sets of objects, a set of points denoted by lower-case letters and a set of lines denoted by capital letters, a relation of equality in each set, a relation "lies on" between elements of different sets (i.e., a point and a line, or a line and a point, being so related), and having the following properties:

G1. For any point b and line A, b lies on A if and only if A lies on b; i.e., "lies on" is a symmetric relation.

G2. Each line is determined by the points which lie on it.

For example, x and y both lie on L, but they do not both lie on any other line; so that specifying the pair (x, y) of points also specifies the line L.

G3. Any two distinct points determine (i.e., jointly lie on) a unique line.

Thus each pair of points corresponds to one and only one line, the correspondence being $(x, y) \leftrightarrow L$, $(y, z) \leftrightarrow M$, $(z, x) \leftrightarrow N$, $(x, w) \leftrightarrow R$, $(y, w) \leftrightarrow S$, and $(z, w) \leftrightarrow T$.

G4. For any given line A, there is a point b which lies on A, and a point c which does not lie on A.

Actually, of course, there are two points on the line, and two points not on the line; but, for purposes of later interpretations, we do not wish to state everything possible.

G5. For any line A and any point b which does not lie on A, there is a unique line B such that b lies on B, and no point c lies on both A and B.

This property is essentially the famous fifth postulate of Euclid's plane geometry. That is, for any given line and given point not on it, there is a unique line through the given point parallel to the given line. The reader may at this point object that if, for example, we were to extend the line T it would intersect the line L, and thus they would have a point in common and not be parallel. But we must remember that what we are calling lines are actually line segments and hence may not be so extended; and moreover, the only points we are permitted to consider are x, y, z, and w; in our miniature geometry there are no other "points." Thus, while T and M may not look parallel, they do satisfy the criterion of being distinct lines with no point in common.

G6. There are exactly four points.

This is an observation we must obviously include since none of G1–G5 would require that our geometry be finite. Indeed, the observant reader will perhaps have noticed that G1–G5 are all properties valid in ordinary Euclidean plane geometry, and in that system there are infinitely many points and lines.

Although we shall not do so here, we could use properties G1–G6 to derive all the other properties of this system. For example, we could prove that for any line there are exactly two distinct points which lie on it, that there are exactly six lines, and that each point lies on exactly three lines. We may caution the reader that if he only assumes G1–G6, it is not as easy as it might appear to derive these results; but if he is interested he may try to obtain one or more, using plenty of sketching to guide his reasoning. In this chapter, however, we are not greatly concerned with proofs, preferring to wait until the next chapter when we shall wish to prove several results in the formal, or postulational, natural number system. For the present we are primarily interested in seeing something of how one abstracts a postulational system from an intuitive one, and then develops alternative interpretations of the postulational system.

So let us phrase the formal system G corresponding to our miniature geometry. G is composed of two sets, $\mathcal{H}$ and $\mathcal{K}$, the elements of $\mathcal{H}$ being denoted by lower-case letters and those of $\mathcal{K}$ by capital letters; a relation of equality in each of $\mathcal{H}$ and $\mathcal{K}$; and a relation on pairs of elements, one each from $\mathcal{H}$ and $\mathcal{K}$, which we denote by a tilde "$\sim$," and which satisfy the following postulates.

G1. For any b in $\mathcal{H}$, and any A in $\mathcal{K}$, $b \sim A$ if and only if $A \sim b$.

G2. Each A in $\mathcal{K}$ is determined by the set of b's in $\mathcal{H}$ such that $A \sim b$.

G3. For any distinct a and b in $\mathcal{H}$ there is a unique A in $\mathcal{K}$ such that $a \sim A$ and $b \sim A$.

G4. For each A in $\mathcal{K}$ there are elements a and c in $\mathcal{H}$ such that $a \sim A$ but $c \nsim A$ (i.e., $c \sim A$ is false, the notation $\nsim$ corresponding to $\neq$ meaning "unequal").

G5. For any A in $\mathcal{K}$ and any c in $\mathcal{H}$ such that $c \nsim A$, there is a unique B in $\mathcal{K}$ such that $c \sim B$ and for no d in $\mathcal{H}$ do $d \sim A$ and $d \sim B$ both hold.

G6. There are exactly four elements in $\mathcal{H}$.

As a first alternative interpretation, let us see what happens if we
interpret the elements of $\mathcal{K}$ as
"lines," those of $\mathcal{K}$ as "points," and
$\sim$ as "lies on." That is, we exactly
reverse the roles of point and line
from those of our original miniature
geometry. If this is to be a permis-
sible interpretation of G, we must
obtain a figure having four lines,
any two of which determine one of
six points, and satisfying the rest

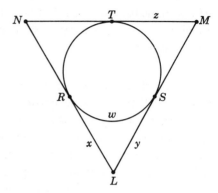

Figure 3.20

of the postulates. The diagram of
Fig. 3.20 indicates a possible solution to the problem, provided we
agree to consider the inner circle as one of the lines.

Thus here again we have a kind of duality, since when we interchange
the roles of "point" and "line" our postulates, or defining properties,
remain realizable, although not in terms of the original interpretation.
The reader should of course verify that G1–G6 are valid for this "six-
point" interpretation of G. Postulate G5 in particular is interesting
when rephrased in this way.

As another interpretation of G, we may consider elements of $\mathcal{K}$ to
be committees and elements of $\mathcal{K}$ to be the (six) members of a club.
We leave it to the reader to verify the postulates in this interpretation.
Also, the reader may construct the dual of this interpretation.

EXERCISES

1. State and verify G1–G6 in the language of the "six-point" interpretation
   of G.

2. Do similarly for both of the "committee" interpretations of G.

3. By interchanging the roles of points and lines, draw a finite geometry
   dual to the following:

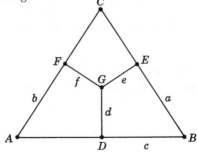

Note that the dual geometry must have seven lines and six points. (We may note that the given geometry does not satisfy a Euclidean "parallel postulate" since, while point C is not on line c, there is no line through C not meeting c. Also, through each of E and F there is exactly one line not meeting c, while through G there are two lines not meeting c.)

4. Give committee interpretations of both the original and dual geometries of Exercise 3.

5. Draw a geometry dual to the following:

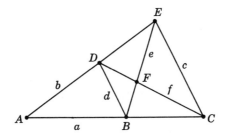

6. Does the geometry of Exercise 5 satisfy a Euclidean "parallel postulate?"

7. Construct (i.e., draw) a miniature geometry satisfying

a. There is a point and a line not on the point.

b. Every line lies on at least two distinct points.

c. Any two distinct points lie on just one line.

d. Any two distinct lines lie on at least one point.

(NOTE: There are many different correct answers to this exercise.)

4

**THE
NATURAL
NUMBERS
AS A
MATHEMATICAL
SYSTEM**

4.1 Introduction

In the preceding chapters we have considered the system of natural numbers as it developed in response to man's inventiveness and the need to compare "sizes" of sets. In Chapter 2 we considered twelve properties which always hold true in the arithmetic of the natural numbers, and then saw that in another arithmetic, that of an ordinary clock, some of these properties of the natural numbers were laws (that is, were always true), and some were not. We also saw that clock arithmetic has some laws which do not hold in the arithmetic of the natural numbers.

In the last chapter we focused attention on the basic laws of a mathematical system. Indeed, we saw that the listing of the basic laws of a mathemetical system is all-important, since this list actually defines the mathemetical system. Further, we saw that a given mathematical system

119

may have many different concrete interpretations. This is certainly the case in regard to the system of natural numbers. That is, the intuitive system may have developed from man's noting the combinatorial properties of flocks of sheep, bundles of sticks, or piles of stones. Once he had invented the natural numbers, or the symbols "1," "2," "3," etc. (or their ancient equivalents) together with their rules of combination with respect to "addition" and "multiplication," he was then able to interpret this system in a multitude of concrete situations which might appear at first glance to be totally unrelated.

We now wish to present formally the system of natural numbers in somewhat the way it may be subconsciously formulated by the student of arithmetic when he reaches that point at which he feels he "knows what the natural numbers are," even though he may be quite unable to raise this intuition to the conscious level of a precise definition.

4.2 Postulates for the Natural Numbers

In defining the natural number system in a formal way, we start with a set N of undefined elements together with two operations on these elements, or methods of combining them, which we shall call addition and multiplication. We shall denote the elements of N by lower-case italic letters $a, b, c, \ldots$, when we do not wish to refer to specific elements, and by Hindu–Arabic numerals when we do wish to be specific. The result of applying addition to a and b, in that order, will be denoted by "$a + b$" and will be called "the sum of a and b" or "a plus b;" and, likewise, the result of applying multiplication to a and b in that order will be denoted by "$a \cdot b$," or by "ab," and will be called "the product of a and b" or "a times b." The notation "$a = b$" shall mean that "a" and "b" are but two names for the same element of N. Note that "a," "b," and so forth are not the elements of N, but merely names used to denote these elements. That is, the elements of N are abstract concepts, whereas "a," "b," and so forth are configurations of ink or particular vocal sounds.

Further, we shall adopt the following postulates with regard to any elements a, b, and c of N and our two operations.

N1. Closure of addition and closure of multiplication.

$a + b$ is a unique element of N and ab is a unique element of N.

N2. Commutativity of addition and commutativity of multiplication.

$$a + b = b + a \quad \text{and} \quad ab = ba.$$

N3. Associativity of addition and associativity of multiplication.

$$(a + b) + c = a + (b + c) \quad \text{and} \quad (ab)c = a(bc).$$

N4. Distributivity of multiplication over addition.

$$a(b + c) = ab + ac.$$

N5. Cancellation of addition and cancellation of multiplication.

$$\text{If } a + b = a + c, \text{ then } b = c; \quad \text{if } ab = ac, \text{ then } b = c.$$

N6. Trichotomy. Exactly one of the following holds

$$a = b; \quad \text{or}$$

$$a = b + r \text{ for some } r \text{ in } N; \quad \text{or}$$

$$a + s = b \text{ for some } s \text{ in } N.$$

N7. N has a multiplicative identity, or unity element.

There exists an element 1 in N such that $1a = a$ for every a in N.

N8. Induction.

If T is a subset of N such that both

1 is in T;

$a + 1$ is in T whenever a is in T;

then $T = N$; i.e., T is the set of all natural numbers.

The reader will recognize that these postulates are just the laws of the natural numbers discussed in Chapter 2, although here we have listed them in a different sequence, and have also combined certain parallel properties of addition and multiplication into single postulates. We recall that the notation "$a(b + c)$" means "a times the sum of b and c," whereas "$ab + ac$" means the sum of the two products "a times b" and "a times c."

4.3   Reasons for the Postulates

In the normal course of developing a mathematical system, we would now proceed to deduce theorems as logical consequences of the postulates we have assumed in defining the system. But before doing so, let us remember that what we hope to have here is a postulational formulation of the intuitive natural number system. Thus it may be appropriate to consider briefly the reasons for assuming these particular axioms.

In the first place, we know that in the intuitive natural number system there are two distinct ways of combining elements, and in each case a unique natural number results. Thus we not only assume the existence of two operations in the formal system, but postulate that each operation is closed. In Chapter 2, examples were given of ways of combining elements of a set which do not produce other elements of the same set, such as the fact that adding two odd numbers does not produce an odd number. But while such examples serve very well to illustrate the concept of closure in the intuitive system, the important idea at this point is that in the formal natural number system we have at our disposal *only* this set N of things called natural numbers, otherwise undefined. It would be completely meaningless to speak of an operation, or method of combining elements, which did not always produce an element of N when applied to elements of N. There simply are no other elements available for us to discuss than those of N. Thus, if $a + b$ were not always a natural number whenever a and b are natural numbers, then $a + b$ would not be anything at all, and " $+$ " would be meaningless as a defining operation for the system of natural numbers. Hence, postulate N1 is quite essential.

Postulates N2 and N3 clearly must be assumed if our addition and multiplication are to mean what we want them to mean, and again Chapter 2 has provided illustrations of operations that do not have these properties.

At this point we may note that N1, N2, and N3 are, except for the notation employed, precisely the same as postulates B1, B2, and B3 of Boolean algebra, and we know that the character of a system is not dependent on the notation we employ in defining it. In Boolean algebra, our postulates continued to state parallel properties for the two operations throughout, with the result that there was really no way of telling which was which; that is, we could interchange their roles and get the same postulates back again. We certainly do not want this to be the situation in our natural number system, for here we know perfectly well that intuitive addition and multiplication are not interchangeable.

As soon as we state postulate N4, which assets only one of the two possible distributive laws, we have distinguished between our operations of addition and multiplication. By doing so, we of course sacrifice any possibility of getting "free theorems" by means of a duality principle, as we were able to do in Boolean algebra. But just as we can't have our cake and eat it, too, so we can't have a duality principle and at the same time be dealing with the natural number system.

The cancellation properties, postulate N5, further clarify what we are to mean by our addition and multiplication. Thus, if the lack of a second distributive property had not already made the natural number system distinct from that of Boolean algebra, the assertion of these cancellation properties would certainly do so, as neither cancellation property holds in Boolean algebra, as may be seen from specific examples. We may also observe that while N1 through N4 all are valid in clock arithmetic, only the additive cancellation law holds in the arithmetic of the ordinary twelve-hour clock. Again, postulate N5 makes it clear that we are not dealing here with the arithmetic of the integers (positive, negative, and zero), since from the fact that $0 \cdot 3 = 0 \cdot 7$ we certainly cannot conclude that $3 = 7$.

The arithmetic of a clock also serves as an example of a system in which the trichotomy axiom N6 does not hold. For, as noted in Chapter 2, if a and b are any two numbers in clock arithmetic, then there are clock numbers r and s such that both $a = b +_{12} r$ and $a +_{12} s = b$; and if it happens that $a = b$, then we have all three of the possibilities holding simultaneously, rather than just one as N6 requires.

The reader may convince himself that all of postulates N1 through N6 are valid in the system of positive even numbers. As soon as we consider N7, however, it is clear that the positive even numbers are not what we are talking about, for in that system there is no multiplicative identity element. But this is not the most important assertion of postulate N7, for without this postulate it would be quite possible that we are dealing with a set N of elements which is empty. It is only at this point that we actually postulate that there is even one natural number.

The assertion that the set N of natural numbers has at least one element, 1, is however not enough to assure us that N contains the right number of elements, or even elements of the right sort. If we consider N1 through N7 jointly, we may deduce that N contains infinitely many elements. From N7 we have 1 in N, and hence from N1 we have $1 + 1$, which we call 2, in N. Now N6, the property of trichotomy, assures us that 2 is not the same element as 1. N1 now says that $2 + 1 = 3$ is in N, and N6 says that 3 is not equal to either 1 or 2. Next we have $3 + 1 = 4$ in N by N1, and from N6 we obtain that 4 is different from any of 1, 2, or 3. This process continues indefinitely since the new number, $a + 1$, which we obtain at any stage, must be different from all those previously obtained. This is so since clearly $a + 1$ is not a; whereas if $a + 1 = b$ for any b obtained previous to a, we would have $b + c = a$ for some c. But trichotomy says that $a + 1 = b$ and $b + c = a$ can not both hold. Thus it is impossible for this "add one" process to ever "circle back," and we must obtain infinitely many natural numbers in this way.

At this stage in our list of postulates we have almost obtained what we want. But we still have no way of being sure, on the basis of N1–N7, that the numbers we get by starting with 1 and using the "add one" process are *all* the natural numbers. For example, we do not know from N1-N7 alone that fractions such as $\frac{1}{2}$, $\frac{5}{3}$, etc., are not natural numbers. And we certainly wish to exclude such fractions as these from the list of natural numbers. We recall that, in giving postulates for a system, we must state enough postulates to determine the system; we can not simply say "everybody knows that $\frac{1}{2}$ isn't a natural number." What "everybody knows" has no place in a *formal* system where we can use only the properties we explicitly assume. Thus we must add the inductive property N8 to our list of postulates. N8 says just what we need to say at this point, namely that, by starting with 1 and applying the "add one" process indefinitely, we do obtain all the natural numbers.

Nowadays we deal with a great many mathematical systems. In particular, we deal with many different number systems, and the number of these continues to increase. Each of these various systems has been devised by man to do a certain job. It is important that we be able to distinguish between these systems so that we may select a system appropriate to whatever problem we have at hand. Also, we certainly need to avoid ascribing to a system properties which it does not possess. We need to be well aware of properties that characterize the natural number system in order to work efficiently and correctly with this system. Moreover, we need to be aware of cases where properties of the natural number system fail to hold in some alternative system. Thus, in discussing the reasons for choosing postulates N1 to N8, we have noted several instances of other systems which fail to satisfy some of these postulates.

Another reason for being familiar with properties characterizing the natural numbers is that we shall subsequently use the natural number system as a foundation upon which to build more complicated number systems. Clearly, if one is not well grounded in the basic system, then the more complex systems will be much less intelligible than they should be.

We have frequently referred to postulates N1–N8 as characterizing the intuitive natural numbers. That this is so can be proven, but only by the use of methods far too sophisticated for this book. We shall therefore be content with merely asserting that all the properties of the intuitive natural numbers can indeed be deduced as consequences of this particular list of postulates. There are many alternative postulate systems which also characterize the natural number system, the most famous being that devised by the Italian mathematician Guiseppi Peano (1858–1932).

EXERCISES

In each of Exercises 1 *through* 10, *determine which of* N1–N8 *are true for the sets and operations listed.*

1. The set of natural numbers, with ordinary multiplication, but with ordinary addition replaced by an operation $*$ defined by $a * b = 2 \cdot a + 2 \cdot b$; e.g., $3 * 5 = 2 \cdot 3 + 2 \cdot 5 = 16$.

2. The same as Exercise 1, except that the set of all natural numbers is to be replaced by the set of all even natural numbers.

3. The same as Exercise 1, except that the operation $*$ is defined by $a * b = a + 2b$; e.g., $2 * 3 = 2 + 2 \cdot 3 = 8$.

4. The same as Exercise 3, except that the set of all natural numbers is to be replaced by the set of all odd natural numbers.

5. The set of all natural numbers, with ordinary multiplication, but with ordinary addition replaced by an operation $*$ defined by $a * b =$ the larger of a and b; e.g., $2 * 3 = 3$; $3 * 3 = 3$; $4 * 3 = 4$.

6. The same as Exercise 5, except that ordinary multiplication is to be replaced by an operation defined by $a \bigcirc b =$ the smaller of a and b; e.g., $2 \bigcirc 3 = 2$; $3 \bigcirc 3 = 3$; $4 \bigcirc 3 = 3$.

7. The set $\{a, b\}$ with "addition" and "multiplication" defined by the following tables:

+	a	b			a	b
a	a	b		a	a	a
b	b	b		b	a	b

8. The set $\{1, 2, 3\}$ with the operations of addition and multiplication on a three-hour clock.

9. The set $\{1, 2, 3, 4\}$ with the operations of addition and multiplication on a four-hour clock.

10. The set $\{1, 2, 3, \ldots, 11, 12\}$ with the operations of addition and multiplication on a twelve-hour clock.

11. Give additional postulates which, together with those of N1–N8 that are true of twelve-hour clock arithmetic, will serve to define this arithmetic.

12. Give a list of postulates which may be used to define the arithmetic of a seven-hour clock.

4.4 Using the Postulates to Prove Theorems

While we do not intend to prove, on the basis of postulates N1–N8, any great number of the familiar facts about the natural numbers, we do wish to illustrate this use of the postulates in a few simple cases. In giving proofs of theorems, we shall list in parentheses the reason justifying each statement or "line" of the proof. In these justifications we shall abbreviate "Theorem 1" to "T1," and so forth, and if a previous line of the proof, say the third, is referred to, we will indicate this by "L3."

We have agreed that "$u = v$" is to mean that u and v are but two names for the same element, or number of our system. Thus, if we have $u = v$ we may freely substitute either u or v for the other whenever this is convenient. If we also have $v = w$ it of course follows at once that $u = w$ also. We write this in the abbreviated form $u = v = w$.

In many theorems we shall wish to establish that, say, $u = x$. To establish this, we might start with u and argue successively that $u = v$,

$v = w$, and $w = x$. A convenient style for such a proof will be the following:

$$u = v \qquad \text{(Reason)}$$

$$= w \qquad \text{(Reason)}$$

$$= x \qquad \text{(Reason)}$$

Here the continued equality $u = v = w = x$ is broken up so that we may state the reason for each of the component equalities. We shall use this style of proof in our first theorems.

The reader will doubtless have noticed that postulates N4, N5, and N7 are all "left-handed" in the sense that they respectively postulate that multiplication distributes over addition from the left; like summands on the left may be deleted or cancelled and a given equality will be preserved; similarly for like factors on the left; and that 1 is a left identity for multiplication. We naturally do not wish to have to appeal to the commutativity axiom N2 together with one of these axioms each time we need the "right-handed" version of one of these properties, so our first few theorems will establish the right-handed versions once and for all.

We first establish that multiplication distributes over addition from the right as well as from the left.

THEOREM 4.1.   For any a, b, and c in N, $(b + c)a = ba + ca$.

Proof:

$$b + c \text{ is a natural number} \qquad \text{(N1)}$$

$$(b + c)a = a(b + c) \qquad \text{(L1 and N2)}$$

$$= ab + ac \qquad \text{(N4)}$$

$$= ba + ca \qquad \text{(N2)}$$

In constructing this proof, we had to proceed from the initial expression $(b + c)a$ to the final expression $ba + ca$. To do this, we clearly needed to apply N4, the distributive postulate. But we first needed to get $(b + c)a$ into the form $a(b + c)$ to which N4 applies. This of course required an application of N2, commutativity of multiplication. In turn this required the preliminary observation that $b + c$ is a single natural number by virtue of N1, the closure of N with respect to addition. Thus our first two steps were taken in order to set the stage for the application of N4. Then a final application of N2 produced the desired result.

The process of first identifying what will be the central idea of the proof, in this case the application of N4, and then constructing the proof around this idea, is quite typical of the thinking that goes into a proof. The reader will find it helpful in reading and analyzing proofs to make a practice of thus locating the central idea of the proof in order to see how the whole proof is built around it. The use of this idea is easily seen in the proofs of our next two theorems, which together establish the right-hand versions of the cancellation postulate N5.

THEOREM 4.2.   For any a, b, and c in N, if $b + a = c + a$, then $b = c$.

Proof:

$$a + b = b + a \qquad\qquad \text{(N2)}$$
$$= c + a \qquad\qquad \text{(Hypothesis)}$$
$$= a + c \qquad\qquad \text{(N2)}$$
$$b = c \qquad\qquad \text{(N5)}$$

Here the essential idea of the argument is to apply N5, the cancellation postulate. In order to apply N5 we needed to convert the hypothesis, namely $b + a = c + a$, into the form $a + b = a + c$ by the use of N2. An alternative scheme of proof to that given above could have been:

$$b + a = c + a \qquad\qquad \text{(Hypothesis)}$$
$$b + a = a + b; \text{ and } c + a = a + c \qquad\qquad \text{(N2)}$$
$$a + b = a + c \qquad\qquad \text{(Substitution)}$$
$$b = c \qquad\qquad \text{(N5)}$$

Thus we see that while the essential idea of the proof is, in this case, fixed, nevertheless it may be expressed in differing sequences of steps. Where such alternative proofs are available, any one is as valid as any other. Of course, a given individual may prefer one to another, but that is a matter of personal taste, not of mathematical soundness. As one gains experience in constructing proofs, he will likely develop the ability to recognize certain proofs as being "more elegant" or "neater" than others which are equally valid. This is closely akin to the difference between, say, an essay which is beautifully written and another which presents the same ideas but in a poorer style. And, as in the case of the use of the English language, so in mathematics we seek to express ourselves in good style. Indeed, good style contributes to both understanding and appreciation of mathematics. However, when first beginning to do formal mathematics, our emphasis must be on the validity of our arguments above all else.

THEOREM 4.3. For any a, b, and c in N, if $ba = ca$, then $b = c$.

Proof: (We leave this proof, which parallels that of Theorem 4.2, as an exercise for the reader.)

The proof that 1 is a multiplicative identity on the right is particularly simple.

THEOREM 4.4. For any a in N, $a \cdot 1 = a$.

Proof: $$a \cdot 1 = 1 \cdot a \qquad \text{(N2)}$$

$$= a \qquad \text{(N7)}$$

As we know, there is only one identity element for multiplication in the natural number system, namely 1. We now wish to prove that given N1–N8 this must be so.

THEOREM 4.5. If e is an element of N such that $ae = a$ for some a in N, then $e = 1$.

Proof:

$$ae = a \text{ for some } a \qquad \text{(Hypothesis)}$$

$$= a \cdot 1 \qquad \text{(T4.4)}$$

$$e = 1 \qquad \text{(N5)}$$

By now we should be able to carry out a somewhat longer proof. In particular, we wish to give an example of an "if and only if" type of theorem. In this type of theorem we assert that two apparently rather different statements are logically equivalent, that is, either is a consequence of the other. Our proof must then consist of two parts. In the first part we assume the first statement and deduce the second as a consequence; and we reverse roles in the second part of the proof, there assuming the second statement and deducing the first as a consequence. As an illustration, we establish an alternative characterization of the natural number 1.

THEOREM 4.6. For any a in N, $a = 1$ if and only if $aa = a$.

Proof: We first assume as our hypothesis that $a = 1$.

$$aa = aa \qquad \text{(Identity)}$$

$$a = 1 \qquad \text{(Hypothesis)}$$

$$aa = 1 \cdot 1 \qquad \text{(Substitution)}$$

$$= 1 \qquad \text{(N7)}$$

$$= a \qquad \text{(Hypothesis)}$$

Having established the first part of our theorem, we next assume as hypothesis that $aa = a$.

$$aa = a \qquad \text{(Hypothesis)}$$

$$= a \cdot 1 \qquad \text{(T4.4)}$$

$$a = 1 \qquad \text{(N5)}$$

Thus the second part of our theorem is also established and the proof is complete.

Besides the relation of equality, or identity, there are other relations which we are often interested in when dealing with natural numbers, namely those relations of "greater than" and "less than." We shall define "less than" and leave the reader to give a definition of "greater than."

Definition of Less Than, and of Least Element. If a and b are natural numbers, then we define $a < b$ (read "a is less than b") to mean that there is some natural number c such that $a + c = b$. If S is a set of natural numbers, and s in S has the property that for each t in S either $s = t$ or $s < t$, then we call s a least element of S.

In terms of the relation "less than" we may replace the postulate of trichotomy by a postulate which may seem more familiar.

N6′. For any natural numbers a and b, exactly one of $a = b$, $b < a$, or $a < b$ holds.

We now turn our attention to deriving some of the basic properties of the relation "less than."

THEOREM 4.7. 1 is a least natural number; that is, for all natural numbers a, either $1 = a$ or $1 < a$.

Proof: We need to show that the set T consisting of all natural numbers a, such that either $1 = a$ or $1 < a$, is actually the set of all natural numbers. If we can show that the two conditions of N8 are true for this set T, then N8 will assure us of our result. We first show that 1 is in T.

1 is in T	(Definition of T)

We now suppose k is in T, and need to show that then $k + 1$ is in T. We have

k is in N	(Definition of T as subset of N)
$1 < 1 + k$	(Definition of $<$)
$1 < k + 1$	(N2)
$k + 1$ is in T	(Definition of T)

Having shown that the conditions of N8 are satisfied by T, we may conclude that $T = N$.

The verification that our subset T of N satisfies the two hypotheses, 1 is in T and $k + 1$ is in T if k is in T, is very easy, requiring only the definitions of T and of $<$, and one postulate, N2. It may appear to be such a simple argument that one wonders how it really proves anything. That it does is of course due to the very powerful nature of the inductive postulate itself, which, as we have noted before, really tells us how we obtain the entire set of natural numbers. In this application, we argue that if 1 is less than or equal to k, then 1 is also less than or equal to $k + 1$. Thus 1 is less than or equal to 2, 1 is less than or equal to 3, and so on indefinitely; hence 1 is less than or equal to every natural number.

Usually one says that 1 is *the* least natural number, rather than the weaker statement we have made that 1 is *a* least natural number. We leave it to the reader to show, by invoking the trichotomy postulate N6, that there can not be two distinct least natural numbers; and hence 1 is indeed *the* least natural number.

As final illustrations of theorems and their proofs we give the basic theorems used in dealing with inequalities; that is, statements of the form $a < b$.

THEOREM 4.8.   For any a, b, and c in N, if $a < b$, then $ca < cb$ and $c + a < c + b$.

Proof: We will show that $a < b$ implies $c + a < c + b$ and leave the argument that also $ca < cb$ as an exercise for the reader.

$a < b$	(Hypothesis)
$a + d = b$ for some d in N	(Definition of $<$)
$c + (a + d) = c + b$	(Substitution)
$(c + a) + d = c + b$	(N3)
$c + a < c + b$	(Definition of $<$)

This proof happens to be the first in which we have used the associative axiom N3. This delay in its use does not mean that it is in general infrequently used, as nothing could be further from the truth, but merely that the theorems we have considered have been exceptionally simple ones. We may give the reader a hint for use in constructing the second part of the proof of Theorem 4.8 by noting that, in the second part, the role played by N3 will be taken over by N4, the distributive postulate.

Next we have the *transitive* property of the relation $<$, that is

THEOREM 4.9. For any a, b, and c in N, if $a < b$ and $b < c$, then $a < c$.

Proof:

$a < b$, $b < c$	(Hypothesis)
$a + r = b$, $b + s = c$ for some r and s in N	(Definition of $<$)
$(a + r) + s = c$	(Substitution)
$a + (r + s) = c$	(N3)
$r + s$ is in N	(N1)
$a < c$	(Definition of $<$)

This transitive property of our order relation is also referred to sometimes as the property of being a linear order relation; that is, the natural numbers are ordered like points on a line, where if a is to the left of b, and b is to the left of c, then clearly a is to the left of c.

While the theorems we have given are but a very few of those needed for the purposes of doing ordinary arithmetic in the natural number system, they should provide some idea of how one proceeds from the axiomatic formulation of the natural number system to develop the other intuitively known and very useful properties.

EXERCISES

1. Show by example that $a + (bc)$ is in general unequal to $(a + b)(a + c)$ in the natural number system. (This will show, by exhibiting a counterexample, that "addition distributes over multiplication" is *false* for natural numbers.)

2. Show by example that $a \cup b = a \cup c$ does not imply $b = c$ in the algebra of sets. Similarly, show that $a \cap b = a \cap c$ does not imply $b = c$ in this algebra. That is, both possible cancellation properties fail to hold in the algebra of sets.

3. What cancellation properties hold for the arithmetic of a four-hour clock? A five-hour clock? A seven-hour clock? Can you generalize to the case of an n-hour clock, where n is some arbitrary natural number?

4. Show that the natural number system as defined by N1–N8 cannot consist of just one element; of just two elements.

5. Supply a proof of Theorem 4.3.

6. Define the relation "greater than" in the set of all natural numbers.

7. Show that there can be only one least natural number.

8. Supply the second part of the proof of Theorem 4.8; that is, show that, for any natural numbers a, b, and c, if $a < b$ then $ca < cb$.

9. If a, b, and c are natural numbers such that $a + b < a + c$, does it necessarily follow that $b < c$?

10. Prove the theorem "x is a natural number such that $3x + 1 = x + 5$ if and only if $x = 2$," being sure to prove both parts of the theorem. (Finding the correct theorem and then proving it constitute what is often called "solving the equation $3x + 1 = x + 5$.")

11. Using the definitions of the place-value system of notation for natural numbers, justify each step in the usual procedure for computing the product 26 times 37; that is, in the form

$$
\begin{array}{r}
26 \\
37 \\
\hline
182 \\
78 \\
\hline
962
\end{array}
$$

give a postulate, definition, or theorem to justify each step of the procedure.

12. Defining 2 as $1 + 1$, 3 as $2 + 1$, 4 as $3 + 1$, and so on *ad infinitum*, use these definitions and the postulates N1–N8 to prove that $2 \cdot 2 = 4$ and that $3 + 2 = 5$.

4.5 An Alternative to the Postulate of Induction

We have already mentioned that the list of postulates N1–N8, which we have used to define the natural numbers, can be replaced by other, equivalent, lists of postulates. In particular, we may replace N8, the postulate of induction, by a postulate which may seem more obviously true of the intuitive natural number system.

N8′. If S is any non-empty set of natural numbers, then S contains a least element; i.e., if S is a non-empty subset of N, then there is some s in S such that for any t in S either $s = t$ or $s < t$. We call N8′ the *well ordered* property of the natural numbers.

We now wish to show that, assuming N1–N7, either of N8 or N8′ implies the other. We begin by arguing that N8 implies N8′. To do this we must somehow bring the two conditions of N8 into the picture. Since any non-empty set S of natural numbers must contain some natural number n, we define T to be the set of natural numbers n such that any subset of N containing an element less than or equal to n must contain a least element. We will then show that T satisfies both the conditions of N8, from which it will follow that $T = N$, and hence N8′ holds.

Clearly 1 is in T, since we already know by Theorem 4.7 that 1 is a least element of N and hence any subset S of N containing an element less than or equal to 1 must contain 1, which is then a least element of S.

Now, suppose it is true that any subset of N containing an element less than or equal to k has a least element, and that S is some subset of N containing an element less than or equal to $k + 1$. Then either $k + 1$ is itself a least element of S, or else S contains an element a such that $a < k + 1$. If we can show that a is less than or equal to k we will be finished, as it will then follow that S has a least element. By virtue of N6, or N6′, we have that just one of $a < k$, $a = k$, or $k < a$ holds, and we need to show that $k < a$ is impossible.

Now, $a < k + 1$ means that $a + b = k + 1$ for some b. If $k < a$ were true, it would mean that $k + c = a$ for some c. We would then have

$$k + (c + b) = (k + c) + b = a + b = k + 1$$

by N3 and substitution. Then N5 would imply that $c + b = 1$, which is impossible since 1 is a least natural number. Thus $k < a$ is impossible when $a < k + 1$, and we conclude that $a < k$ or $a = k$, whence S has a least element. We have verified both conditions of N8 for our set T; and hence T is the set of all natural numbers, thus completing the argument that N1–N8 imply N8′.

To show that N1–N7 and N8′ imply N8, we first need to show that N1–N7 and N8′ imply that 1 is a least natural number. To do so we argue as follows. By N7 we know that N is not empty, since 1 is in N; and then N8′ says that N must have a least element which we will call b. By N6′, we must have $b = 1$, $b < 1$, or $1 < b$. The last of these three alternatives is impossible since b, as a least element of N, is less than or equal to every natural number. Also, if $b < 1$ were the case, then we would have $b + c = 1$ for some c, and

$$bb + bc = b(b + c) = b \cdot 1 = b$$

would hold. Since bb and bc are natural numbers by postulate N1, this would mean $bb < b$, contrary to b being a least natural number. Thus $b = 1$ is the only possibility, 1 is a least natural number, and our argument is complete.

Notice that we ruled out $b < 1$ since it led to a contradiction. Although we shall not attempt here to prove that the natural number system contains no contradictions, we shall appeal to our experience with it to make this seem reasonable. We shall therefore freely use arguments of the above type when convenient.

In order to establish N8, we suppose that T is a subset of N such that 1 is in T and $(a + 1)$ is in T if a is in T; and we need to show that $T = N$. Equally well we may show that $\bar{T}$, the complement of T, is empty. If $\bar{T}$ is not empty, then, by N8′, $\bar{T}$ has a least element x. Now x is not 1, since x is in $\bar{T}$ and 1 is in T. Since 1 is a least natural number, we conclude that $1 < x$, or $1 + t = t + 1 = x$ for some natural number

t. This says that $t < x$; hence, t is not in $\bar{T}$, as no natural number less than x can be in $\bar{T}$. Thus t is in T, which by our initial assumption regarding T implies that $t + 1 = x$ is also in T. Here we have a contradiction of x in $\bar{T}$; that is, x cannot be in both T and $\bar{T}$. Hence $\bar{T}$ must have been empty, or $T = N$; and we have established that N1–N7 and N8′ imply N8.

Having established that, assuming N1–N7, N8 and N8′ are equivalent, from now on we may freely use whichever of N8 or N8′ is most convenient for the purpose at hand. It is also interesting to know that a statement as intuitively obvious as N8′ is (together with N1–N7) equivalent to the often mysterious N8.

5

FRACTIONS

5.1 Introduction

Our treatment of the fundamental concepts of arithmetic has been limited primarily to a discussion of the natural numbers. We have seen that the numbers themselves, the operations of addition and multiplication, and the postulates or axioms governing the use of these operations were products of man's imagination, and that they were suggested by practical considerations arising from man's need for a means of counting.

But man had many quantitative needs aside from that of answering the relatively simple question, "How many?" Problems of measurement, involving such questions as how long, how heavy, how much, how strong, how bright, how loud, and so on, confronted man at every turn and could not always be solved in terms of natural numbers. Such problem necessitated an extension of the number system.

Our discussion of this extension of the number system will be given in two parts. The first part is intuitive and is intended to show how the notions of fractions, equivalence of fractions, and addition and multiplication of fractions arise from the practical demands of a system of measurement. The second part contains a more rigorous treatment that shows how the properties of fractions can be developed from the basic definitions.

5.2   Measurement and Fractions

Measurement would be only a counting problem if the measurements of time, length, area, volume, and so on were always to come out as integral multiples of the units of measure. A given distance would be measured by counting the number of miles from one end to the other if the distance were an exact number of miles. To measure the volume of a certain barrel, we would simply have to count the number of gallons of liquid it would hold if the barrel contained an integral number of gallons.

However, it can easily happen that a quantity cannot be measured exactly by a whole number of the standard units. In such a situation, it is natural to say that the given quantity can be measured by a certain number of the standard units plus a *part* of one additional unit. Alternatively, and more accurately, one might divide the standard unit into several equal subunits, and it might then turn out that the desired quantity can be measured by, say, r units plus s subunits. For example, suppose one desires to measure the length of the object in Fig. 5.1 and

Six inch ruler

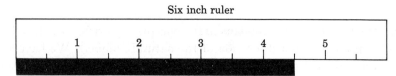

Figure 5.1   Measurement of a line segment.

chooses an inch as the standard unit of length. Clearly, the measurement does not come out even. Without further subdivision, one can only say that this object is something over four inches long. However, if one divides the inch into two equal parts, he can say that the object is four and one-half inches long or, entirely in terms of the subunit, that it is nine half-inches long.

Even after dividing the standard unit into equal subunits, it still may not be possible to get an exact measurement in a given case. In such a situation, the process of subdivision might be continued by further dividing the subunit into smaller and smaller subunits.* As is well known, our standard systems of measurement are constructed in just this way so that we have meters, decimeters, centimeters, and millimeters in the metric system and yards, feet, inches, half-inches, quarter-inches, and so on, in the English system. The same is true in systems for measuring time, volumes, weights, angles, and the like.

If we divide a given standard unit into n equal subunits and measure a quantity exactly equivalent to m of these subunits, the result of the measurement can be expressed by the number pair (m, n) since the natural number n uniquely determines the size of the subunit and the natural number m determines the number of subunits required for the measurement. For example, $(2, 3)$ would designate a measurement requiring 2 subunits where the size of the subunit is determined by dividing the chosen unit into 3 equal parts. Similarly $(3, 2)$ would denote a measurement of 3 subunits where the size of the subunit is determined by dividing the standard unit into 2 equal parts. The usual notation in situations of this sort is to denote by $1/n$ the length of each subunit if the standard unit is divided into n equal subunits and let m/n denote a measurement requiring precisely m of these subunits. However, one should realize that *any* convenient notation involving two natural numbers could be used just as well.

We make the following definition.

DEFINITION 5.1   If m and n are any two natural numbers, the number pair m/n is called a *fraction*.

It is common to call m the *numerator* of the fraction and n the *denominator*. The word "denominator" is related to the word "denomination" and so, in terms of measurement, tells the name or size of the subunit involved. "Numerator" is related to "numeration" or "counting" and tells how many of the subunits are involved. The fraction $1/n$ with a numerator of one is called a *unit fraction*.

---

* Surprisingly, it may not be possible to obtain an exact measurement in this way no matter how far the process of subdivision is carried out. This poses a very difficult mathematical problem, which we consider in some detail in Chapter 8.

5.3   Equivalence of Fractions

Continuing our intuitive approach, we say that two fractions are equivalent if they can be used to designate the same measurement in terms of a single standard unit. To indicate equivalence of fractions, we use the equality sign.

If subunits of the same size are used in both cases, it is clear that two measurements will be the same if and only if the same number of subunits are involved. For example, a measurement of a thirds will be equal to a measurement of b thirds if and only if the natural numbers a and b are equal. Thus, in accord with our criterion for equivalence of fractions, we say that $a/3 = b/3$ if and only if $a = b$. More generally, it is clear that we ought to have the following rule.

RULE 5.1   For any three natural numbers a, b, and c, $a/c = b/c$ if and only if $a = b$.

This rule simply says that fractions with common denominators are equivalent if and only if they are identical fractions. However, equivalence of fractions in general involves more than simple identity of symbols, and it will be necessary to return to our measurement criterion for equivalence of fractions to see what is meant in the general case.

In terms of measurement, fractions with different denominators represent measurements in subunits of different sizes. This makes it somewhat difficult to compare the measurements and, thus, determine the question of equivalence of the fractions involved. On the other hand, if the two measurements can be converted to measurements in terms of a single common subunit, the desired comparison can easily be made. For example, consider a measurement of 2/3 units, as shown in Fig. 5.2. If each subunit of size 1/3 is further divided into 5 equal parts, the original unit will then contain 15 subunits each of size 1/15 and two subunits of length 1/3 will contain precisely 10 subunits of length 1/15.

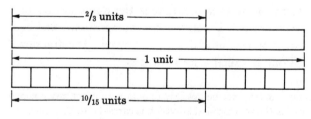

Figure 5.2   Equality of 2/3 and 10/15.

It is apparent that 2/3 and 10/15 can be used to designate the same measurement where we have a single fixed unit as standard. Thus, in line with our basic principle, we say that 2/3 = 10/15. Note that this is not identity of symbols since "2/3" and "10/15" are clearly different.

The preceding argument could be repeated in general with a, b, and c in place of 2, 3, and 5, and we would be led to the following conclusion.

RULE 5.2 For any three natural numbers a, b, and c, $a/b = ac/bc$.

The criterion for the equivalence of fractions in general now follows easily from Rules 5.1 and 5.2. Consider fractions a/b and c/d. According to Rule 5.2, $a/b = ad/bd$ and $c/d = cb/db$. Also, $cb/db = bc/bd$ by N2, the commutative law for multiplication of natural numbers. Thus, $c/d = bc/bd$, and the fractions a/b and c/d are clearly equivalent if and only if ad/bd and bc/bd are equivalent. But, by Rule 5.1, these fractions are equivalent if and only if $ad = bc$. This, then, is the desired condition for equivalence of a/b and c/d, and we state the following rule.

RULE 5.3 For any four natural numbers a, b, c, and d, $a/b = c/d$ if and only if $ad = bc$.

For example, it is very easy to see, by Rule 5.3, that 4/6 = 10/15 since $4 \cdot 15 = 6 \cdot 10$, and that $3/5 \neq 6/9$ since $3 \cdot 9 \neq 5 \cdot 6$. Also, by Rule 5.2, 3/7 = 15/35 and 8/26 = 4/13.

EXERCISES

1. Rule 5.2 is the principal tool used in "reducing fractions to their lowest terms," as we usually say. For example, to reduce 34/51 to its lowest terms, we find the largest natural number which evenly divides 34 and 51 (in this case it is 17), and write $34/51 = 2 \cdot 17/3 \cdot 17 = 2/3$. If the largest natural number which evenly divides both numerator and denominator of a fraction is 1, we say that the fraction is in its *lowest terms*.

   In reducing a fraction like 34/51 to its lowest terms, many people write $34/51 = 2 \cdot \cancel{17}/3 \cdot \cancel{17} = 2/3$ and say that they have *cancelled* the 17 in both numerator and denominator. Cancelling is a physical act that consists of striking a line through certain numbers and it must be *justified* by some mathematical reason or law. The cancelling just described can be justified by Rule 5.2. Essentially, it involves *dividing* both numerator and denominator of the fraction by the same number. The physical act of cancelling without justification often leads students to make errors.

Reduce the following fractions to their lowest terms.

(a) $\dfrac{12}{16}$ (b) $\dfrac{38}{57}$ (c) $\dfrac{45}{60}$ (d) $\dfrac{200}{75}$

(e) $\dfrac{63}{84}$ (f) $\dfrac{132}{504}$ (g) $\dfrac{315}{445}$ (h) $\dfrac{1819}{1853}$

Note that, for large numerators and denominators, it becomes increasingly difficult to reduce a fraction to its lowest terms. The problem here, which is basically that of finding the divisors of a given natural number, will be considered in more detail in Chapter 7.

2. Is $93/155 = 3/5$? Justify your answer in two different ways.

3. Is $205/451 = 4/9$? Explain.

5.4 Addition of Fractions

Again we rely on the notion of measurement to suggest how fractions should be added. Suppose, for example, that we desire the sum of $3/10$ and $4/10$. One might think of the problem of finding the total length of two strings of length $3/10$ and $4/10$ units respectively. Since the subunit of measurement is the same in each case, this is simply a matter of adding 3 and 4 to determine the number of subunits in the total measurement. Thus, the total length is $7/10$ units. This suggests that we should have that three-tenths plus four-tenths equals seven-tenths or, in symbols, that we ought to have $3/10 + 4/10 = 7/10$. More generally, if the preceding argument were repeated with 3, 4, and 10 replaced by a, b, and c respectively, we would obtain $a/c + b/c = (a + b)/c$ for any three natural numbers a, b, and c. Thus, the sum of two fractions, a/c and b/c, which have the same denominator ought to be the fraction whose numerator is the sum of the numerators of the original fractions and whose denominator is the common denominator of the original fractions. This is formalized in the following rule.

RULE 5.4   For any natural numbers a, b, and c, $\dfrac{a}{c} + \dfrac{b}{c} = \dfrac{a + b}{c}$.

The rule for addition of fractions that do not have a common denominator can be deduced from Rules 5.2 and 5.4. Consider the fractions a/b and c/d. By Rule 5.2, we have that $a/b = ad/bd$ and $c/d = cb/db$.

Also, by N2, the commutative law for multiplication of natural numbers, $cb/db = bc/bd$. Therefore, it follows that

$$\frac{a}{b} + \frac{c}{d} = \frac{ad}{bd} + \frac{bc}{bd}$$

But this last sum is equal to $(ad + bc)/bd$ by Rule 5.4, and so

$$\frac{a}{b} + \frac{c}{d} = \frac{ad + bc}{bd}$$

Thus, we have obtained the following general rule.

RULE 5.5   If a, b, c, and d are any four natural numbers, then

$$\frac{a}{b} + \frac{c}{d} = \frac{ad + bc}{bd}$$

Note in particular that, by Rule 5.5, the sum of any two fractions is again a fraction so that *the set of all fractions is closed under addition.*

As an example of Rule 5.5, we may note that

$$\frac{2}{3} + \frac{4}{5} = \frac{2 \cdot 5 + 3 \cdot 4}{3 \cdot 5} = \frac{10 + 12}{15} = \frac{22}{15}$$

EXERCISES

1. Add the following fractions and reduce the result to lowest terms.

(a) $\dfrac{1}{2} + \dfrac{1}{3}$ (b) $\dfrac{1}{7} + \dfrac{3}{10}$ (c) $\dfrac{2}{3} + \dfrac{1}{6}$ (d) $\dfrac{7}{24} + \dfrac{5}{16}$

(e) $\dfrac{3}{34} + \dfrac{7}{51}$ (f) $\dfrac{2}{63} + \dfrac{5}{84}$ (g) $\dfrac{17}{540} + \dfrac{101}{1800}$

The work involved in adding fractions can often be minimized by converting both fractions to fractions with a common denominator that is the smallest natural number divisible by both denominators involved. For example, since 48 is the smallest natural number divisible by both 16 and

24 the addition in part (d) can be carried out, as follows:

$$\frac{7}{24} + \frac{5}{16} = \frac{7 \cdot 2}{24 \cdot 2} + \frac{5 \cdot 3}{16 \cdot 3} = \frac{14}{48} + \frac{15}{48} = \frac{14 + 15}{48} = \frac{29}{48}$$

This computation should be compared with the solution by the method of Rule 5.5. Also, the computation here can easily be shortened by doing much of the work mentally.

2. Carry out the additions in Exercise 1 by the method of finding a least common denominator.

3. Compute the following pairs of sums.

(a) $\dfrac{2}{5} + \dfrac{7}{8}$ and $\dfrac{7}{8} + \dfrac{2}{5}$

(b) $\dfrac{5}{42} + \dfrac{8}{35}$ and $\dfrac{8}{35} + \dfrac{5}{42}$

(c) $\dfrac{5}{4} + \dfrac{6}{9}$ and $\dfrac{6}{9} + \dfrac{5}{4}$

4. Compute the following pairs of sums.

(a) $\left(\dfrac{1}{2} + \dfrac{1}{6}\right) + \dfrac{1}{3}$ and $\dfrac{1}{2} + \left(\dfrac{1}{6} + \dfrac{1}{3}\right)$

(b) $\left(\dfrac{1}{3} + \dfrac{1}{6}\right) + \dfrac{1}{9}$ and $\dfrac{1}{3} + \left(\dfrac{1}{6} + \dfrac{1}{9}\right)$

(c) $\left(\dfrac{7}{45} + \dfrac{7}{30}\right) + \dfrac{7}{12}$ and $\dfrac{7}{45} + \left(\dfrac{7}{30} + \dfrac{7}{12}\right)$

5.5 Multiplication of Fractions

Although we did not mention it at the time, multiplication was involved in the intuitive reasoning leading up to the very definition of fractions. Recall that we first associated the fraction m/n with a measurement requiring precisely m subunits each of length $1/n$. Thus, m/n can be conceived as the sum of m numbers each equal to $1/n$. In terms of our earlier understanding, this says that m/n can be thought of as the *product*, or natural multiple, $m(1/n)$. Similarly, the product $2(a/b)$ could be interpreted as the sum

$$\frac{a}{b} + \frac{a}{b} = \frac{(a+a)}{b} = \frac{2a}{b}$$

The product $3(a/b)$ could be interpreted as the sum

$$2\left(\frac{a}{b}\right) + \left(\frac{a}{b}\right) = \frac{2a}{b} + \frac{a}{b} = \frac{(2a+a)}{b} = \frac{3a}{b}$$

and, in general, the product $r(a/b)$ could be interpreted as the fraction ra/b. Thus, a natural multiple of a fraction should be the fraction whose numerator is the product of the natural number and the numerator of the original fraction, and whose denominator is the denominator of the original fraction; e.g., we should have $3(2/5) = 6/5$; $5(3/21) = 15/21$; and $4(2/9) = 8/9$.

It is somewhat more difficult to see that the product of a fraction and a natural number in the reverse order to that in the preceding paragraph should yield the same result as before since we have no *a priori* grounds for suspecting that the commutative law must necessarily hold. Suppose we think of the problem of finding a line segment two-fifths as long as a segment three units long; that is, suppose we think of finding 2/5 of 3. This can be accomplished schematically, as shown in Fig. 5.3, by dividing each of the three units into 5 subunits each of

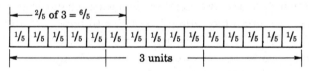

Figure 5.3   Geometrical interpretation of 2/5 of 3.

length 1/5 so that the total measurement of three units is divided into fifteen subunits. Grouping the subunits three at a time divides the total measurement into five equal parts each of length 3/5. Thus, one-fifth of the total measurement is given by the fraction 3/5 and two-fifths of the total measurement is given by 6/5. In other words, two-fifths of 3 is 6/5. Since taking 2/5 of 3 gives the same result as the natural multiple 3 times 2/5, it is reasonable to think of 2/5 of 3 as the product $(2/5)\cdot 3$. Thus, it is apparent that we should have $3\cdot(2/5) = (2/5)\cdot 3 = 6/5$. In general, we think of a fractional part *of* a natural number as the product of the fraction *times* the number. Thus, we have $a(b/c) = (b/c)a = ab/c$ for any natural numbers a, b, and c. Of course, $ab = ba$ by N2, so that the result may be written as either ab/c or ba/c.

If we extend this interpretation of the term "of" from multiplication of a fraction times a natural number to multiplication of two fractions, then it is not difficult to discover what the general rule for multiplication of fractions ought to be. For example, let us consider the product $(2/5)(3/4)$ and interpret this to mean 2/5 of 3/4. This is depicted geometrically in Fig. 5.4, where we begin by dividing the unit into four

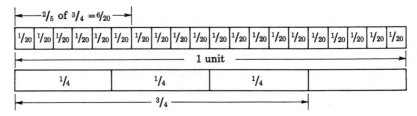

Figure 5.4   Geometrical interpretation of 2/5 of 3/4.

subunits each of length 1/4, and then further subdivide each one-fourth into 5 still smaller equal subunits. This divides the unit into twenty subunits each of length 1/20, and three-fourths of the unit contains 15 of the smaller subunits. If these 15 subunits are now grouped by threes, we shall have divided the measurement of 3/4 into five equal parts each of length 3/20. Thus, one-fifth of the measurement of 3/4 is given by the fraction 3/20 and two-fifths of the measurement is given by 6/20. Finally, since we are interpreting 2/5 of 3/4 to mean 2/5 times 3/4, we have $(2/5)(3/4) = 6/20$. The argument that $(3/4)(2/5) = 6/20$ is exactly analogous to the one we have just made and so we do not go through the details. However, the diagram for this product is given in Fig. 5.5.

The preceding argument indicates that the product of any two fractions ought to be the fraction whose numerator is the product of the numerators of the original fractions and whose denominator is the product of the denominators of the original fractions. Thus, we ought to have $(3/5)(2/7) = 6/35$; $(1/10)(3/9) = 3/90$; and so on. Hence, we state the following rule.

RULE 5.6   If a, b, c, and d are any four natural numbers, then

$$\frac{a}{b} \cdot \frac{c}{d} = \frac{ac}{bd}$$

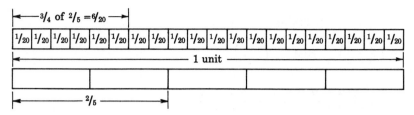

Figure 5.5   Geometrical interpretation of 3/4 of 2/5 or (3/4) (2/5).

EXERCISES

1. Determine the following products and reduce the resulting fractions to lowest terms.

   (a) $\dfrac{2}{5} \cdot \dfrac{7}{8}$ (b) $\dfrac{13}{24} \cdot \dfrac{5}{6}$ (c) $\dfrac{12}{13} \cdot \dfrac{5}{24}$ (d) $\dfrac{15}{32} \cdot \dfrac{56}{105}$ (e) $\dfrac{24}{270} \cdot \dfrac{15}{9}$

Since, in multiplying fractions, we multiply numerators and denominators together, it is clear that we can often use Rule 5.2 to simplify the work. For example, we can divide both the 12 and 24 in part (c) by 12 as follows.

$$\frac{\overset{1}{\cancel{12}}}{13} \cdot \frac{5}{\underset{2}{\cancel{24}}} = \frac{5}{26}$$

This can be justified by first multiplying in the usual way and then simplifying by use of Rule 5.2.

2. Compute the following products as shown in Exercise 1.

   (a) $\dfrac{18}{25} \cdot \dfrac{10}{24}$ (b) $\dfrac{38}{18} \cdot \dfrac{8}{104}$ (c) $\dfrac{54}{27} \cdot \dfrac{4}{150}$ (d) $\dfrac{36}{49} \cdot \dfrac{42}{1024}$

3. Compute the following pairs of products.

   (a) $\dfrac{2}{5} \cdot \dfrac{3}{8}$ and $\dfrac{3}{8} \cdot \dfrac{2}{5}$

   (b) $\dfrac{3}{5} \cdot \dfrac{15}{9}$ and $\dfrac{15}{9} \cdot \dfrac{3}{5}$

   (c) $\dfrac{27}{33} \cdot \dfrac{11}{18}$ and $\dfrac{11}{18} \cdot \dfrac{27}{33}$

4. Compute the following pairs of products.

(a) $\left(\dfrac{1}{3}\cdot\dfrac{2}{5}\right)\cdot\dfrac{4}{7}$ and $\dfrac{1}{3}\cdot\left(\dfrac{2}{5}\cdot\dfrac{4}{7}\right)$

(b) $\left(\dfrac{6}{10}\cdot\dfrac{4}{27}\right)\cdot\dfrac{9}{15}$ and $\dfrac{6}{10}\cdot\left(\dfrac{4}{27}\cdot\dfrac{9}{15}\right)$

5. Compute the following:

(a) $\dfrac{2}{3}\cdot\left(\dfrac{1}{5}+\dfrac{1}{4}\right)$ and $\dfrac{2}{3}\cdot\dfrac{1}{5}+\dfrac{2}{3}\cdot\dfrac{1}{4}$

(b) $\dfrac{18}{25}\cdot\left(\dfrac{1}{4}+\dfrac{1}{6}\right)$ and $\dfrac{18}{25}\cdot\dfrac{1}{4}+\dfrac{18}{25}\cdot\dfrac{1}{6}$

5.6 A More Rigorous Approach

In the preceding sections, we developed criteria for equivalence of fractions and rules for adding and multiplying fractions. The intuitive arguments were based on the notion of measurement and were not intended to *prove* that the rules given are true. Rather they were offered in an attempt to show why these particular rules should be required to hold in a system adequate to meet the needs of measurement.

In this section, we offer a more formal development of the arithmetic of fractions, beginning with three definitions which are simply restatements of three of the rules developed intuitively earlier.

DEFINITION 5.2 *Equivalence of fractions.* If a, b, c, and d are any four natural numbers, $a/b = c/d$ if and only if $ad = bc$.

DEFINITION 5.3 *Addition of fractions.* If a, b, c, and d are any four natural numbers, then

$$\frac{a}{b}+\frac{c}{d}=\frac{ad+bc}{bd}$$

DEFINITION 5.4 *Multiplication of fractions.* If a, b, c, and d are any four natural numbers, then

$$\frac{a}{b}\cdot\frac{c}{d}=\frac{ac}{bd}$$

From these definitions, and the postulates for the system of natural numbers, we can now derive a number of interesting and important consequences. In the first place we note that, by Definitions 5.3 and 5.4 and the closure laws for addition and multiplication of natural numbers, the set of fractions is closed with respect to both addition and multiplication. Verification of these facts is left as an exercise for the reader. The following sequence of theorems shows that the commutative and associative laws hold for addition and multiplication of fractions and that the distributive law is also valid. It should be observed that the key step in each of the following proofs is the use of the corresponding postulate for the system of natural numbers.

THEOREM 5.1 *Commutative law for addition.* If a/b and c/d are any two fractions then

$$\frac{a}{b} + \frac{c}{d} = \frac{c}{d} + \frac{a}{b}$$

Proof:

$$\frac{a}{b} + \frac{c}{d} = \frac{ad + bc}{bd} \qquad \text{(by Definition 5.3)}$$

$$= \frac{bc + ad}{bd} \qquad \text{(by N1 and N2)}$$

$$= \frac{cb + da}{db} \qquad \text{(by N2)}$$

$$= \frac{c}{d} + \frac{a}{b} \qquad \text{(by Definition 5.3)}$$

Therefore, $a/b + c/d = c/d + a/b$ as claimed.

THEOREM 5.2 *Associative law for addition.* If a/b, c/d, and e/f are any three fractions, then

$$\left(\frac{a}{b} + \frac{c}{d}\right) + \frac{e}{f} = \frac{a}{b} + \left(\frac{c}{d} + \frac{e}{f}\right)$$

Proof:

$$\left(\frac{a}{b} + \frac{c}{d}\right) + \frac{e}{f} = \frac{ad + bc}{bd} + \frac{e}{f} \qquad \text{(by Definition 5.3)}$$

$$= \frac{(ad + bc)f + (bd)e}{(bd)f} \qquad \text{(by N1 and Definition 5.3)}$$

$$= \frac{[(ad)f + (bc)f] + (bd)e}{(bd)f} \qquad \text{(by Theorem 4.1)}$$

$$= \frac{[a(df) + b(cf)] + b(de)}{b(df)} \qquad \text{(by N3)}$$

$$= \frac{a(df) + [b(cf) + b(de)]}{b(df)} \qquad \text{(by N1 and N3)}$$

$$= \frac{a(df) + b(cf + de)}{b(df)} \qquad \text{(by N1 and N4)}$$

$$= \frac{a}{b} + \frac{cf + de}{df} \qquad \text{(by N1 and Definition 5.3)}$$

$$= \frac{a}{b} + \left(\frac{c}{d} + \frac{e}{f}\right) \qquad \text{(by Definition 5.3)}$$

and the proof is complete.

THEOREM 5.3 *Commutative law for multiplication.* If a/b and c/d are any two fractions, then

$$\frac{a}{b} \cdot \frac{c}{d} = \frac{c}{d} \cdot \frac{a}{b}$$

Proof:

$$\frac{a}{b} \cdot \frac{c}{d} = \frac{ac}{bd} \qquad \text{(by Definition 5.4)}$$

$$= \frac{ca}{db} \qquad \text{(by N2)}$$

$$= \frac{c}{d} \cdot \frac{a}{b} \qquad \text{(by Definition 5.4)}$$

THEOREM 5.4 *Associative law for multiplication.* If a/b, c/d, e/f are any three fractions, then

$$\frac{a}{b} \cdot \left(\frac{c}{d} \cdot \frac{e}{f} \right) = \left(\frac{a}{b} \cdot \frac{c}{d} \right) \cdot \frac{e}{f}$$

Proof:

$$\frac{a}{b} \cdot \left(\frac{c}{d} \cdot \frac{e}{f} \right) = \frac{a}{b} \cdot \frac{ce}{df} \qquad \text{(by Definition 5.4)}$$

$$= \frac{a(ce)}{b(df)} \qquad \text{(by N1 and Definition 5.4)}$$

$$= \frac{(ac)e}{(bd)f} \qquad \text{(by N3)}$$

$$= \frac{ac}{bd} \cdot \frac{e}{f} \qquad \text{(by N1 and Definition 5.4)}$$

$$= \left(\frac{a}{b} \cdot \frac{c}{d} \right) \frac{e}{f} \qquad \text{(by Definition 5.4)}$$

and the proof is complete.

Before proving that the distributive law for fractions we prove as theorems two results which we had previously obtained intuitively.

THEOREM 5.5 If a, b, and c are any three natural numbers, then $a/b = ac/bc$.

Proof:

$$a(bc) = (ab)c \qquad \text{(by N3)}$$
$$= (ba)c \qquad \text{(by N2)}$$
$$= b(ac) \qquad \text{(by N3)}$$

Therefore

$$\frac{a}{b} = \frac{ac}{bc} \qquad \text{(by Definition 5.2)}$$

As noted earlier, Theorem 5.5 guarantees that an equivalent fraction is obtained by multiplying both numerator and denominator of a fraction by the same number or by dividing a common factor out of both numerator and denominator of a fraction.

THEOREM 5.6   If a, b, and c are any three natural numbers, then

$$\frac{a}{c} + \frac{b}{c} = \frac{a+b}{c}$$

Proof:

$$\frac{a}{c} + \frac{b}{c} = \frac{ac + cb}{cc} \qquad \text{(by Definition 5.3)}$$

$$= \frac{ac + bc}{cc} \qquad \text{(by N2)}$$

$$= \frac{(a+b)c}{cc} \qquad \text{(by Theorem 4.1)}$$

$$= \frac{a+b}{c} \qquad \text{(by Theorem 5.5)}$$

We are now in a position to prove the distributive law for fractions.

THEOREM 5.7   *Distributive law.* If a/b, c/d, and e/f are any three fractions, then

$$\frac{a}{b} \cdot \left(\frac{c}{d} + \frac{e}{f} \right) = \frac{a}{b} \cdot \frac{c}{d} + \frac{a}{b} \cdot \frac{e}{f} = \frac{ac}{bd} + \frac{ae}{bf}$$

Proof:

$$\frac{a}{b}\cdot\left(\frac{c}{d}+\frac{e}{f}\right)=\frac{a}{b}\cdot\left(\frac{cf+de}{df}\right) \qquad \text{(by Definition 5.3)}$$

$$=\frac{a(cf+de)}{b(df)} \qquad \text{(by N1 and Definition 5.4)}$$

$$=\frac{a(cf)+a(de)}{b(df)} \qquad \text{(by N4)}$$

$$=\frac{a(cf)}{b(df)}+\frac{a(de)}{b(df)} \qquad \text{(by Theorem 5.6)}$$

$$=\frac{a(cf)}{b(df)}+\frac{a(ed)}{b(fd)} \qquad \text{(by N2)}$$

$$=\frac{a}{b}\cdot\frac{cf}{df}+\frac{a}{b}\cdot\frac{ed}{fd} \qquad \text{(by N1 and Definition 5.4)}$$

$$=\frac{a}{b}\cdot\frac{c}{d}+\frac{a}{b}\cdot\frac{e}{f} \qquad \text{(by Theorem 5.5)}$$

$$=\frac{ac}{bd}+\frac{ae}{bf} \qquad \text{(by Definition 5.4)}$$

THEOREM 5.8. *Existence of a multiplicative identity.* If a/b is any fraction, then

$$\frac{a}{b}\cdot\frac{1}{1}=\frac{1}{1}\cdot\frac{a}{b}=\frac{a}{b}$$

and hence 1/1 is a multiplicative identity for the set of fractions.

Proof:

$$\frac{1}{1}\cdot\frac{a}{b}=\frac{1\cdot a}{1\cdot b} \qquad \text{(by Definition 5.4)}$$

$$=\frac{a}{b} \qquad \text{(by N7)}$$

It is possible to continue our sequence of theorems showing that the cancellation laws for addition and multiplication hold and that the law of trichotomy is also valid. We leave the proof of their results to the reader.

1. Show that the fractions in the set $T = \{\frac{1}{1}, \frac{2}{2}, \frac{3}{3}, \ldots\}$ are all equivalent. That is, if a and b are any two natural numbers, show that $a/a = b/b$.

2. Show directly that any one of the equivalent fractions in set T of Exercise 1 is a multiplicative identity for the set of fractions. That is, if a, b, and c are any three natural numbers, show that

$$\frac{c}{c} \cdot \frac{a}{b} = \frac{a}{b}$$

3. *Cancellation law for addition.* Supply a reason for each step in the following proof that, if a/b, c/d, and e/f are any three fractions with

$$\frac{a}{b} + \frac{c}{d} = \frac{a}{b} + \frac{e}{f}$$

then $c/d = e/f$.

Proof:

$$\frac{a}{b} + \frac{c}{d} = \frac{a}{b} + \frac{e}{f}$$

$$\frac{ad + bc}{bd} = \frac{af + be}{bf}$$

$$(ad + bc)(bf) = (bd)(af + be)$$

$$(bf)(ad + bc) = (bd)(af + be)$$

$$b[f(ad + bc)] = b[d(af + be)]$$

$$f(ad + bc) = d(af + be)$$

$$f(ad) + f(bc) = d(af) + d(be)$$

$$f(ad) + f(bc) = (da)f + (db)e$$

$$f(ad) + (bc)f = f(da) + (bd)e$$

$$f(ad) + (bc)f = f(ad) + (bd)e$$

$$(bc)f = (bd)e$$

$$b(cf) = b(de)$$

$$cf = de$$

$$\frac{c}{d} = \frac{e}{f}$$

4. *Cancellation law for multiplication.* If a/b, c/d, and e/f are any three fractions with

$$\frac{a}{b} \cdot \frac{c}{d} = \frac{a}{b} \cdot \frac{e}{f}$$

prove that $c/d = e/f$. As in Exercise 3, start with the given statement of equivalence and work down to the desired equivalence. Note that the result will follow if you can show that $cf = de$.

5. Suppose that addition of fractions were defined so that

$$\frac{a}{b} + \frac{c}{d} = \frac{a+c}{b+d}$$

for any two positive rational fractions a/b and c/d. Would the closure, commutative, and associative laws hold for this addition? Prove each of your answers.

6. If addition of fractions were defined as in Exercise 5 and multiplication were defined in the usual way, would the distributive law for multiplication over addition hold? Explain.

7. Solve the following equations using the cancellation law for addition of fractions. Check each of your answers. HINT: In (a) one should write $5/7 = 3/7 + 2/7$ and in (c) one should write $2/5 = 8/20$ and $7/4 = 35/20 = 8/20 + 27/20$.

(a) $\dfrac{3}{7} + x = \dfrac{5}{7}$ (b) $\dfrac{13}{29} + x = \dfrac{27}{29}$

(c) $\dfrac{2}{5} + x = \dfrac{7}{4}$ (d) $\dfrac{5}{7} + x = \dfrac{4}{5}$

8. Solve the following equations using the cancellation law for multiplication of fractions. Check each of your answers. HINT: In (a) note that

$$\frac{10}{21} = \frac{2}{3} \cdot \frac{5}{7}$$

and in (c) note that

$$\frac{7}{11} = \frac{3}{4} \cdot \left(\frac{4}{3} \cdot \frac{7}{11}\right) = \frac{3}{4} \cdot \frac{28}{33}$$

(a) $\dfrac{2}{3} \cdot x = \dfrac{10}{21}$ (b) $\dfrac{6}{7} \cdot x = \dfrac{12}{35}$

(c) $\dfrac{3}{4} \cdot x = \dfrac{7}{11}$ (d) $\dfrac{3}{5} \cdot x = \dfrac{17}{24}$

9. Solve the following equations and check your answers.

(a) $\dfrac{3}{4} \cdot \left(x + \dfrac{3}{5} \right) = \dfrac{19}{20}$

(b) $\dfrac{1}{3} + \dfrac{5}{6} \cdot x = \dfrac{2}{3}$

(c) $\dfrac{3}{4} + \dfrac{5}{7} \cdot x = \dfrac{21}{10}$

5.7   Division and Fractions

Division of m by n is defined in terms of multiplication and may be thought of as answering the question, "What number multiplied by n gives m?" For example, $6 \div 3 = 2$ and $6 = 3 \cdot 2$ are simply two different ways of expressing the *same* relationship between the numbers 6, 3, and 2. Division of numbers is always understood in this way and we make the following definition.

DEFINITION 5.5   If $a = bc$, then $a \div b = c$ and conversely.

In view of the definition, the statement that

$$\frac{a}{b} \div \frac{c}{d} = \frac{e}{f}$$

is equivalent to the assertion that

$$\frac{a}{b} = \frac{c}{d} \cdot \frac{e}{f}$$

We have noted earlier that the set of natural numbers is not closed under division. For example, there is no natural number c such that $8 \div 3 = c$. In contrast, the following theorem shows that the set of fractions is closed under division. It also justifies the commonplace rule of "invert and multiply" for division of fractions, which is so often used without understanding.

THEOREM 5.9   If a, b, c, and d are any four natural numbers, then

$$\frac{a}{b} \div \frac{c}{d} = \frac{a}{b} \cdot \frac{d}{c} = \frac{ad}{bc}$$

Proof: By Definition 5.5, it suffices to show that

$$\frac{c}{d} \cdot \frac{ad}{bc} = \frac{a}{b}$$

$$\frac{c}{d} \cdot \frac{ad}{bc} = \frac{c(ad)}{d(bc)} \quad \text{(by N1 and Definition 5.4)}$$

$$= \frac{(ad)c}{(bc)d} \quad \text{(by N2)}$$

$$= \frac{a(dc)}{b(cd)} \quad \text{(by N3)}$$

$$= \frac{a(cd)}{b(cd)} \quad \text{(by N2)}$$

$$= \frac{a}{b} \quad \text{(by N1 and Theorem 5.5)}$$

As an example of the Theorem 5.9, we note that $(3/5) \div (7/8) = (3/5) \cdot (8/7) = 24/35$ and that $(6/11) \div (6/11) = (6/11) \cdot (11/6) = 66/66 = 1/1$. This last computation is typical of the general case and is of particular importance. Thus, for any fraction a/b, we have that

$$\frac{a}{b} \div \frac{a}{b} = \frac{a}{b} \cdot \frac{b}{a} = \frac{ab}{ba} = \frac{ab}{ab} = \frac{1}{1}$$

and we note that 1/1 is a multiplicative identity for the set of fractions. The fraction b/a is frequently called the *reciprocal* of a/b, but, for our purpose, it is much more meaningful to call it the *multiplicative inverse* of a/b.

More generally, if we have a system S of elements, an operation $*$, and an identity element e such that $s * e = e * s = s$ for every element s in S, then the element b is said to be the *inverse of the element* a *with* *respect to the operation* ✳ in case $a * b = b * a = e$. In twelve-hour clock arithmetic, for example, it is clear that 5 is its own multiplicative inverse since 5 $\underset{12}{\times}$ 5 = 1. Also, 4 has no multiplicative inverse since there is no number a in the arithmetic such that $a \underset{12}{\times} 4 = 1$. The reader should check to find the other three elements in twelve-hour clock arithmetic which have multiplicative inverses. The reader should also note that *every* number in clock arithmetic has an *additive inverse*. Thus, 4 is the additive inverse of 8 since 4 $\underset{12}{+}$ 8 = 12 and 12 is the additive identity; 5 is the additive inverse of 7 since 5 $\underset{12}{+}$ 7 = 12; and so on.

The importance of the notion of an inverse can be illustrated by considering multiplication and division of fractions. In the first place, since

$$\left(\frac{a}{b} \cdot \frac{c}{d}\right) \cdot \frac{d}{c} = \frac{a}{b} \cdot \left(\frac{c}{d} \cdot \frac{d}{c}\right) = \frac{a}{b} \cdot \frac{1}{1} = \frac{a}{b}$$

it is clear that, if we multiply one fraction by a second fraction, and then multiply the result by the multiplicative inverse of the second fraction, we obtain the first fraction as a final result. That is to say, multiplication by the multiplicative inverse of a number nullifies the effect of multiplication by the number. If the reader will compare the preceding computation with that involved in the proof of Theorem 5.9, he will see that this property of the multiplicative inverse was the key to the proof. Also, Theorem 5.9 shows that *division of one fraction by another can be accomplished by multiplying the first fraction by the multiplicative inverse of the second*. This fact is of considerable importance; it will play a prominent role in Chapter 6.

EXERCISES

1. Compute the following quotients and reduce your answers to lowest terms.

(a) $\frac{2}{3} \div \frac{3}{4}$ (b) $\frac{2}{3} \div \frac{4}{3}$ (c) $\frac{7}{11} \div \frac{21}{66}$

(d) $\frac{39}{42} \div \frac{26}{36}$ (e) $\frac{501}{315} \div \frac{213}{285}$

2. Compute the following products.

(a) $\left(\frac{2}{3} \cdot \frac{5}{7}\right) \cdot \frac{7}{5}$ (b) $\left(\frac{13}{15} \cdot \frac{7}{11}\right) \cdot \frac{11}{7}$

3. Equations like $\frac{3}{5} \cdot x = \frac{7}{11}$ are most easily solved using division; that is, if $\frac{3}{5} \cdot x = \frac{7}{11}$, then

$$x = \frac{7}{11} \div \frac{3}{5} = \frac{7}{11} \cdot \frac{5}{3} = \frac{35}{33}$$

Use this idea to solve the following equations. Check your answers.

(a) $\frac{7}{9} \cdot x = \frac{5}{2}$ (b) $\left(\frac{1}{3} + \frac{2}{5}\right) \cdot x = \frac{11}{17}$ (c) $\frac{2}{3} \cdot x + \frac{1}{7} = \frac{9}{8}$

4. Solve the following equations and check your answers.

(a) $x \div \frac{3}{4} = \frac{5}{7}$ (b) $x \div \frac{11}{7} = \frac{15}{16}$ (c) $\left(\frac{2}{3} \cdot x\right) \div \frac{4}{5} = \frac{7}{8}$

5. Prove that $\left(\dfrac{a}{b} + \dfrac{c}{d}\right) \div \dfrac{e}{f} = \left(\dfrac{a}{b} \div \dfrac{e}{f}\right) + \left(\dfrac{c}{d} \div \dfrac{e}{f}\right).$

6. Which numbers in 12-hour clock arithmetic have multiplicative inverses? What is the multiplicative inverse of each of these numbers?

7. Which numbers in 7-hour clock arithmetic have multiplicative inverses? What is the multiplicative inverse of each of these numbers?

8. Repeat Exercises 6 and 7 for additive inverses.

9. Would the additive identity have a multiplicative inverse in any clock arithmetic? Why or why not?

10. Show that no divisor of zero in a clock arithmetic can have a multiplicative inverse. HINT: Let 0 denote the additive identity in a clock arithmetic. Suppose that a is a divisor of zero. Then there exists b with $b \neq 0$ such that $ab = 0$. Suppose also that a has a multiplicative inverse. Then there exists c such that $ac = 1$. Consider the product $1 \cdot b = (ac)b$, and show that this is impossible.

11. Consider a clock arithmetic. If a has a multiplicative inverse, and if $ab = ac$, show that $b = c$.

5.8 The Positive Rational Numbers

Equivalence of fractions is not simply identity of symbols. Clearly 2/3 and 4/6 are different symbols; and yet, by definition, they are equivalent fractions. Recall that the motivation for our definition of the equivalence of fractions was that the two fractions in question could be used to represent the same measurement. This amounts to saying that 2/3 and 4/6 both represent the same number. Of course, infinitely many other fractions also represent this number since, by Theorem 5.5, we have 2/3 = 4/6 = 6/9 = 8/12 = 10/15 and so on. Technically, the abstract number represented by any one of a set of equivalent fractions is called a *positive rational number*, and any one of the set of equivalent fractions is called a *representive* of the rational number. At the same time, this distinction between the rational number and any particular representative of the rational number is not consistently made, and 2/3, 5/7, ..., are often called rational numbers as well as fractions. In fact, the name "rational number" comes from the fact that a/b is the *ratio* of a and b where "ratio" means "quotient of."

The set of rational numbers $N' = \{\frac{1}{1}, \frac{2}{1}, \frac{3}{1}, \frac{4}{1}, \ldots\}$ is of particular interest. Reverting to the notion of measurement for a moment, the fraction $n/1$ could be interpreted as a measurement of n subunits where the size of the subunit is determined by "dividing" the unit chosen as standard into one part. Since dividing the standard unit into only one subunit is no division at all, it follows that $n/1$ denotes a measurement requiring precisely n of the standard units. Thus, at least in the case of measurement, one might reasonably use the symbols n and $n/1$ interchangeably.

Let us see whether we have more rigorous grounds for identifying the natural number n and the rational number $n/1$. We set up a correspondence between the sets

$$N = \{1, 2, 3, \ldots\} \quad \text{and} \quad N' = \{\tfrac{1}{1}, \tfrac{2}{1}, \tfrac{3}{1}, \ldots\}$$

in the obvious way indicated by

$$n \leftrightarrow \frac{n}{1}$$

Thus, to each element n in N there corresponds precisely one element $n/1$ in N', and conversely. Moreover

$$n + m \leftrightarrow \frac{n+m}{1} = \frac{n}{1} + \frac{m}{1}$$

and

$$n \cdot m \leftrightarrow \frac{nm}{1} = \frac{n}{1} \cdot \frac{m}{1}$$

If, for any natural number n, we call $n/1$ the *image* of n, then the preceding shows that the image of $n + m$ is the sum of the images of n and m, and the image of $n \cdot m$ is the product of the images of n and m. This means that, if a result involving addition and multiplication of natural numbers is valid, the corresponding result is valid for the images. For example, since $a(b + c) = ab + ac$ for any natural numbers a, b, and c, we must also have that

$$\frac{a}{1} \cdot \left(\frac{b}{1} + \frac{c}{1} \right) = \frac{a}{1} \cdot \frac{b}{1} + \frac{a}{1} \cdot \frac{c}{1}$$

for any three elements $a/1$, $b/1$, and $c/1$ in N', and conversely. Again, since $1 \cdot a = a$ for every natural number a, we have that

$$\frac{1}{1} \cdot \frac{a}{1} = \frac{a}{1}$$

where $a/1$ is any element in N', and conversely. Thus, it follows that the rational numbers in N' satisfy all of the postulates of the system of natural numbers. Moreover, we have seen that a mathmatical system is actually defined by its postulates and, thus, N' essentially *is* the system of natural numbers. In fact, the distinction between the natural number n and its rational image $n/1$ is not always made, and one says that a natural number n is a rational number and writes

$$n = \frac{n}{1}$$

Thus, the system of positive rational numbers contains the set of natural numbers as a subsystem, and so may be viewed as an extension of the system of natural numbers.

We have seen that many of the properties of the natural numbers also hold for the system of positive rational numbers. Thus, the closure, commutative, and associative laws with respect to addition and multiplication, the distributive law, the law of trichotomy, and the cancellation laws hold; and $1 = 1/1$ is a multiplicative identity. Moreover, we have gained some properties which the natural numbers did not possess. In particular, the system of positive rational numbers provides a tool adequate for the problems of counting and every-day measurement; and, more importantly, it is closed under division. However, the principle of mathematical induction does *not* hold for the set of all positive rational numbers. That is, it is not true that any set of positive rational numbers which contains 1 and also contains $r + 1$ whenever it contains the rational number r, contains all positive rational numbers. For example, the set $\{\frac{1}{2}, 1, \frac{3}{2}, 2, \frac{5}{2}, 3, \frac{7}{2}, 4, \frac{9}{2}, \ldots\}$ satisfies these conditions and yet does not contain all positive rationals.

EXERCISES

1. Show that if a/b is a multiplicative identity for the positive rational numbers, then $a/b = 1/1$, and hence the multiplicative identity is unique.

2. Show that the multiplicative inverse of a positive rational number is unique.

5.9   Ratio and Proportion

In the preceding section, we remarked that the name "rational number" comes from the fact that the fraction a/b is the *ratio* or *quotient* of the natural numbers a and b. To see that this is so, we must show that $a \div b = a/b$. But, since we have identified the natural numbers a and b with the rational numbers or fractions $a/1$ and $b/1$, we have that

$$a \div b = \frac{a}{1} \div \frac{b}{1} = \frac{a}{1} \cdot \frac{1}{b} = \frac{a \cdot 1}{1 \cdot b} = \frac{a}{b}$$

as desired.

Since $a/b = a \div b$ when a and b are natural numbers, the fraction notation is often used to indicate division even when the numerator and denominator are not natural numbers. Thus, one might write

$$\frac{2/3}{4/7} = \frac{2}{3} \cdot \frac{7}{4} = \frac{14}{12} = \frac{7}{6}$$

and

$$\frac{3/7 + 2/5}{5/6} = \frac{6}{5}\left(\frac{3}{7} + \frac{2}{5}\right)$$

$$= \frac{6}{5} \cdot \frac{29}{35}$$

$$= \frac{174}{175}$$

The reader would do well to work out many examples of this sort of his own devising.

The fraction a/b is the ratio of a to b, and the indicated equality of two fractions is called a *proportion*. Thus, 6/9 and 10/15 are ratios and the equality

$$\frac{6}{9} = \frac{10}{15}$$

is a proportion. Also, the numbers 6 and 10 are said to be *proportional* to the numbers 9 and 15. Instances of proportions are commonplace in daily life. For example, if oranges cost 45 cents a dozen, the number of oranges a person buys is proportional to the amount of money he spends. If he buys 2 dozen oranges he spends 90 cents, and if he buys 3 dozen oranges he spends 135 cents; and 2 and 90 are proportional to 3 and 135; i.e.

$$\frac{2}{3} = \frac{90}{135}$$

Similarly, if a train travels at a constant rate of speed, the distance traveled is proportional to the elapsed time. Traveling at 65 miles per hour for 3 hours, a train will progress 195 miles. If the same pace is maintained for 5 hours, 325 miles will be traversed. The numbers 3 and 195 are clearly proportional to 5 and 325 since

$$\frac{3}{5} = \frac{195}{325}$$

An interesting instance of proportion in mathematics occurs in connection with similar geometrical figures. It is a theorem in plane geometry that the lengths of corresponding sides of similar geometrical figures are proportional. For example, the two triangles in Fig. 5.6 are similar and each side of the smaller triangle is just one-third as long as the corresponding side of the larger triangle; that is, side AB' is one-third the length of side AB, and so on. Roughly speaking, geometrical figures are similar in case one figure is just a magnification of

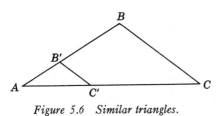

Figure 5.6   Similar triangles.

the other. This happens to be the case for triangles, for example, if the corresponding sides of the triangles are parallel.

Suppose now that one wants to give a geometrical representation of the product of 6 and 2. This can be accomplished by drawing two intersecting straight lines 𝔐 and 𝔑 as in Fig. 5.7. Choosing any convenient

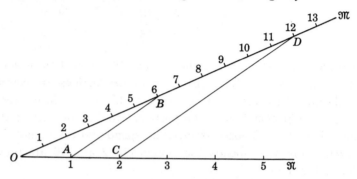

Figure 5.7   *Geometrical construction of 6·2.*

unit of length, we begin at the point of intersection and mark off successively points one unit from O, two units from O, etc., on 𝔑 as shown. Similarly, with another (or the same; it makes no difference) unit of length we lay off and number successive points on 𝔐. Let A denote the point numbered 1 on 𝔑 and let B denote the point numbered 6 on 𝔐. Join these two points with a straight line segment. Now, let C denote the point numbered 2 on 𝔑 and draw a line through C parallel to the line segment through A and B. This will meet line 𝔐 at the point numbered 12 and designated by D, and 12 is the product of 6 and 2. What we have done is simply to construct two similar triangles OAB and OCD. Since OC is twice as long as OA, it follows that OD is twice as long as OB. Thus, OD is 12 (the product of 6 and 2) units long, as desired. The process is completely general, and the reader should construct several additional examples for himself.

To summarize, the product of a and b can be represented geometrically by drawing intersecting numbered lines like 𝔐 and 𝔑 in Fig. 5.7, drawing a line from 1 on 𝔑 to the point numbered a on 𝔐, and drawing a line through the point numbered b on 𝔑 parallel to the line just drawn from 1 to a. This line meets 𝔐 at a point ab units from O, the point of intersection of 𝔐 and 𝔑. Figure 5.8 gives the geometrical construction of 5·3.

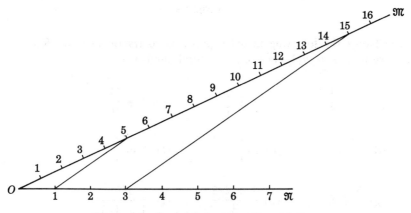

Figure 5.8   Geometrical construction of 5·3.

A moment's reflection will reveal how the preceding construction could be reversed to effect the geometrical representation of a quotient. Thus, to divide 15 by 3 geometrically, one might begin by joining 3 on 𝔫 to 15 on 𝔪 by a line segment. Then, through 1 on 𝔫 draw a line parallel to the first line. This line will (for the same reason as before) meet 𝔪 at a point representing the quotient of 15 and 3. Similarly the diagram of Fig. 5.7 could be viewed as the construction for the quotient of 12 and 2.

Suppose now that we want a geometrical representation of the rational number 5/8. This amounts to representing 5 ÷ 8 geometrically according to the scheme outlined in the preceding paragraph. The work is shown in Fig. 5.9.

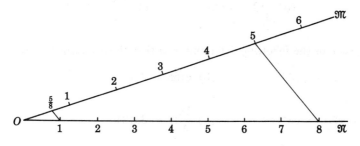

Figure 5.9   Geometrical construction of 5/8.

We shall have occasion to return to these constructions in the sequel.

EXERCISES

1. Change the following mixed expressions to fractional form. Recall that we write $n = n/1$ where n is a natural number.

(a) $3 + \dfrac{4}{5}$ (b) $1 + \dfrac{2}{7}$ (c) $3 + \dfrac{11}{9}$

(d) $\dfrac{31}{7} + 4$ (e) $5 \cdot \dfrac{3}{4}$ (f) $5 \div \dfrac{3}{4}$

(g) $\dfrac{3}{4} \div 5$ (h) $\dfrac{1 + 2/5}{3}$ (i) $\dfrac{5/7}{1 + 1/5}$

2. If a, b, and c are any three natural numbers, show that $a(b/c) = ab/c$.

3. If r, s, and t are any three natural numbers, show that $(r/s) \div t = r/st$.

4. Show that $1/a$ is the multiplicative inverse of the natural number a.

5. Show that $a \div b = a(1/b)$, where a and b are natural numbers; that is, the quotient of a and b can be found by multiplying a by the multiplicative inverse of b.

6. The proportion $a/b = c/d$ is often written in the form $a:b = c:d$ which is read "a is to b as c is to d." Which of the following proportions are true?

(a) $3:4 = 21:28$ (b) $20:35 = 65:91$ (c) $42:35 = 70:60$

(d) $\dfrac{2}{3}:2 = 6:18$ (e) $\dfrac{3}{7}:\dfrac{7}{5} = 16:25$

7. In each of the following determine x so that the proportion is true.

(a) $2:7 = x:35$ (b) $6:66 = 2:x$

(c) $x:26 = 65:169$ (d) $\dfrac{11}{4}:x = 33:24$

8. A road has a grade of 6 per cent, which means that it rises 6 feet for every 100 feet measured horizontally. How much does the road rise in a mile? Figure the answer to the nearest foot.

9. A telephone pole 18 feet high casts a shadow 10 feet long. How tall is a church steeple which, at the same time, casts a shadow 45 feet long?

10. A car travels at the rate of 60 miles per hour. How many feet per second is this?

11. Draw geometrical configurations to represent the product $5 \cdot 7$ and the product $6 \cdot (3/4)$.

12. Draw geometrical configurations to represent the quotients $18 \div 6$; $12 \div 8$; and $6 \div 2/3$.

6

THE
RATIONAL
NUMBER
SYSTEM

6.1 Introduction

In the preceding chapter we discussed the extension of the system of natural numbers to the system of positive rational numbers. The extension was motivated by the practical demands of an adequate system of measurement, but the resulting system of numbers was seen to possess properties of theoretical as well as practical importance. In particular, we noted that the system of positive rational numbers possesses all the properties of the natural numbers (except for the principle of mathematical induction) and moreover is closed under the operation of division. The need for closure under the operation of division might well have served as motivation for the extension of the natural numbers to the positive rational numbers. In the present chapter, we will see how the need for closure under the operation of subtraction prompts a further extension of the number system.

171

6.2 Subtraction

Subtraction of m from n is defined in terms of addition, and it may be thought of as answering the question, "What number added to m gives n?" For example, $8 - 5 = 3$ and $5 + 3 = 8$ are simply two different ways of expressing the same relationship between the numbers 8, 5, and 3.

DEFINITION 6.1 *Subtraction.* If $a = b + c$, then $a - b = c$, and conversely.

It is immediately clear that the set of positive rational numbers is *not* closed with respect to subtraction since, for example, there is no positive rational number which is equal to $3 - 5$. If there were a positive rational number $c = 3 - 5$, this would imply that $3 = 5 + c$, and this is clearly impossible by the law of trichotomy since we already have $5 = 3 + 2$. Indeed, if a and b are any positive rational numbers with b greater than a, then there can be no positive number equal to $a - b$.

Now we must either be satisfied with the impossibility of subtracting b from a if b is larger than a, or we must *create* new numbers to serve as the results of such subtractions. Our plan is to take the latter course and to extend our system of numbers in such a way that it will be closed under subtraction as well as under addition, multiplication, and division. However, instead of an intuitive approach, based on physical counting and measuring situations as used in the case of the positive rational numbers, we employ a somewhat more formal approach, taking our cue from the structure of the system of positive rational numbers. This approach provides a good example of reasoning by analogy, which is another form of intuitive reasoning. One does not know at the outset that such an approach will be successful, but it is certainly worth trying. Before attempting to obtain closure under subtraction in this way, however, it will be helpful to see how the positive rational numbers might have been created had we begun with the idea of obtaining closure under division.

6.3 Critique on the Positive Rational Number System

Aside from the principle of mathematical induction, the system of positive rational numbers possesses all of the properties of the natural numbers and is also closed with respect to the operation of division.

In particular, we note that 1 is the multiplicative identity for the set of positive rationals as well as for the natural numbers, and that for each positive rational number r there is another positive rational number s such that $rs = 1$. More specifically, if $r = a/b$, then $s = b/a$, and s is called the multiplicative inverse of r.

Theorem 5.9 makes it clear that division of the positive rational number a/b by the positive rational number c/d is equivalent to multiplication of a/b by the multiplication inverse of c/d. Thus, had the need for closure under division been the motivating principle behind the extension of the natural numbers to the positive rational numbers, we might very well have begun by creating new numbers to serve as multiplicative inverses. We would then have required that these new numbers obey the same basic laws of combination as the natural numbers and we might then have proceeded to develop precise rules for multiplication and addition. Accordingly, we approach the problem of obtaining closure under subtraction by introducing new numbers to serve as the additive identity and as additive inverses, and by requiring that these new numbers obey the basic rules of combination satisfied by the positive rational numbers.

6.4 The Rational Number System

Recall that by a positive rational number we mean a number which can be represented as the quotient of two natural numbers.

DEFINITION 6.2 If r is a positive rational number, the symbol r' denotes a number called the *negative* of r. The set of all such r' is called the set of *negative rational numbers*. The symbol "0" denotes a number called zero. The *rational number system* is the set R of all positive rational numbers, all negative rational numbers, and zero, with a relation of equality and operations of addition and multiplication, and satisfying the following postulates.

R1. *Closure law for addition and multiplication.* If a and b are any two elements of R, then $a + b$ and ab are unique elements of R.

R2. *Commutative law for addition and multiplication.* If a and b are any two elements of R, then $a + b = b + a$ and $ab = ba$.

R3. *Associative law for addition and multiplication.* If a, b, and c are any three elements of R, then $(a + b) + c = a + (b + c)$ and $(ab)c = a(bc)$.

R4. *Distributive law.* If a, b, and c are any three elements of R, then $a(b + c) = ab + ac$.

R5. *Additive identity.* If r is any element of R, then $0 + r = r + 0 = r$.

R6. *Additive inverses.* If r is any positive rational number, then $r + r' = r' + r = 0$.

R7. *Multiplicative identity.* If r is any positive rational number, then $1 \cdot r = r \cdot 1 = r$.

R8. *Multiplicative inverses.* If r is any positive rational number, then there exists a positive rational number s such that $rs = 1$.

The effect of Definition 6.2 is to extend the positive rational number system by introducing zero and the negative rational numbers to serve as the additive identity and as additive inverses. Furthermore, it requires that the newly introduced numbers combine with themselves and with the positive rational numbers according to the closure, commutative, associative, and distributive laws.

We now proceed to develop formal rules for the addition, multiplication, subtraction, and division of rational numbers.

6.5   Addition and Subtraction of Rational Numbers

By the general definition of an inverse, if r and s are rational numbers and $r + s = s + r = 0$, then s is an additive inverse of r. Thus, by R6, every positive rational number has an additive inverse r'. By R5, $0 + 0 = 0$ so that 0 is an additive inverse for itself. The following theorem shows that every negative rational number also has an additive inverse.

THEOREM 6.1   Let r' be any negative rational number. Then r is an additive inverse of r'.

Proof: By the general definition of additive inverse, it is necessary to show that $r' + r = r + r' = 0$. But this is true by R6.

It follows that *every* rational number has an additive inverse and we can make the following definition.

DEFINITION 6.3   An additive inverse of any rational number r will be denoted by r'. Thus, $r + r' = r' + r = 0$ for any rational number r.

THEOREM 6.2   *Cancellation law for addition.* If r, s, and t are any three rational numbers such that $r + s = r + t$, then $s = t$.

Proof:

$$
\begin{aligned}
s &= 0 + s & &\text{(by R5)} \\
&= (r' + r) + s & &\text{(by Definition 6.3)} \\
&= r' + (r + s) & &\text{(by R3)} \\
&= r' + (r + t) & &\text{(by hypothesis)} \\
&= (r' + r) + t. & &\text{(by R3)} \\
&= 0 + t & &\text{(by R6)} \\
&= t & &\text{(by R5)}
\end{aligned}
$$

THEOREM 6.3   There is only one additive inverse for any rational number.

Proof: Suppose that s and t are both additive inverses of the rational number r. Then $r + s = 0 = r + t$. But then, by Theorem 6.2, $s = t$. Thus, there cannot be two different additive inverses of r.

The importance of Theorem 6.3 is this. If we find any number s such that $r + s = s + r = 0$, then s is *the* additive inverse of r. Thus, in Theorem 6.1, r is not only *an* additive inverse of r', it is *the* additive inverse of r'; that is, $r = (r')'$. Thus, we have proved Theorem 6.4.

THEOREM 6.4   For any rational number r, $r = (r')'$.

As examples of the preceding results, we note that the additive inverse of 3 is $3'$ and that $(4')' = 4$ so that the additive inverse of $4'$ is 4. Instead of writing $3'$, $4'$, and $(4')'$, it is customary to write -3, -4, and $-(-4)$. However, there is good reason to use $3'$; for example, as we have here in order to distinguish between the *number* − 3 and the *operation of subtracting three*. We discuss this point in more detail following Theorem 6.8. In this standard notation, Theorem 6.4 states that − (− 4) = 4 or, more generally, that − (− a) = a for any rational number a.

Theorem 6.5 shows that zero is the only additive identity for the set of rational numbers.

THEOREM 6.5   Zero is the only additive identity for R.

Proof: Suppose that some number e were also an additive identity for the set of rational numbers. Then $e = e + 0 = 0$.

Theorem 6.6 answers the question, "What is the additive inverse of the sum of two rational numbers?"

THEOREM 6.6   If r and s are any two rational numbers, then $(r + s)' = r' + s'$.

Proof: As a result of Theorem 6.3, it is now only necessary to show that $(r + s) + (r' + s') = 0$. We have

$$
\begin{aligned}
(r + s) + (r' + s') &= r + [s + (r' + s')] && \text{(by R1 and R3)}\\
&= r + [(r' + s') + s] && \text{(by R2)}\\
&= r + [r' + (s' + s)] && \text{(by R3)}\\
&= r + (r' + 0) && \text{(by Definition 6.3)}\\
&= r + r' && \text{(by R5)}\\
&= 0 && \text{(by Definition 6.3)}
\end{aligned}
$$

Thus, $r' + s' = (r + s)'$.

Theorem 6.6 states that the additive inverse of the sum of two rational numbers is the sum of their additive inverses. In particular, this provides a rule for the addition of negative rational numbers. For example, it follows from Theorem 6.6 that $3' + 2' = (3 + 2)'$ or, in standard notation, that $(-3) + (-2) = -(3 + 2) = -5$. Similarly, we would obtain $(-4) + (-2/5) = -(4 + 2/5) = -22/5$.

The motivation for extending the positive rational number system to the rational number system, by the addition of zero and the negative rational numbers, was the hope of obtaining a system closed with respect to the operation of subtraction. Theorem 6.7 shows that this is, in fact, the case. It also shows that subtracting a rational number s from a rational number r can be accomplished by adding the additive inverse of s to r in exact analogy to dividing r by s by multiplying r by the multiplicative inverse of s.

THEOREM 6.7 If r and s are any two rational numbers, then $r - s = r + s'$.

Proof: In view of Definition 6.1, it is only necessary to show that $s + (r + s') = r$. We have

$$s + (r + s') = s + (s' + r) \qquad \text{(by R2)}$$

$$= (s + s') + r \qquad \text{(by R3)}$$

$$= 0 + r \qquad \text{(by Definition 6.3)}$$

$$= r \qquad \text{(by R5)}$$

Thus, $r + s' = r - s$ as claimed.

For example, it follows from Theorem 6.7 that

$$3 = 5 - 2 = 5 + 2' \quad \text{and} \quad 7 - 4' = 7 + (4')' = 7 + 4 = 11$$

In standard notation this would have been written

$$3 = 5 - 2 = 5 + (-2)$$
and
$$7 - (-4) = 7 + [-(-4)] = 7 + 4 = 11$$

and we see that Theorem 6.7 provides means for addition as well as subtraction of negative and positive rational numbers in many cases. The difficulty is that while $2 - 5 = 2 + 5'$ by Theorem 6.7, it is still not completely clear what rational number is equal to $2 + 5'$. More generally, if s is larger than r, Theorem 6.7 does not reveal what rational number is equal to $r - s = r + s'$. Theorem 6.8 provides the answer.

THEOREM 6.8   For any rational numbers r and s, $r + s' = (r' + s)'$.

Proof:

$$(r' + s)' = r'' + s' \qquad \text{(by Theorem 6.6)}$$

$$= r + s' \qquad \text{(by Theorem 6.4)}$$

Theorem 6.8 says that $r - s = -(s - r)$. For example, $2 - 5 = -(5 - 2) = -3$. Also, the results of the two preceding theorems could be written

$$r - s = r + (-s) \quad \text{and} \quad r + (-s) = -[(-r) + s]$$

It is common practice to say that $-r$ is *the negative of* r. In using this terminology, care must be taken that the notions *negative number* and *negative of a number* are not confused. A negative rational is always the negative of a positive rational, whereas every rational number is the negative of its additive inverse. For example, 4 is not a negative rational, but is the negative of -4.

Denoting the negative of s by $-s$ and subtraction of s from r by $r - s$ clearly involves a double use of the minus sign. Our use of s' to denote the negative of s avoided this duplicity. The reader should have no difficulty with the standard notation and should find it easy to tell from the context whether the minus sign is being used to indicate subtraction or a negative. For example, the equation $r - s = r + (-s)$, which is simply and expression of the result of Theorem 6.7, says that to *subtract* r from s one has to add *the negative of* s to r.

Finally, the preceding theorems do not explain the actual mechanics of taking differences of rational numbers. It is easy to see by inspection that

$$\frac{1}{3} - \frac{1}{6} = \frac{1}{6}$$

but it is not immediately obvious that

$$\frac{8}{11} - \frac{5}{13} = \frac{49}{143}$$

On the other hand

$$\frac{8}{11} - \frac{5}{13} = \frac{8 \cdot 13}{11 \cdot 13} - \frac{5 \cdot 11}{13 \cdot 11} = \frac{104}{143} - \frac{55}{143}$$

Since we must add $\frac{49}{143}$ to $\frac{55}{143} = \frac{5}{13}$ to obtain $\frac{104}{143} = \frac{8}{11}$, it follows that

$$\frac{8}{11} - \frac{5}{13} = \frac{104}{143} - \frac{55}{143} = \frac{104 - 55}{143} = \frac{49}{143}$$

The following theorem shows that this is typical of the general case.

THEOREM 6.9 If a, b, c, and d are any four natural numbers, then

$$\frac{a}{b} - \frac{c}{d} = \frac{ad - bc}{bd} \quad \text{if} \quad bc < ad$$

$$= -\left(\frac{bc - ad}{bd}\right) \quad \text{if} \quad ad < bc.$$

Proof: Suppose first that $bc < ad$. Then

$$\frac{c}{d} + \frac{ad - bc}{bd} = \frac{bc}{bd} + \frac{ad - bc}{bd} \qquad \text{(by Theorem 5.5)}$$

$$= \frac{bc + (ad - bc)}{bd} \qquad \text{(by Theorem 5.6)}$$

$$= \frac{bc + [ad + (bc)']}{bd} \qquad \text{(by Theorem 6.7)}$$

$$= \frac{bc + [(bc)' + ad]}{bd} \qquad \text{(by R2)}$$

$$= \frac{[bc + (bc)'] + ad}{bd} \qquad \text{(by R3)}$$

$$= \frac{0 + ad}{bd} \qquad \text{(by Definition 6.3)}$$

$$= \frac{ad}{bd} \qquad \text{(by R5)}$$

$$= \frac{a}{b} \qquad \text{(by Theorem 5.5)}$$

Therefore, by Definition 6.1

$$\frac{a}{b} - \frac{c}{d} = \frac{ad - bc}{bd}$$

In case $ad < bc$, we have

$$\frac{a}{b} - \frac{c}{d} = -\left(\frac{c}{d} - \frac{a}{b}\right) \qquad\qquad\qquad \text{(by Theorem 6.8)}$$

$$= -\left(\frac{cb - da}{db}\right) \qquad\qquad \text{(by the first part of this proof)}$$

$$= -\left(\frac{bc - ad}{bd}\right) \qquad\qquad \text{(by R2)}$$

As examples of the preceding theorem we have that

$$\frac{3}{4} - \frac{1}{3} = \frac{9 - 4}{12} = \frac{5}{12}$$

and

$$\frac{2}{3} - \frac{4}{5} = -\left(\frac{4}{5} - \frac{2}{3}\right) = -\left(\frac{12 - 10}{15}\right) = -\frac{2}{15}$$

EXERCISES

1. Compute the following sums, justifying your work by the preceding theorems.

(a) $7 + (-3)$

(b) $(-7) + 3$

(c) $(-7) + (-3)$

(d) $(-7) + 0$

(e) $(-4) + \left(-\frac{2}{5}\right)$

(f) $6 + \left(-\frac{2}{7}\right)$

(g) $\frac{3}{4} + \frac{3}{5}$

(h) $\left(-\frac{3}{4}\right) + \frac{2}{7}$

(i) $\left(-\frac{3}{4}\right) + \left(-\frac{2}{7}\right)$

(j) $\left(-\frac{3}{8}\right) + 17$

(k) $(-5) + 7 + (-4)$

(l) $6 + \left(-\frac{1}{3}\right) + \left(-\frac{1}{6}\right)$

(m) $\left(\frac{3}{5}\right) + \left(-\frac{2}{6}\right) + \left(\frac{1}{3}\right)$

(n) $(-2) + \left(-\frac{2}{11}\right) + \left(-\frac{1}{5}\right)$

2. Compute the following differences.

(a) $7 - 3$

(b) $7 - (-3)$

(c) $(-7) - 3$

(d) $(-7) - (-3)$

(e) $5 - \dfrac{3}{7}$

(f) $5 - \left(-\dfrac{3}{7}\right)$

(g) $(-5) - \left(-\dfrac{3}{7}\right)$

(h) $(-5) - \dfrac{3}{7}$

(i) $\dfrac{3}{4} - \left(-\dfrac{2}{3}\right)$

(j) $\left(-\dfrac{3}{4}\right) - \left(-\dfrac{2}{3}\right)$

(k) $\left(-\dfrac{3}{4}\right) - \dfrac{2}{3}$

(l) $(7 - 4) - 5$

(m) $7 - (4 + 5)$

(n) $7 - (4 - 5)$

(o) $[7 - (-4)] - 5$

(p) $7 - [(-4) + 5]$

3. Solve and check the following equations.

(a) $x - 7 = 12$

(b) $x - \dfrac{3}{5} = -3$

(c) $x + \dfrac{5}{11} = -\dfrac{2}{5}$

(d) $x - \dfrac{3}{5} = -\dfrac{2}{7}$

(e) $2x + 5 = 27$

(f) $2x - 5 = 27$

4. *Distributive law for multiplication over subtraction.* Give a reason for each step of the following proof that $r(s - t) = rs - rt$ for any three rational numbers r, s, and t.

$$rt + r(s - t) = rt + r(s + t')$$
$$= r[t + (s + t')]$$
$$= r[t + (t' + s)]$$
$$= r[(t + t') + s]$$
$$= r[0 + s]$$
$$= rs$$

Therefore, $rs - rt = r(s - t)$ by _____. Illustrate this result with several examples.

5. For any three rational numbers r, s, and t, prove that

$$r - (s - t) = (r - s) + t$$

SUGGESTION: Begin with $(r - s) + t = (r + s') + t$.

6. For any three rational numbers r, s, and t, prove that

$$r - (s + t) = (r - s) - t.$$

SUGGESTION: Begin with $(r - s) - t = (r + s') + t'$.

7. Use the results of Exercises 5 and 6 to compute the following:

(a) $12 - (5 - 7)$ (b) $(17 - 5) - 8$

(c) $(15 - 8) - 21$ (d) $[(28 - 2) - 31] + 25$

8. For any three rational numbers r, s, and t, prove that

$$r + (s - t) = (r + s) - t$$

6.6 Multiplication of Rational Numbers

In the following sequence of theorems we develop rules for multiplication of rational numbers, positive, negative, and zero.

THEOREM 6.10 If s is any rational number, then $s \cdot 0 = 0 \cdot s = 0$.

Proof: Let r denote a rational number, then

$$sr + 0 = sr \qquad \text{(by R1 and R5)}$$
$$= s(r + 0) \qquad \text{(by R5)}$$
$$= sr + s \cdot 0 \qquad \text{(by R4)}$$

Therefore

$$0 = s \cdot 0 = 0 \cdot s \qquad \text{(by Theorem 6.2 and R2)}$$

THEOREM 6.11 For any rational number r, $1 \cdot r = r$. Hence, 1 is the multiplicative identity for R.

Proof: If r is a positive rational number, then $1 \cdot r = r$ by R7. If $r = 0$, then $1 \cdot 0 = 0$ by Theorem 6.10. Thus, it only remains to show that the result is true for negative rationals. Let r' be any negative rational. We must show that $1 \cdot r' = r'$.

$$0 = 1 \cdot 0 \qquad\qquad \text{(by Theorem 6.10)}$$
$$= 1 \cdot (r + r') \qquad\qquad \text{(by R6)}$$
$$= 1 \cdot r + 1 \cdot r' \qquad\qquad \text{(by R4)}$$
$$= r + 1 \cdot r' \qquad\qquad \text{(by R7)}$$

But since $r + 1 \cdot r' = 0$, it follows from Theorem 6.3 that $1 \cdot r'$ is the additive inverse of r. Thus, $1 \cdot r' = r'$.

THEOREM 6.12   If r and s are any two rational numbers, then $rs' = s'r = (rs)'$.

Proof:

$$rs + (rs)' = 0 \qquad\qquad \text{(by Definition 6.3)}$$
$$= r \cdot 0 \qquad\qquad \text{(by Theorem 6.10)}$$
$$= r\,(s + s') \qquad\qquad \text{(by Definition 6.3)}$$
$$= rs + rs' \qquad\qquad \text{(by R4)}$$

Therefore

$$(rs)' = rs' = s'r \qquad\qquad \text{(by Theorem 6.2 and R2)}$$

In words, the preceding theorem states that the product of r and the negative of s is the negative of the product of r and s. Thus, for example

$$2 \cdot 3' = 3' \cdot 2 = 6' \quad \text{and} \quad 8 \cdot \left(\frac{5}{2}\right)' = \left(\frac{5}{2}\right)' \cdot 8 = 20'$$

In standard notation this would be written

$$2 \cdot (-3) = (-3) \cdot 2 = -6 \quad \text{and} \quad 8 \cdot \left(-\frac{5}{2}\right) = \left(-\frac{5}{2}\right) \cdot 8 = -20$$

More generally, $r(-s) = (-s)\,r = -rs$ where $-rs$ is understood to mean $-(rs)$.

Theorem 6.13 gives a rule for finding the product of the negative of two rational numbers.

THEOREM 6.13   If r and s are any two rational numbers, then $r's' = rs$.

Proof:

$$(rs)' + rs = 0 \qquad\qquad\qquad\qquad \text{(by Definition 6.3)}$$
$$= r' \cdot 0 \qquad\qquad\qquad\qquad \text{(by Theorem 6.10)}$$
$$= r'\,(s + s') \qquad\qquad\qquad \text{(by Definition 6.3)}$$
$$= r's + r's' \qquad\qquad\qquad \text{(by R4)}$$
$$= (rs)' + r's' \qquad\qquad\qquad \text{(by Theorem 6.12)}$$

Therefore

$$rs = r's' \qquad\qquad\qquad\qquad \text{(by Theorem 6.2)}$$

Theorem 6.13 states that the product of the negative of r and the negative of s is the same as the product of r and s for any rational numbers r and s. In standard notation, we would have $(-r)(-s) = rs$ so that, for example

$$(-2)(-3) = 2 \cdot 3 = 6 \quad \text{and} \quad [-(-3)] \cdot (-5) = (-3) \cdot 5 = -15$$

6.7   Division in the Set of Rational Numbers

The preceding sequence of theorems develops the rules for multiplication in the set of all rational numbers. Since we already understand division in terms of multiplication, these theorems also give rules for division. For example: $6 \div (-2) = -3$ since $6 = (-2)(-3)$; $(-6) \div (-2) = 3$ since $-6 = (-2) \cdot 3$; and $-6 \div 2 = -3$ since $-6 = 2(-3)$. These examples illustrate Theorem 6.14.

THEOREM 6.14   If r and s are any rational numbers with $s \neq 0$, then

(a) $\qquad\qquad\qquad\qquad r \div s' = (r \div s)'$

(b) $\qquad\qquad\qquad\qquad r' \div s = (r \div s)'$

(c) $\qquad\qquad\qquad\qquad r' \div s' = r \div s$

Proof: Let $r \div s = t$ so that $r = st$. It follows from Theorems 6.12 and 6.13 that $r' = (st)' = s't = st'$ and that $r = s't'$. But, by the definition of division, these equalities imply that

$$r \div s' = t' = (r \div s)'$$
$$r' \div s = t' = (r \div s)'$$

and

$$r' \div s' = t = r \div t$$

In standard notation we would have

$$r \div (-s) = -(r \div s)$$
$$(-r) \div s = -(r \div s)$$

and

$$(-r) \div (-s) = r \div s$$

Also, in fractional notation, we would have

$$\frac{r}{-s} = -\left(\frac{r}{s}\right)$$

$$\frac{-r}{s} = -\left(\frac{r}{s}\right)$$

and

$$\frac{-r}{-s} = \frac{r}{s}$$

In Theorem 6.14 we required that s be different from zero. This was necessary and division by zero is undefinable. To illustrate, suppose we try to divide 6 by 0. If there were a rational number c such that $6 \div 0 = c$ then we should have $6 = 0 \cdot c$. But this is impossible since $0 \cdot c = 0$ by Theorem 6.10. Of course, this same difficulty arises if we try to divide by 0 any number r different from 0 since again $r \div 0 = c$ would imply that $r = 0 \cdot c = 0$. A difficulty of a different sort arises if we try to divide 0 by 0. The equation $0 \div 0 = c$ implies that $0 = 0 \cdot c$ and this is true of *every* rational number c. This is just as objectionable as having *no* number c serve as quotient and so we must leave division by zero *undefined*.

Since the positive rational number system is closed under division, Theorem 6.14 shows that, except for division by zero, the set of all rational numbers is closed under division. The next two theorems, which are really corollaries of Theorem 6.14, show that every rational number other than zero has a multiplicative inverse and that a modified cancellation law for multiplication also holds.

THEOREM 6.15   The multiplicative inverse of r is $1/r$, if r is any rational number other than zero.

Proof: Let $1/r = 1 \div r = s$. Then, by the definition of division

$$1 = rs = r\left(\frac{1}{r}\right)$$

Also, $(1/r)r = r(1/r)$ by R2 and we have that $1/r$ is the desired multiplicative inverse of r.

THEOREM 6.16   *Cancellation law for multiplication.* If r, s, and t are any three rational numbers with $r \neq 0$, and if $rs = rt$, then $s = t$.

Proof:

$$
\begin{aligned}
s &= 1 \cdot s && \text{(by Theorem 6.11)} \\[2mm]
&= \left(\frac{1}{r} \cdot r\right) \cdot s && \text{(by Theorem 6.15)} \\[2mm]
&= \frac{1}{r} \cdot (rs) && \text{(by R3)} \\[2mm]
&= \frac{1}{r} \cdot (rt) && \text{(by hypothesis)} \\[2mm]
&= \left(\frac{1}{r} \cdot r\right) \cdot t && \text{(by R3)} \\[2mm]
&= 1 \cdot t && \text{(by Theorem 6.15)} \\[2mm]
&= t
\end{aligned}
$$

If the reader will compare the preceding proof with the proof of Theorem 6.2, he will see that they are parallel. In each case the proof of the cancellation law depended on the existence of appropriate inverse elements. The added restriction was necessary in Theorem 6.16 since zero has no multiplicative inverse.

EXERCISES

1. Compute the following products and quotients. Reduce all answers in fractional form to lowest terms. Justify your work.

(a) $\dfrac{2}{3} \cdot \dfrac{7}{8}$

(b) $\dfrac{2}{3} \cdot \left(-\dfrac{7}{8}\right)$

(c) $\dfrac{5}{7} \cdot \dfrac{-6}{11}$

(d) $(-3) \cdot \left(-\dfrac{5}{7}\right)$

(e) $0 \cdot \left(-\dfrac{2}{11}\right)$

(f) $\left(-\dfrac{5}{8}\right)\left(-\dfrac{22}{35}\right)$

(g) $\dfrac{6}{5} \div \dfrac{3}{20}$

(h) $\left(-\dfrac{5}{2}\right) \div \dfrac{15}{8}$

(i) $\left(-\dfrac{6}{7}\right) \div \left(-\dfrac{3}{2}\right)$

(j) $(-2) \div \left(-\dfrac{3}{5}\right)$

(k) $\dfrac{3}{7} \div (-6)$

(l) $\left(-\dfrac{2}{3}\right) \div 0$

(m) $0 \div 3$

(n) $\dfrac{-2}{3} \div \dfrac{4}{9}$

(o) $\dfrac{3/4}{2 - 2/3}$

(p) $\dfrac{2/7 - 10/35}{3/5}$

(q) $\dfrac{7/25}{6/5 - 30/25}$

(r) $\dfrac{3 + 5/2}{1/6 - 1/3}$

(s) $\dfrac{(-5/7) \div 4}{7/8}$

(t) $\left(-\dfrac{3}{11}\right)\left(\dfrac{1001}{13}\right)\left(-\dfrac{5}{27}\right)$

2. If r, s, and t are any rational numbers with $s \neq 0$ and $t \neq 0$, prove that

$$\frac{r}{s} = \frac{rt}{st} = \frac{tr}{ts}$$

SUGGESTION: Since the rational number system is closed under division, $r/s = q$ where q is rational. Therefore $r = sq$. Proceed by considering rt.

3. The result of the preceding exercise can often be used to simplify the work involved in computing a quotient like that of Exercise 1(r). The method also depends on the fact that $a(b/c)$ is an integer in case c evenly divides a. Now since 6 is the least common denominator of the fractions involved in

$$\frac{3 + 5/2}{1/6 - 1/3}$$

it follows that

$$\frac{(3 + 5/2)}{(1/6 - 1/3)} = \frac{6 \cdot (3 + 5/2)}{6 \cdot (1/6 - 1/3)}$$

$$= \frac{6 \cdot 3 - 6(5/2)}{6(1/6) - 6(1/3)}$$

$$= \frac{18 + 15}{1 - 2}$$

$$= \frac{33}{-1}$$

$$= -33$$

Use this method to simplify the following quotients.

(a) $\dfrac{1/2 + 1/3}{2/3 + 1/6}$

(b) $\dfrac{3/5 - 2/7}{6 + 1/2}$

(c) $\dfrac{2 - 17/32}{21/48 - 2}$

(d) $\dfrac{(-3) - 2/3}{2/7 - 1/11}$

(e) $\dfrac{5 + 2/11}{\dfrac{2}{3} + \dfrac{1/2}{1 - 2/3}}$

4. Negative numbers were introduced in this chapter to satisfy the purely mathematical need of obtaining closure under subtraction. List as many practical uses of negative numbers as you can.

5. Compute the following.

(a) $\dfrac{5 + 7}{6}$ and $\dfrac{5}{6} + \dfrac{7}{6}$

(b) $\dfrac{8 + (-3)}{7}$ and $\dfrac{8}{7} + \dfrac{-3}{7}$

(c) $\dfrac{2/3 + 7/8}{5/24}$ and $\dfrac{2/3}{5/24} + \dfrac{7/8}{5/24}$

6. For any three rational numbers r, s, and t with $t \neq 0$, prove that

$$\frac{r+s}{t} = \frac{r}{t} + \frac{s}{t}$$

6.8 The Number Line

The notion of length can be made the basis of an interesting and useful graphical representation of the entire rational number system. We begin by drawing a line as in Fig. 6.1 and arbitrarily choosing a point to which

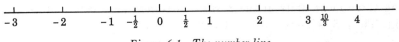

Figure 6.1   The number line.

we assign the number 0. Then, choosing any arbitrary length as a unit, we lay off this distance successively to the right and left of the zero point, labeling the points to the right of zero 1, 2, 3, ..., and those to the left -1, -2, -3, ..., as shown. Also, the point one-half unit to the right of zero is labeled 1/2, and so on. In general, the point r units to the right of zero is labeled r, and the point r units to the left of zero is labeled $-r$. Thus, to each rational number corresponds one and only one point on the line (considered to extend infinitely far in each direction) and so we have a graphical or geometrical representation of the rational number system. This representation, for obvious reasons, is called *the number line.*

The number line serves a useful purpose in discussing elementary facts of arithmetic, particularly with regard to addition and subtraction. For this purpose, it is useful to think of direction to the right as the positive direction on the number line, and direction to the left as the negative direction. Now, in adding two to three (or, more appropriately, positive two to positive three), one can think of starting at zero, going two units in the positive direction, then going three more units in the positive direction, and ending at five. Of course, this is simply a counting process where one counts units on the number line to determine that $2 + 3 = 5$. This extends to the addition of negative numbers as well. For example, to add negative two and negative three one may think of starting at zero, going two units in the *negative* direction, then going three more units in the negative direction, and ending at negative five. Thus,

$(-2) + (-3) = -5$, as we already know by Theorem 6.6. Similarly, to add positive 2 and negative 3, one can think of starting at zero, going two units in the positive direction, then going three units in the negative direction, and ending at negative one. Thus, $2 + (-3) = -1$, as we already know from Theorems 6.7 and 6.8.

Subtraction, too, is easily described on the number line. For example, to subtract positive three from positive five, one can think of starting at zero, going five units in the positive direction, then going three units in the *negative* direction, and ending at positive two. Thus, $5 - 3 = 2$. Again, to subtract negative three from positive five, one can think of starting at zero, going five units in the positive direction, then going three more units in the *positive* direction, and ending at positive eight. Thus, $5 - (-3) = 5 + 3 = 8$.

In Section 5.9 the geometrical representations for products and quotients involved the use of two halves of number lines. It is interesting to see how these constructions extend to products involving negative

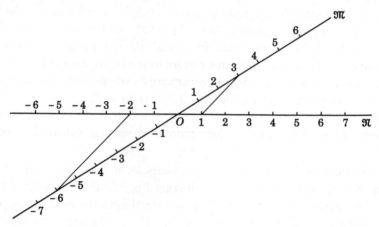

Figure 6.2   Geometrical construction of $3 \cdot (-2)$.

numbers. Consider Fig. 6.2 with intersecting number lines $\mathfrak{M}$ and $\mathfrak{N}$. Suppose we wish to represent the product $3 \cdot (-2)$. Recall that we begin by joining 1 on $\mathfrak{N}$ and 3 on $\mathfrak{M}$ by a line segment. Then we draw a line through -2 on $\mathfrak{N}$ parallel to the first line. This will meet $\mathfrak{M}$ at -6, the product of 3 and -2. The representation of $(-3)(-2) = 6$ is given in Fig. 6.3.

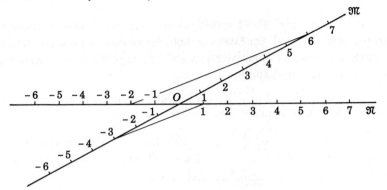

Figure 6.3   Geometrical construction of $(-3)(-2) = 6.$

EXERCISES

1. Geometrically represent the following products and quotients.

   (a) $5 \cdot (-2)$ (b) $(-6)(-3)$ (c) $8 \div (-5)$

   (d) $(-15) \div (-3)$ (e) $\dfrac{3}{5}(-10)$

   The last construction can be easily carried out in three steps.

2. Adding and subtracting on the number line can be indicated by the use of arrows. For example, the sum $8 + (-3)$ can be indicated as follows.

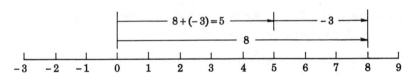

   Use this method to indicate geometrically the following sums and differences.

   (a) $5 + 2$ (b) $5 + (-2)$ (c) $(-5) + 2$
   (d) $(-5) + (-2)$ (e) $5 - 2$ (f) $5 - (-2)$
           (g) $(-5) - 2$ (h) $(-5) - (-2)$

6.9   Order and the Law of Trichotomy

Since $7 + 2 = 9$ and $9 + (-2) = 7$, it is apparent that the law of trichotomy as stated for the natural numbers and the positive rational numbers is not valid for the set of all rational numbers. However, appropriately modified, the law does hold for the set of rational numbers. Recall that, for the set of positive rational numbers, the law of trichotomy can be rephrased by saying:

> If a and b are any two rational numbers, then precisely one of $a = b$, $a < b$, or $b < a$ holds.

As we will soon show, the law in this form is valid for the set of all rational numbers. First we must have a better understanding of the relations of "less than" and "greater than."

DEFINITION 6.4   If a and b are any two rational numbers and if there exists a positive rational number r such that $a + r = b$, then a is said to be *less than* b and we write $a < b$. Also, we say that b is *greater than a*, and write $b > a$. We also write $a \leq b$ to mean that a is less than or equal to b, and $b \geq a$ to mean that b is greater than or equal to a.

For example, we observe that $2 < 7$ since $2 + 5 = 7$; that $-3 < 5$ since $(-3) + 8 = 5$; and that $-(\frac{2}{3}) < -(\frac{1}{6})$ since $-(\frac{2}{3}) + \frac{1}{2} = -(\frac{1}{6})$. Also, if a is a member of the set $T = \{1, 2, 3, 4, 5\}$, it would be appropriate to say that $a \leq 5$.

The following theorems deal with the properties of inequalities.

THEOREM 6.17   If a, b, and c are rational numbers with $a < b$, then $a + c < b + c$ and $a - c < b - c$.

Proof: Since $a < b$, there exists a positive rational number r such that $a + r = b$. Therefore

$$b + c = (a + r) + c \qquad \text{(by substitution)}$$
$$= a + (r + c) \qquad \text{(by R3)}$$
$$= a + (c + r) \qquad \text{(by R2)}$$
$$= (a + c) + r \qquad \text{(by R3)}$$

Therefore, there exists a positive rational number r whose sum with $a + c$ gives $b + c$ and so $a + c < b + c$ by Definition 6.4. Also, since subtracting c from a number is accomplished by adding the additive inverse of c, the result for subtraction clearly follows from the result for addition.

THEOREM 6.18 Let a, b, and c be rational numbers with $a < b$. If $c > 0$, then $ac < bc$. If $c < 0$, then $ac > bc$.

Proof: Since $a < b$, there exists a positive rational number r such that $a + r = b$. Suppose that $c > 0$. Then

$$bc = (a + r)c \qquad \text{(by substitution)}$$
$$= c(a + r) \qquad \text{(by R1 and R2)}$$
$$= ca + cr \qquad \text{(by R4)}$$
$$= ac + rc \qquad \text{(by R2)}$$

Since r and c are both positive, it follows that rc is positive and so $ac < bc$.

We still obtain $bc = ac + rc$ if c is negative. This time, however, rc would be negative. Thus

$$bc + (rc)' = (ac + rc) + (rc)' \qquad \text{(by substitution)}$$
$$= ac + [rc + (rc)'] \qquad \text{(by R3)}$$
$$= ac + 0 \qquad \text{(by Definition 6.3)}$$
$$= ac \qquad \text{(by R5)}$$

and $ac > bc$ since $(rc)'$ is positive.

THEOREM 6.19 If a, b, and c are rational numbers with $a < b$ and $b < c$, then $a < c$.

Proof: Since $a < b$ and $b < c$, there exist positive rational numbers r and s such that $a + r = b$ and $b + s = c$. Therefore

$$c = b + s \qquad \text{(by hypothesis)}$$
$$= (a + r) + s \qquad \text{(by substitution)}$$
$$= a + (r + s) \qquad \text{(by R3)}$$

Since the positive rational numbers are closed with respect to addition, $r + s$ is a positive rational number. Therefore $a < c$ by Definition 6.4.

As examples of the preceding theorems, we observe that since $-2 < 3$, it follows that

$$-2 + 5 < 3 + 5, \qquad -2 - 5 < 3 - 5, \qquad (-2) \cdot 3 < 5 \cdot 3,$$

and

$$(-2)(-3) > 5 \cdot (-3)$$

Also, since $3 < 5$, it follows that $-2 < 5$. The reader will find it instructive to state and prove theorems for the relations $>$, $\leq$, and $\geq$ analogous to those we have just demonstrated.

THEOREM 6.20 *Law of Trichotomy.* If r and s are any two rational numbers, then precisely one of the following hold: (1) $r = s$, (2) $r < s$, or (3) $r > s$.

Proof: Since the rational numbers are closed under addition, $r - s = r + s'$ is a rational number. The rational numbers comprise the positive rational numbers, zero, and the negative rational numbers. Therefore, $r - s$ must be in one of these three classes of numbers. If $r - s = 0$, then $r = s + 0 = s$. If $r - s$ is a negative rational, $s - r = -(r - s) = u$ is a positive rational. But then $s = r + u$ and $r < s$ by definition of "less than." Finally, if $r - s = v$ is a positive rational number, then $r = s + v$ and $r > s$ by the definition of "greater than."

EXERCISES

1. Which of the following are true?
   (a) $-3 > -1$
   (b) $-3 < 1$
   (c) $(-2)(-3) > -2$
   (d) $5 + (-17) > 2 + (-17)$
   (e) $3(-5) < 3(-7)$
   (f) $5 - (-17) > 2 - (-17)$
   (g) If r is an element of $S = \{2, 4, 6, \ldots\}$ then $r \geq 2$.

2. List the following numbers in order from the smallest to the largest: 3, -5, $-\frac{3}{2}$, $\frac{2}{3}$, $\frac{2}{7}$, $\frac{5}{7}$, $\frac{3}{2}$.

3. If $1 < a$, prove that $a < a^2$.

4. If $0 < a < 1$, prove that $a^2 < a$.

5. If $a < 1$, does it necessarily follow that $a^2 < a$? Explain.

6. If a, b, c, and d are positive integers and $ad > bc$, prove that $a/b > c/d$.

7. If a, b, c, and d are natural numbers with $a/b > c/d$, prove that $ad > bc$.

8. If a and b are rational numbers with $0 < a < b$, prove that $1/b < 1/a$.

9. For what rational numbers x are the following inequalities true?

(a) $x + 4 < 7$ (b) $x - 4 < 7$

(c) $x + (-4) > -7$ (d) $3x < -12$

(e) $4x + 7 < 35$ (f) $5 - 2x < -17$

(g) $3(x - 4) > 15$ (h) $2x + 1 > x$

(i) $5x - 6 > 11x$ (j) $6 - 3x < 2 - x$

10. If a and b are rational numbers with $a > b$, prove that $a + c > b + c$ for any rational number c.

11. If a and b are any rational numbers with $a \leq b$ and c is a rational number with $c > 0$, prove that $ac \leq bc$.

6.10   Absolute Value

In terms of the number line with the positive direction to the right, it is apparent that $a < b$ if and only if a is to the left of b on the line. For example, $1 < 3$ since $1 + 2 = 3$, and 1 is to the left of 3 on the number line.

Figure 6.4   Order on the number line.

Again, $-\left(\frac{3}{2}\right) < \frac{4}{3}$ since $\left(-\frac{3}{2}\right) + \frac{17}{6} = \frac{4}{3}$, and $-\frac{3}{2}$ is to the left of $\frac{4}{3}$ on the number line.

Also, it is apparent that, for $a < b$, $b - a$ gives the distance from a to b on the number line. Thus, $3 - (-1) = 4$, and it is 4 units from -1 to 3 on the number line. Again, $(-1) - (-2) = 1$, and it is one unit from -2 to -1.

If one does not know, or does not care to specify, that $a < b$, it is still possible to determine the distance between a and b on the number line. In fact, since $a - b = -(b - a)$, it is clear that the positive one of $a - b$ and $b - a$ is the desired distance. For example, $7 - (-4) = 11$, and $(-4) - 7 = -11$; and 11 is the distance from -4 to 7 on the number line. In order to express this idea more succinctly, we introduce the notion of absolute value.

DEFINITION 6.5   If a is any rational number, we define the absolute value of a, denoted by $|a|$, to be

$$|a| = a \qquad \text{if } a \geq 0$$

$$= -a \qquad \text{if } a < 0$$

For example, $|-5| = 5$; $|5| = 5$; $|-\frac{5}{2}| = \frac{5}{2}$; $|4 - 7| = 3$; and $|7 - 4| = 3$. Since $|r| = |-r|$ for any rational number r, it is clear that $|a - b| = |b - a|$ for any rational numbers a and b and that this absolute value gives the distance between a and b on the number line.

Theorem 6.21 gives an interesting inequality involving absolute values that we will have occasion to use in Chapter 8.

THEOREM 6.21   For any two rational numbers a and b, $|a + b| \leq |a| + |b|$.

Proof: The proof is effected by considering individually the possible cases which may arise.

Case 1. If $a = 0$ or $b = 0$, then it is clear that equality holds.

Case 2. If $a > 0$ and $b > 0$, then $a + b > 0$. Also

$$|a + b| = a + b = |a| + |b|$$

by Definition 6.5.

Case 3. If $a < 0$, $b < 0$, then $a + b < 0$. Therefore

$$|a + b| = -(a + b) = (-a) + (-b) = |a| + |b|$$

by Definition 6.5.

Case 4. If $a > 0$, $b < 0$, and $a + b \geq 0$, then $b < -b$ since b is negative and $-b$ is positive. Therefore, by Theorem 6.17 and the hypothesis

$$0 \leq a + b < a + (-b)$$

Hence, by Definition 6.5

$$|a + b| = a + b < a + (-b) = |a| + |-b| = |a| + |b|$$

Case 5. If $a > 0$, $b < 0$, and $a + b < 0$, then we have $-a < a$ since a is positive and $-a$ is negative. Therefore, by Theorem 6.17,

$$(-a) + (-b) < a + (-b)$$

Also, since $a + b < 0$ by hypothesis, we have $-(a + b) > 0$ by Theorem 6.18. Therefore

$$0 < -(a + b) = (-a) + (-b) < a + (-b)$$

Hence, by Definition 6.5

$$|a + b| = |-(a + b)| = -(a + b) < a + (-b) = |a| + |-b| = |a| + |b|$$

Case 6 with $a < 0$, $b > 0$, $(a + b) \geq 0$ and *Case 7* with $a < 0$, $b > 0$, $(a + b) < 0$ are treated exactly like *Cases 4* and *5*.

In all of these cases we have either

$$|a + b| = |a| + |b| \quad \text{or} \quad |a + b| < |a| + |b|$$

Therefore, $|a + b| \leq |a| + |b|$ as claimed.

EXERCISES

1. Find the distance between the following pairs of points on the number line.

   (a) 6 and 15   (b) 7 and -22

   (c) -31 and -25 (d) $-\dfrac{5}{2}$ and 7

   (e) -52 and 401   (f) -52 and -401

2. If x is rational and $x > 0$, show that $0 < x/2 < x$.

3. If x is rational and $x < 0$, show that $x < x/2 < 0$.

4. If x and y are rational numbers with $x < y$, show that $(x + y)/2$ is rational and that $x < (x + y)/2 < y$.

5. If x and y are rational numbers with $x < y$, show that $2x + y$ lies on the number line one-third of the way from $3x$ to $3y$.

6. If a and b are rational numbers, prove that $|ab| = |a| \cdot |b|$. SUGGESTION: Consider all possible cases.

6.11   Ordered Fields

The reader will recall the discussion in Chapter 3 of the algebra of sets and its generalization, Boolean algebra. In the same way, the rational number system is an example of an abstract mathematical system called a *field*.

A field is a set 𝔉 of at least two distinct elements *r, s, t,* ..., together with a relation of equality and operations which we call addition and multiplication and which we denote in the usual way, such that the following postulates are satisfied.

F1. *Closure laws.* If *a* and *b* are any two elements of 𝔉, then $a + b$ and ab are unique elements of 𝔉.

F2. *Commutative laws.* If *a* and *b* are any elements of 𝔉, then

$$a + b = b + a \quad \text{and} \quad ab = ba$$

F3. *Associative laws.* If *a, b,* and *c* are any elements of 𝔉, then

$$(a + b) + c = a + (b + c) \quad \text{and} \quad (ab)c = a(bc)$$

F4. *Distributive law.* If *a, b,* and *c* are any elements of 𝔉, then

$$a(b + c) = ab + ac$$

F5. *Identities.* There exist elements *e* and *o* in 𝔉 such that

$$o + a = a + o = a \quad \text{and} \quad ea = ae = a$$

for any element *a* in 𝔉.

F6. *Inverses.* For any element *a* in 𝔉, there exists an element *a'* such that

$$a' + a = a + a' = o$$

And for any element *a* in 𝔉 other than *o*, there exists an element *â* such that

$$a\hat{a} = \hat{a}a = e$$

It should now be apparent that the discussion of this chapter has largely been devoted to showing that the rational number system is a field. This is not the only field we have seen, however, for clock arithmetic is a field for any *p*-hour clock where *p* is a prime number; that is, where *p* is not evenly divisible by any natural number other than itself and 1. The reader will find it instructive to show that this is so for a number of examples of this kind.

We have seen that the rational number system possesses certain order properties in addition to satisfying the field postulates. In particular, the rational number field satisfies the law of trichotomy. A field 𝔉 is said to be ordered if, in addition to the field properties, the following postulate is satisfied.

F7. *Order.* There is a relation of order denoted by " $<$ " such that: (a) for any element a in $\mathfrak{F}$ precisely one of the following holds: $a = 0$, $a < 0$, or $0 < a$; and (b) if $0 < a$ and $0 < b$, then $0 < a + b$ and $0 < ab$.

Thus, we see that the rational number system forms an ordered field.

EXERCISES

1. Show that clock arithmetic for a 2-hour clock is a field.

2. Show that clock arithmetic for a 4-hour clock is not a field. Which postulates are not satisfied?

3. Let a/b denote the quotient of a and b in 7-hour clock arithmetic. That is, $a/b = c$ means the same as $a = b \not\times c$. Evaluate the following quotients whenever they are defined.

(a) $\dfrac{3}{5}$ (b) $\dfrac{4}{3}$ (c) $\dfrac{1}{5}$

(d) $\dfrac{7}{4}$ (e) $\dfrac{6}{7}$ (f) $\dfrac{5}{3}$

4. Solve the following equations in 7-hour clock arithmetic.

(a) $(2 \not\times y) +_7 5 = 4$ (b) $3 \not\times (y +_7 3) = 2$

(c) $(5 \not\times y) +_7 2 = 6$ (d) $(3 \not\times y) +_7 4 = 1$

7

PRIME
NUMBERS
AND THE
FUNDAMENTAL
THEOREM
OF
ARITHMETIC

We are now going to speak of some aspects of that kind of arithmetic which is indeed the *arithmos* of the Greek mathematicians of more than twenty centuries ago. These mathematicians realized that the natural numbers possess important intrinsic properties of their own. We shall look into a few of these. In this chapter, when we speak of a *number*, we shall mean a *natural number*, 1, 2, 3, ... When we say an *integer*, we shall mean one of these same *positive integers*.

7.1 What is a Prime?

If a, b, and c are natural numbers and if $a = bc$, the integers b and c are called the *divisors* or *factors* of a and we say that a is divisible by b and by c.

A *prime number*, or simply a *prime*, is any one of the natural numbers that is greater than unity and that has no factors (or divisors) except itself and unity. Thus, for example, the first seven primes are 2, 3, 5, 7, 11, 13, 17. We always exclude unity from the list of primes simply because it is a convenience to do so.

Every natural number greater than unity that is not a prime is called a *composite number*. For example, the first seven composite numbers are

$$4 = 2 \times 2 = 2^2, \qquad 6 = 2 \times 3, \qquad 8 = 2 \times 2 \times 2 = 2^3$$
$$9 = 3 \times 3 = 3^2, \qquad 10 = 2 \times 5, \qquad 12 = 2^2 \times 3$$
$$14 = 2 \times 7, \qquad\quad 15 = 3 \times 5, \qquad 16 = 2 \times 2 \times 2 \times 2 = 2^4$$

The student will make a fundamental observation at once: *The only even prime is* 2. The proof is clear.

Obviously, every prime is divisible by a prime, itself. A fundamental question is whether every composite number is always divisible by a prime, or, as one often says, has a prime factor. Moreover, we might ask, could it be that every composite number, and therefore every natural number greater than unity, can be expressed as a product of primes? And if this be the case, is the representation of a natural number as a product of primes possible in only one way; or, in other words, is the factorization of a natural number into primes unique? These questions lie at the heart of "arithmetic" in the classic sense and will be answered in this chapter.

The argument which we shall employ is an indirect one such as we have already used in earlier proofs, making use of the postulate of the excluded middle: *Of two mutually contradictory statements, one is true and the other false.* We establish the truth of a proposition which is either true or false by assuming it to be false and then proving this assumption false.

7.2   Divisibility of a Natural Number by Primes

THEOREM 7.1   Every integer larger than unity is divisible by a prime.

Proof: Consider the integer $n > 1$. If n is itself a prime, the theorem is of course true. However, if n is not a prime, it is composite and must have a factor greater than 1 and less than n. There must be a smallest such factor and let s be this smallest factor. The integer s must be a prime for if it is not, then this number s itself must have a factor between 1 and s. Since such a factor of s would also be a factor of n, we have contradicted the assumption that s is the smallest divisor of n between 1 and n.

1. Apply the spirit and principle of this argument to the numbers: 7, 8, 17, 28, 44, and 385.

This result can be readily extended by considering some of its implications, and leads to the proof of the following theorem:

THEOREM 7.2 Every integer is a product of primes (which are not necessarily distinct).

Proof: If n is a composite number, then, as a consequence of Theorem 7.1, there is a least prime between 1 and n, say p_1, such that

$$n = p_1 n_1$$

where n_1 is some integer. If n_1 is a prime, Theorem 7.2 is established; but if n_1 is composite, there is a smallest prime, say p_2, between 1 and n_1 such that

$$n_1 = p_2 n_2$$

We continue to argue in this way for n_1, n_2, n_3, and so on. The natural numbers n_1, n_2, n_3, ... are steadily decreasing in size, $n_1 > n_2 > n_3 > \cdots$ and there can only be a finite number of these. Hence, at some point we arrive at the last of these n's, say n_k, which must be a prime, which we call p_k. Therefore

$$n = p_1 \cdot p_2 \cdot p_3 \cdots p_k$$

where p_1, p_2, p_3, ..., p_k are primes. These need not be distinct primes.

1. Find in this way the decomposition of 154 and 8470 into prime factors.

Subsequently we shall return to this question of the factorization of a natural number into primes and prove the crucial theorem that this factorization is unique.

7.3 The Sieve of Eratosthenes

The Greek mathematician and astronomer Eratosthenes ($c.$ 225 B.C.) is celebrated for many accomplishments. In Chapter 1 we referred to his marvelously accurate determination of the diameter of the earth, which he believed to be round. What concerns us here is his method of sorting out the primes in any given finite range of numbers.

This procedure of finding primes is appropriately called the *Sieve of Eratosthenes*. In the description of the *Sieve* that follows, it is to be explicitly noted that we find the primes by *counting* and only by counting. Suppose we wish to sieve out the primes from among the first fifty numbers. Starting with 2, we write the numbers up to 50:

2	3	4	5	6	7	8	9	10
11	12	13	14	15	16	17	18	19	20
21	22	23	24	25	26	27	28	29	30
31	32	33	34	35	36	37	38	39	40
41	42	43	44	45	46	47	48	49	50

Now leave 2, but, counting, cross out (or underline) every second number thereafter: 4, 6, 8, 10, ... Clearly, every second number following 2 is a multiple of 2. Having done this, leave 3, but cross out (or underline) every third number, even though some, for example 6, 12, ..., have already been crossed out. These doubly eliminated numbers, 6, 12, ..., which are divisible by both 2 and 3, are doubly underlined above. Already 4 has been eliminated. So leaving 5, now cross out each fifth number. Some of these of course have already been eliminated: 10, 15, 30, ..., but there are new deletions like 25, 35, ... Now leaving 7, delete every seventh number. The next remaining number is 11. Leave it, and cross out every eleventh number. Next is 13; leave it, and cross out every thirteenth number. Next is 17; leave it, and cross out every seventeenth number. Next is 19; leave it, and cross out every nineteenth number. Next is 23; leave it and cross out every twenty-third number. We find that in our list to 50 there is only one such number, namely 46. Next is 29; leave it, and cross out every twenty-ninth number. The next multiple of 29 is not in our list up to 50 and, clearly, there is no need to investigate the remaining numbers in our list, namely 31, 37, 41, 43, and 47.

Hence the fourteen numbers remaining uncrossed out are the primes up to 50, namely 2, 3, 5, 7, 11, 13, 17, 19, 23, 29, 31, 37, 41, 43, and 47.

There are 25 primes between 1 and 100, and the reader may wish to sieve these out for himself. In doing so he will make an important observation for economy of time and effort in using the sieve. It is this. Already in the numbers up to 50 we have had no need to consider primes beyond 7 in sieving for the primes after 7. The same is true if we seek the primes between 1 and 100, because the next prime after 7 is 11 and 11×11 exceeds 100. If we seek the primes in the interval between 1 and any integer N, we need not examine for multiples of any prime whose square exceeds N. Thus, in the search for primes included in the first thousand numbers, the last prime whose multiples we need examine is 31, for the next prime, 37, is such that 37×37 exceeds 1000.

EXERCISES

1. Construct a Sieve of Eratosthenes to find the primes first up to 100 and then up to 300.

2. Prove that to find by sieving the primes less than an integer N, we need not examine any prime whose square exceeds N.

7.4 Factor Tables

Even though, in searching for the primes between 1 and any given integer N, we need not continue our sieving process beyond any prime whose square exceeds N, nevertheless the sieving our of primes when N is large is very tedious indeed. We could resort to various short cuts. For example, just as the number symbols are abstractions to replace concrete objects in the counting process, we could, so to speak, turn the idea completely around and use concrete objects such as punched holes in cards for the numbers themselves, since indeed there is no need to write out the number symbol for the purpose at hand. This has in fact been done.

There are many tricks to the reckoning trade. For example, we have no difficulty in determining whether a number is divisible by 2. Nor is there any trouble in ascertaining which numbers have 5 as a factor, since all such numbers end only in 0 or 5. All numbers ending in zero have both 2 and 5 as factors. Similarly, but less obviously, we can ascertain fairly readily those numbers which have 3, 7, or even 11 as a factor.

Some people have not been averse to the work involved in identifying the prime factors of very large numbers, even up to a hundred million.

Tables have been constructed which give the smallest prime factor of numbers up to some very large integer. Such tables are called "factor tables."

A factor table for the first 500 integers is exhibited below in Table 7.1. Notice the economy of statement in the presentation. The primes are indicated by the absence of any entry. For composite numbers, the least prime factor is given. Thus, for the number 121, reading 100 at the left and 21 across the top, we first find the entry of 11, which is the least prime factor of 121. Similarly for 289, reading 200 at the left and 89 across the top, we find the entry 17. The number 17 here enters the factor table for it is the least prime factor of 289, which is the square of 17.

TABLE 7.1 FACTOR TABLE FOR INTEGERS FROM 1 TO 500

	1	3	7	9	11	13	17	19	21	23
0	—	—	—	3	—	—	—	—	3	—
100	—	—	—	—	3	—	3	7	11	3
200	3	7	3	11	—	3	7	3	13	—
300	7	3	—	3	—	—	—	11	3	17
400	—	13	11	—	3	7	3	—	—	3

	27	29	31	33	37	39	41	43	47	49
0	3	—	—	3	—	3	—	—	—	7
100	—	3	—	7	—	—	3	11	3	—
200	—	—	3	—	3	—	—	3	13	3
300	3	7	—	3	—	3	11	7	—	—
400	7	3	—	—	19	—	3	—	3	—

	51	53	57	59	61	63	67	69	71	73
0	3	—	3	—	—	3	—	3	—	—
100	—	3	—	3	7	—	—	13	3	—
200	—	11	—	7	3	—	3	—	—	3
300	3	—	3	—	19	3	—	3	7	—
400	11	3	—	3	—	—	—	7	3	11

	77	79	81	83	87	89	91	93	97	99
0	7	—	3	—	3	—	7	3	—	3
100	3	—	—	3	11	3	—	—	—	—
200	—	3	—	—	7	17	3	—	3	13
300	13	—	3	—	3	—	17	3	—	3
400	3	—	13	3	—	3	—	17	7	—

A factor table by D. N. Lehmer for the first ten million integers was published by the Carnegie Institution of Washington in 1909. An unpublished factor table for the first hundred million integers, computed by J. P. Kulik in the early 1800's, is in the archives of the Vienna Academy of Sciences.

The first factor table was published by the Swiss mathematician J. H. Rahn in 1659. It is in this book that the common symbol ÷ for division was first used. An English translation of the book was published later in London by J. Pell and the symbol ÷ was for some time called after him. Pell extended Rahn's factor table to the first 100,000 integers.

EXERCISE

1. Verify the factor table shown in Table 7.1 for integers between 1 and 300.

7.5 The Number of Primes in Selected Ranges

We have determined all of the primes in the range of natural numbers N between 1 and 50, and the quoted factor table (Table 7.1) displays all of the primes between 1 and 500. We have found that there are 14 primes in the range $1 < N < 50$, and the reader no doubt has ascertained that there are 25 primes between 1 and 100. He might ask himself the question of whether there are more or fewer primes between 100 and 200 than between 1 and 100. From our sample factor table, for example, he will find 21 primes in the range $100 < N < 200$. Indeed, from the factor table or by the Eratosthenes Sieve itself he will find the following distribution of primes in 100-intervals for natural numbers N between 1 and 500.

TABLE 7.2   DISTRIBUTION OF PRIMES PER HUNDRED INTEGERS IN THE RANGE
$1 < N < 500$

Range in natural number (N)	Number of primes in this range
$1 < N < 100$	25
$100 < N < 200$	21
$200 < N < 300$	16
$300 < N < 400$	16
$400 < N < 500$	17

We might be led to guess that the number of primes per every hundred integers is of the order of magnitude indicated by this table. Let us examine the frequency distribution of primes in intervals of one thousand integers for larger and larger numbers. Something of the situation is revealed by the following table.

TABLE 7.3 DISTRIBUTION OF PRIMES PER THOUSAND INTEGERS
IN SELECTED RANGES

Range in natural numbers (N)	Number of primes in this range
$1 < N < 1000$	168
$1000 < N < 2000$	135
$2000 < N < 3000$	127
$3000 < N < 4000$	120
$4000 < N < 5000$	119
$9,995,000 < N < 9,996,000$	62
$9,996,000 < N < 9,997,000$	58
$9,997,000 < N < 9,998,000$	67
$9,998,000 < N < 9,999,000$	64
$9,999,000 < N < 10,000,000$	53

The prime numbers in the range from 1 to 10,000,000 have been counted. In selected intervals from ten million to a million million, the number of primes has been ingeniously ascertained without actual count. Something of the character of the distribution that has been found is revealed by giving the approximate number of primes per thousand integers in some selected ranges for larger and larger integers. This is shown in Table 7.4.

TABLE 7.4 DISTRIBUTION OF PRIMES PER THOUSAND INTEGERS
IN VERY LARGE RANGES

Range in natural numbers (N)	Approximate number of primes per thousand of N
$1 < N < 1000$	168
$1000 < N < 10,000$	118
$10,000 < N < 100,000$	93
$100,000 < N < 1,000,000$	77
$1,000,000 < N < 10,000,000$	65
$10,000,000 < N < 100,000,000$	57
$100,000,000 < N < 1,000,000,000$	50
$1,000,000,000,000 < N < 1,000,000,001,000$	37

It might be conjectured that the number of primes in any given range, such as the interval for every thousand integers, gets smaller and smaller as we go to larger and larger numbers. These questions and other interesting ones on the distribution of primes take one into some of the most recondite aspects of mathematics. We shall not pursue the matter here except to ask ourselves whether the primes by any chance eventually die out. In other words, is the number of primes finite or infinite? From the evidence cited above, we might be led to guess that the primes do eventually disappear. Euclid, with no such detailed evidence as we have exhibited, established the answer to this question.

7.6 Euclid's Proof of the Infinity of Primes

Euclid proved the following theorem:

THEOREM 7.3   There are infinitely many primes.

Euclid's proof of this theorem is regarded as one of the most beautiful in all of mathematics. Although it can be phrased so succintly that the point is won quickly and incisively, we shall provide some discussion of the argument involved. The argument is an indirect one: that is, we assume the contrary of the theorem and then prove this assumption to be false. The primes are either finite or infinite in number. There are only these two mutually contradictory alternatives. If we assume the number of primes to be finite and succeed in proving this assumption false, we will have shown that the primes are infinite in extent.

Proof: The contradiction of the theorem is: There are a finite number of primes.

1. Assume the truth of this contradiction. Then there exists a last or largest prime. Call this last prime L. The complete finite list of primes is then 2, 3, 5, 7, ..., L.

2. On the basis of this assumption, construct the following number N

$$N = (2 \times 3 \times 5 \times 7 \times \cdots \times L) + 1$$

In other words, take the finite list of primes from 2 through L, multiply them together, and add one.

Call the resulting number N. This number N may be a prime or it may be composite.

For example

$$(2 \cdot 3 \cdot 5 \cdot 7) + 1 = 211$$

is a prime and

$$(2 \cdot 3 \cdot 5 \cdot 7 \cdot 11) + 1 = 2311$$

is also a prime; but

$$(2 \cdot 3 \cdot 5 \cdot 7 \cdot 11 \cdot 13) + 1 = 30031$$

is composite since $30031 = 59 \times 509$. Similarly

$$(2 \cdot 3 \cdot 5 \cdot 7 \cdot 11 \cdot 13 \cdot 17) + 1 = 510511$$

is also composite, since $510511 = 19 \times 97 \times 277$.

Returning now to our argument, clearly N is larger than L. So if N were a prime, then the assumption that L is the largest prime is false.

On the other hand, N may be composite. We have proved that every natural number is a product of primes. According to the assumption, all of the primes 2, 3, 5, ..., L are involved in the construction of N. So if N is composite, it must have at least one of these primes as a factor. But N cannot be divisible by 2 or 3 or 5 or ... or L, since there is always the remainder of 1. Hence this natural number N must, if it is composite, be divisible by a prime larger than L. Our example

$$(2 \cdot 3 \cdot 5 \cdot 7 \cdot 11 \cdot 13 \cdot 17) + 1$$

illustrates this. If this were our N where, say, we have assumed 17 to be the last prime, the resulting composite number 510511 is not divisible by 2, 3, 5, 7, 11, 13, or 17; but it is divisible by a prime larger than 17, namely, as it turns out, by 19.

Hence, whether N is prime or composite, there is a prime larger than L. Therefore the assumption that the number of primes is finite, with L the largest prime, is false. This contradiction of the assumption establishes the theorem that the number of primes is infinite.

We said that the argument could be put succinctly. Let us do so. Assume the number of primes to be finite. Then there must be a largest one, say, L. Construct the number $N = (2 \cdot 3 \cdot 5 \cdots L) + 1$. Either N is a prime or it is necessarily divisible by a prime greater than L. In either case, L cannot be the largest prime. The number of primes is therefore infinite.

1. Repeat with brevity the proof of Euclid's theorem on the number of primes, using the number $(2 \cdot 3 \cdot 5 \cdot 7 \cdots L) - 1$.

7.7   Some Other Aspects of Primes

There are many famous theorems regarding primes and their properties. The statements of these theorems are usually easy to understand and appreciate. However, the proofs are often extremely difficult; and experienced students of the subject have been heard to say that the easier a result is to state, the harder it seems to be to prove. Of course we never really know whether this is so because, until we have the proof, the statement is at best a mere conjecture. A few very clever people have managed to make what appeared to be shrewd guesses, and their statements were so tantalizing that other people were induced to find proofs of the truth or falsity of the conjectures.

We are going to select three illustrative theorems from many which might have been chosen. Each began as a conjecture and each is named for the man who made it and not after anyone who effected the proofs.

1. *Wilson's Theorem.* The following theorem is commonly ascribed to an amateur English mathematician named Wilson, who lived in the eighteenth century.

THEOREM 7.4   The number $W = [1 \cdot 2 \cdot 3 \cdot 4 \cdots (p - 1)] + 1$, where p is a prime, is divisible by p.

For example, when $p = 5$, we have

$$W = (1 \cdot 2 \cdot 3 \cdot 4) + 1 = 25$$

and 25 is divisible by 5. Or, when $p = 11$, we have

$$W = (1 \cdot 2 \cdot 3 \cdot 4 \cdot 5 \cdot 6 \cdot 7 \cdot 8 \cdot 9 \cdot 10) + 1 = 3,628,801$$

and 3,628,801 is divisible by 11.

This theorem was first proved by the French mathematician and astronomer Lagrange in 1771.

1. Verify Wilson's Theorem for the primes 2, 3, 7, and 13.

2. *Fermat's "Little Theorem."* The following theorem was one of a whole galaxy found by Fermat (1608–1665) who, as we remarked in Chapter 1, although a mathematician by avocation is regarded today as one of the most celebrated mathematicians of the ages.

THEOREM 7.5   If p is a prime and a is any integer, the integer given by $(a^p - a)$ is divisible by p.

Of course, if a is unity, $(a^p - a) = 0$ and zero is divisible by any p. Similarly, if p divides a itself, the result is trivial. Let us, therefore, say that a is not unity and is not divisible by p. Now construct some examples.

$a = 2,\ p = 3$

$$a^p - a = 2^3 - 2 = 6$$

which is divisible by $p = 3$

$a = 3,\ p = 5$

$$3^5 - 3 = 240$$

which is divisible by $p = 5$.

Fermat first gave this result in a letter to a friend, as was his custom, in 1680. He gave no proof and Euler first found the proof in 1736. We suspect that Fermat, who was one of the most ingenious of mathematicians, may have had a proof of his own.

1. Discuss the cases: $a = 3,\ p = 3;\ a = 5,\ p = 3;\ a = 2,\ p = 7;\ a = 3,\ p = 7;\ a = 2,\ p = 11;\ a = 383,\ p = 3;\ a = 4991,\ p = 2$.

3. *Fermat's "Two-Square Theorem."* Another of Fermat's many theorems is the so-called "Two-Square Theorem." We have noted that 2 is the only even prime. Strangely, it often gives us trouble when dealing with theorems on prime numbers. In order to exclude this one number from the infinite set of primes we commonly speak of the "odd primes": 3, 5, 7, 11, ...

It can be ascertained that the odd primes are of two classes, namely:

Class 1: Those which leave the remainder 1 when divided by 4. For example: 5, 13, 17, 29, 37, ...

Class 2: Those which leave the remainder 3 when divided by 4. For example: 3, 7, 11, 19, 23, ...

The "Two-Square Theorem" of Fermat has to do with an unusual property of these two classes.

THEOREM 7.6   Every odd prime of the first class and no odd prime of the second class can be expressed as the sum of two squared integers.

For example, the primes of the first class 5, 13, 17, 29, 37, ... can be represented as

$$5 = 2^2 + 1^2, \qquad 13 = 3^2 + 2^2, \qquad 17 = 4^2 + 1^2,$$

$$29 = 5^2 + 2^2, \qquad 37 = 6^2 + 1^2, \qquad \ldots$$

The reader can easily verify that no examples of the second class 3, 7, 11, 19, 23, ... can be expressed in this way.

It is an extremely difficult matter to prove the part of the theorem which states that every odd prime of the first class can be expressed as the sum of two squared integers. On the other hand, it is comparatively easy to prove the second part of this theorem of Fermat's. Moreover, the proof is an instructive one for our purposes here. Before giving the proof we make a preliminary remark.

What Fermat's theorem is saying is that every odd prime is either of the form $(4k + 1)$ or of the form $(4k + 3)$, where k is 0, 1, 2, 3, ... Of course, it does not say that every integer of the form $(4k + 1)$ or $(4k + 3)$ is a prime, for this is obviously not so. For example, $(4 \cdot 2 + 1) = 9$ and $(4 \cdot 3 + 3) = 15$ are nonprimes.

We now give the proof of the second part of the theorem.

The proof that no odd prime of the form $(4k + 3)$ can be expressed as the sum of two squares is, as follows.

Every even integer is of the form $2m$, where $m = 1, 2, 3, \ldots$. Hence the square of every even integer is of the form $(2m)^2 = 4 \cdot m^2 = 4k$, where k is an integer. On the other hand, every odd integer is of the form $(2m + 1)$, where $m = 0, 1, 2, 3, \ldots$, and the square of every odd integer is therefore of the form

$$(2m + 1)^2 = (4m^2 + 4m + 1) = [4(m^2 + m) + 1] = (4k + 1)$$

where k is an integer. These are merely the proofs of the fact that the square of every even integer is even, and the square of every odd integer is odd.

Hence every squared integer is either of the form $4k$ or $(4k + 1)$. Therefore the sum of two squared integers can only take three forms, namely

$$4k, \quad 4k + 1, \quad 4k + 2 \qquad (k = 0, 1, 2, 3, \ldots)$$

There is no possibility that the sum of two squared integers can be of the form $(4k + 3)$, which establishes the result for the odd primes of this form.

As we have said, the proof of that part of the theorem which states that every odd prime of the form $(4k + 1)$ can be expressed as the sum of two squares is an entirely different matter. It is truely the crux of the result. The great Swiss mathematician Euler gave the proof about 1750. Euler proved the additional fact that the representation of every odd prime of the form $(4k + 1)$ is unique: it can be expressed as the sum of squares in one and only one way.

EXERCISE

1. Give the representations as sums of two squares for all primes between 1 and 300.

7.8   The Axiom of Archimedes

We owe many remarkable theorems in mathematics and physics to Archimedes ($c.$ 225 B.C.). The statement which we are going to call here by his name, following tradition in this respect, is commonly known as the *Axiom of Archimedes*. Before stating it, let us make two remarks. In the first place, it was known and used by Euclid ($c.$ 300 B.C.) and indeed even before Euclid by Eudoxus ($c.$ 370 B.C.). In the second place, it is not strictly an axiom, for it can be proved by the well-ordering principle which we leave to the reader to establish.

The Axiom of Archimedes states that:

If A and B are two natural numbers where $B < A$, there always exists a natural number N such that $N \cdot B > A$.

Thus, if $A = 100$ and $B = 7$, $7 < 100$, there exists a natural number N (indeed many) such that $N \cdot 7 > 100$. For example, N might be 15, since $15 \cdot 7 = 105$, which exceeds 100; but no matter, 15 or not, there is some natural number whose product with 7 is greater than 100. This simple axiom underlies the whole concept of division in arithmetic.

As an immediate consequence of this Archimedean axiom, there always exists, for two natural numbers A and B where $B < A$, a unique natural number Q such that

$$A = Q \cdot B + R \qquad (0 \leq R < B)$$

This very important result is called the *Division Algorithm* or, in other contexts, the *Division Transformation*. It is seen to be true as follows. In the case $B < A$, let $(Q + 1) \cdot B$ be, by the Archimedean Axiom and the well-ordering principle, the first multiple of B greater than A. Hence

$$Q \cdot B \leq A < (Q + 1) \cdot B$$

and so

$$0 \leq (A - Q \cdot B) < B$$

Putting, by definition

$$R = A - Q \cdot B$$

we have an integer R such that

$$0 \leq R < B$$

which was what we set out to establish.

EXERCISES

1. Discuss in detail the corresponding arguments for $A = B$ and for $A < B$.

2. Use the Division Algorithm to show that every natural number can be written either as $4k$, $4k + 1$, $4k + 2$, or $4k + 3$, where k is a positive integer or zero.

3. Show that every odd prime is of the form $4k + 1$ or $4k + 3$.

7.9 The Euclidean Algorithm

From the axiom of Archimedes, there now follows immediately a chain of fundamental ideas. The first of these is a finite set of statements known as the *Euclidean Algorithm.*

The Euclidean Algorithm states that, given two natural numbers A and B, with $B \leq A$, it follows from what we have just said that there exist integers Q_1, Q_2, ..., and R_1, R_2, ..., such that

$$A = Q_1 \cdot B + R_1 \qquad (0 \leq R_1 < B)$$

$$B = Q_2 \cdot R_1 + R_2 \qquad (0 \leq R_2 < R_1)$$

$$R_1 = Q_3 \cdot R_2 + R_3 \qquad (0 \leq R_3 < R_2)$$

$$\cdot \quad \cdot \quad \cdot \qquad\qquad \cdot \quad \cdot \quad \cdot$$

$$R_{n-2} = Q_n \cdot R_{n-1} + R_n \qquad (0 \leq R_n < R_{n-1})$$

$$R_{n-1} = Q_{n+1} \cdot R_n$$

where explicitly $R_{n+1} = 0$ after a finite number of steps 1, 2, 3, 4, ..., n.

The vanishing, finally, of R_{n+1} *must* occur after a *finite* number of steps, since the natural numbers $B, R_1, R_2, \ldots, R_n$ are a steadily decreasing sequence $B > R_1 > R_2 > \ldots > R_n$, and there can be only a finite number of remainders $R_1, R_2, \ldots, R_n$ less than the natural number B.

The following schematic diagram of the successive steps in an example of the use of the Euclidean Algorithm may help the reader.

$$A = (Q_1 \times B) + R_1$$

$$B = (Q_2 \times R_1) + R_2$$

$$R_1 = (Q_3 \times R_2) + R_3$$

$$R_2 = (Q_4 \times R_3) + R_4$$

$$R_3 = (Q_5 \times R_4) + R_5$$

(ETC.)

Let us apply the algorithm to the two numbers 14,287 and 507.

$$14{,}287 = (28 \times 507) + 91 \qquad (0 < 91 < 507)$$

$$507 = (5 \times 91) + 52 \qquad (0 < 52 < 91)$$

$$91 = (1 \times 52) + 39 \qquad (0 < 39 < 52)$$

$$52 = (1 \times 39) + \underline{13} \qquad (0 < 13 < 39)$$

$$39 = (3 \times \underline{13})$$

EXERCISE

1. Apply the Euclidean Algorithm to $A = 225, B = 39; A = 224, B = 39;$ $A = 476, B = 21; A = 5197, B = 296; A = 41213, B = 539.$

7.10 Greatest Common Divisor

If an integer A is a divisor of each of two other integers B and C, it is called a *common divisor* of B and C. Among the common divisors of any two numbers which are not relatively prime, there is a greatest one. It is called their *greatest common divisor* or GCD and is represented by (B, C). If the only common divisor of B and C is unity, then we say that B and C are *relatively prime* and write $(B, C) = 1$.

We now prove the following theorem.

THEOREM 7.7   The last nonzero remainder R_n in the Euclidean Algorithm is the greatest common divisor (GCD) of the numbers A and B.

The proof consists in establishing two facts, namely,

Part I: R_n divides both A and B.

Part II: Every common divisor of A and B is a divisor of R_n.

For example, with

$$(1482, \ 318) = 6$$

Part I states that 6 divides both 1482 and 318. Part II states that, since 3 is a common divisor of both A and B, it also divides 6.

Clearly, in order to establish the theorem itself, we must make a further observation. Specifically, if every common divisor of A and B also divides R_n, which from Part I is itself known to be a common divisor of A and B, then R_n is the greatest common divisor of A and B.

We now give the proofs for Parts I and II.

Proof of Part I: To establish Part I, we must first show that R_n divides both A and B. From the last statement in the algorithm, it is clear that R_n divides R_{n-1}. The next to last statement shows that R_n divides R_{n-2}, since R_n divides itself and R_{n-1}. Similarly from

$$R_{n-3} = Q_{n-1} \cdot R_{n-2} + R_{n-1}$$

we observe that   since R_n divides both R_{n-1} and R_{n-2}, it also divides R_{n-3}. Similarly, working our way up the algorithm, we have that R_n divides R_3 and R_2 and, hence, R_1; that R_n divides R_2 and R_1 and, hence, B; and finally that R_n divides R_1 and B and hence also A. Hence R_n divides both A and B.

Proof of Part II: We now prove that *every divisor, say D, of A and B also divides R_n*, for if this is the case, we can say of the two natural numbers D and R_n, that $D \leq R_n$ and thus R_n must be the largest number that divides both A and B. If D divides A and B, it must divide R_1 since $R_1 = A - Q_1 B$. Similarly, D divides B and R_1 and, hence, R_2. This procedure continues step-by-step down the Euclidean Algorithm until we find that D divides R_{n-2} and R_{n-1} and, hence, R_n. Thus

$$(A, B) = R_n = \text{GCD of } A \text{ and } B$$

EXERCISES

1. Show that $(14287, 507) = 13$, $(225, 39) = 3$, $(224, 39) = 1$, $(476, 21) = 7$ and $(5197, 296) = 1$.

2. Find $(41213, 1764)$, $(30031, 211)$, $(131071, 8191)$, $(157131, 3570)$.

We now prove two theorems to which we shall refer later.

THEOREM 7.8   If k is any integer $(kA, kB) = k(A, B)$.

Proof: In the Euclidean Algorithm involving A and B, multiply through each step by k

$$kA = Q_1 \cdot (kB) + kR_1$$
$$kB = Q_2 \cdot (kR_1) + kR_2$$
$$\cdot \quad \cdot \quad \cdot$$
$$kR_{n-2} = Q_n(kR_{n-1}) + kR_n$$
$$kR_{n-1} = Q_{n+1} \cdot (kR_n)$$

This is the algorithm for kA and kB. Hence, their GCD is kR_n. But $R_n = (A, B)$. Hence

$$(kA, kB) = k(A, B)$$

This result is quite clear for any numerical example. To illustrate the theorem, consider first

$$(48510, \ 1197) = 63$$

This statement is true since by the Euclidean Algorithm

$$48510 = 40 \times 1197 + 630$$
$$1197 = 1 \times 630 + 567$$
$$630 = 1 \times 567 + 63$$
$$567 = 9 \times 63$$

Now consider in place of $A = 48510$ and $B = 1197$ the new numbers $17 \times A = 824670$ and $17 \times B = 20349$. We wish to demonstrate that

$$(824670, \ 20349) = 17(48510, \ 1197) = 17 \times 63$$

We show this in two parallel applications of the Euclidean Algorithm one with the factor 17 displayed and one in which it is absorbed.

(824670, 20349)	(17×48510, 17×1197)
$824670 = 40 \times 20349 + 10710$	$(17 \times 48510) = 40 \times (17 \times 1197) + (17 \times 630)$
$20349 = 1 \times 10710 + 9639$	$(17 \times 1197) = 1 \times (17 \times 630) + (17 \times 567)$
$10710 = 1 \times 9639 + 1071$	$(17 \times 630) = 1 \times (17 \times 567) + (17 \times 63)$
$9639 = 9 \times 1071$	$(17 \times 567) = 9 \times (17 \times 63)$
Hence	Hence
$(82467, 20349) = 1071 = 17 \times 63$ $= 17(48510, 1197)$	$(17 \times 48510, 17 \times 1197) = 17 \times 63$ $= 17(48510, 1197)$

1. In the preceding Exercise the reader was asked to find the GCD of each of four pairs of numbers. Multiply the numbers in the first pair by 2, in the second pair by 4, in the third by 7, and in the fourth by 11. Then illustrate the validity of the foregoing theorem for each of these five pairs of numbers by displays of the Euclidean algorithm as shown above.

2. Prove that if A, B, and C are any three natural numbers then $(A, B) = 1$ implies $(AC, BC) = C$.

Theorem 7.9 is a corollary of Theorem 7.8.

THEOREM 7.9   Let the GCD of two integers A and B be D: $(A, B) = D$. Then, if

$$A = A'D \quad \text{and} \quad B = B'D$$

the two integers A' and B' are relatively prime: $(A', B') = 1$.

Proof: From Theorem 7.8, it follows that

$$D = (A, B) = (A'D, B'D) = D(A'B')$$

and hence $(A', B') = 1$.

It is this theorem that enables us to express a fraction involving the quotient of two integers in an equivalent "reduced" form by cancelling out common divisors; for example, $\frac{9}{24} = \frac{3}{8}$, and, hence, any fraction A/B can be expressed in the form A'/B' where $(A', B') = 1$.

Let us illustrate Theorem 7.9 with a numerical example. Given two numbers $A = 4802$ and $B = 36$, we know that $(4802, 36) = 2$ from the following application of the Euclidean Algorithm.

$$4802 = 133 \times 36 + 14$$
$$36 = 2 \times 14 + 8$$
$$14 = 1 \times 8 + 6$$
$$8 = 1 \times 6 + 2$$
$$6 = 3 \times 2$$

Theorem 7.9 states that since $D = 2$ and $4802 = (2401 \times 2)$ and $36 = (18 \times 2)$, the two numbers $A' = 2401$ and $B' = 18$ are relatively prime. We verify from the following application of the algorithm that $(2401, 18) = 1$.

$$2401 = 133 \times 18 + 7$$
$$18 = 2 \times 7 + 4$$
$$7 = 1 \times 4 + 3$$
$$4 = 1 \times 3 + 1$$
$$3 = 3 \times 1$$

The reader will observe from the comparison of these two applications of the algorithm that the quotients in the second are identical with those in the first, but that the other numbers in the first, when divided by $2 = (4802, 36)$, are the corresponding ones in the second.

Using the letters A, B, A', B' and D, the reader should repeat the argument for the literal expressions of the algorithm corresponding to the statements above and should observe in this way how Theorem 7.9 is a direct corollary of Theorem 7.8.

Finally, we call attention to the fact that $\frac{4802}{36} = \frac{2401}{18}$ by dividing numerator and denominator by the common divisor $2 = (4802, 36)$, and that the fraction $\frac{2401}{18}$ cannot be further reduced since $(2401, 18) = 1$. It is common to say that the fraction A/B is in its *lowest terms* if $(A, B) = 1$, as is the case for $\frac{2401}{18}$.

EXERCISES

1. The GCD of 14287 and 507 is 13. What can you say about the number pair 1099 and 39?

2. Utilizing the foregoing theorem, reduce the fractions $\frac{225}{39}$, $\frac{476}{21}$, and $\frac{157131}{3570}$ to their "lowest terms."

7.11 Euclid's Divisor Theorems

The following crucial theorem results from Euclid.

THEOREM 7.10. If $(A, B) = 1$ and if A divides the product $B \cdot C$, then A divides C, where A, B, and C are natural numbers.

Proof: Construct the Euclidean Algorithm for the relatively prime numbers A and B. We obtain unity as the final remainder: $R_n = 1$.

Multiply the equations of the algorithm throughout by the natural number C

$$(AC) = Q_1 \cdot (BC) + (R_1C) \qquad (0 \leq R_1C < BC)$$
$$(BC) = Q_2 \cdot (R_1C) + R_2C \qquad (0 \leq R_2C < R_1C)$$
$$\cdot \quad \cdot \quad \cdot \qquad\qquad \cdot \quad \cdot \quad \cdot$$
$$(R_{n-2}C) = Q_n \cdot (R_{n-1}C) + C \qquad (\text{Since } R_n = 1)$$
$$(R_{n-1}C) = Q_{n+1} \cdot C$$

Since $(A, B) = 1$, the remainder is now C. It is the GCD of (AC) and (BC) by Theorem 7.10. But A divides (AC) and, by assumption, A divides (BC). Therefore, it divides (R_1C) and, in turn, (R_2C), (R_3C), ..., (R_nC), and finally, therefore, C itself.

From this theorem we readily deduce the following important corollary due to Euclid.

THEOREM 7.11 If P is a prime and if P divides the product $A \cdot B$ where A and B are natural numbers, then P divides A or P divides B.

The proof is clear since, if P does not divide A, $(P, A) = 1$, then Theorem 7.10 tells us that P must divide B.

7.12 The Fundamental Theorem of Arithmetic: The Unique Factorization Theorem

From Theorem 7.11 we are able to establish the following theorem which is known as "the unique factorization theorem" or more commonly as "the fundamental theorem of arithmetic."

THEOREM 7.12. *The Fundamental Theorem of Arithmetic.* Any natural number $N > 1$ can be uniquely represented, apart from the arrangement of factors, as a product of a finite number of primes $P_1, P_2, P_3, \ldots, P_n$. In particular

$$N = P_1^{a_1} \cdot P_2^{a_2} \cdot P_3^{a_3} \cdots P_n^{a_n}$$

where the $a_1, a_2, a_3, \ldots, a_n$ are natural numbers and where the primes $P_1, P_2, P_3, \ldots, P_n$ are all distinct.

For example

$$6 = 2 \cdot 3; \qquad 9 = 3^2; \qquad 12 = 2^2 \cdot 3; \qquad 48 = 2^4 \cdot 3;$$
$$180 = 2^2 \cdot 3^2 \cdot 5; \qquad 132300 = 2^2 \cdot 3^3 \cdot 5^2 \cdot 7^2; \text{ etc.}$$

From Theorem 7.2 we know that N can be expressed as a product of primes. Hence, in order to establish the fundamental theorem we have only to prove the uniqueness of this representation.

From Theorem 7.11 we know that, if P divides the number $(ABC \cdots L)$, then either P divides A, P divides B, P divides C, ..., or P divides L. If A, B, C, ..., L are themselves primes, then P is one of them; that is, P is then either A, B, C, ..., or L.

Now consider the number

$$N = P_1^{a_1} \cdot P_2^{a_2} \cdots P_n^{a_n} = Q_1^{b_1} \cdot Q_2^{b_2} \cdots Q_h^{b_h}$$

where the n primes P_1, ..., P_n are distinct and so also are the h primes Q_1, ..., Q_h. We shall agree to the arrangement $P_1 < P_2 < \cdots < P_n$ and $Q_1 < Q_2 < \cdots < Q_h$. From what we have just said, a P_i from the set P_1, ..., P_n divides the product $Q_1^{b_1} \cdot Q_2^{b_2} \cdots Q_h^{b_h}$ for every $i = 1, 2,$ ..., n, and, hence, every P is a Q. Similarly, every Q is a P. Therefore, $n = h$. Since

$$P_1 < P_2 < \cdots < P_n \quad \text{and} \quad Q_1 < Q_2 < \cdots < Q_h$$

it follows that $P_i = Q_i$ for all $i = 1, 2, \ldots, n = h$. Hence, we have shown so far that

$$N = P_1^{a_1} \cdot P_2^{a_2} \cdots P_n^{a_n} = P_1^{b_1} \cdot P_2^{b_2} \cdots P_n^{b_n}$$

We have now to settle the uniqueness of the exponents a_1, ..., a_n and b_1, ..., b_n. Suppose $a_i \neq b_i$, in particular $a_i > b_i$, for any i of the set $i = 1, 2, \ldots, n$. Divide N, which is ·

$$P_1^{a_1} \cdots P_i^{a_i} \cdots P_n^{a_n} = P_1^{b_1} \cdots P_i^{b_i} \cdots P_n^{b_n}$$

by $P_i^{b_i}$. The result is

$$P_1^{a_1} \cdots P_i^{a_i - b_i} \cdots P_n^{a_n} = P_1^{b_1} \cdots P_{i-1}^{b_{i-1}} \cdot P_{i-1}^{b_{i+1}} \cdots P_n^{b_n}$$

where now P_i is missing from the right-hand side. Hence, the left-hand side is divisible by P_i, but the right-hand side is not. This is a contradiction. As an exercise, the reader may assure himself in the same way that we arrive at a corresponding contradiction if $a_i < b_i$. Hence, we must have $a_i = b_i$ and the theorem is established.

EXERCISE

1. Represent the following numbers as products of primes: 36; 4802; 86436; 172870; 518616; 1037232.

7.13 Least Common Multiple

A concept analogous to the greatest common divisor of two integers A and B is the *least common multiple* (LCM) of A and B.

An integer that is divisible by both A and B is called a *common multiple* of A and B. The smallest common multiple of A and B is called their LCM and we adopt the notation

$$[A, B] = \text{LCM of } A \text{ and } B$$

in contrast to

$$(A, B) = \text{GCD of } A \text{ and } B$$

As an example, consider the three numbers 1037232, 518616, and 172872.

$$1037232 = 6 \times (4802 \times 36)$$

$$518616 = 3 \times (4802 \times 36)$$

$$172872 = 1 \times (4802 \times 36)$$

The three numbers 1037232, 518616, and 172872 are all common multiples of 4802 and 36, and the smallest of these three given numbers is 172872. However, the least common multiple of 4802 and 36 is $[4802, 36] = 86436$.

We now observe that the three common multiples 1037232, 518616, and 172872 are all divisible by the LCM of 4802 and 36, namely by 86436. This is indeed an illustration of the following theorem.

THEOREM 7.13   Any common multiple of A and B is divisible by the LCM.

Proof: Let M be a common multiple of A and B. Divide M by $[A, B]$, the LCM of A and B, and write the result in the form

$$M = Q \cdot [A, B] + R \qquad 0 \leq R < [A, B]$$

By assumption, M and $[A, B]$ are both divisible by A and B. Therefore, R is divisible by both A and B. But $[A, B]$ is the LCM and $R < [A, B]$, which is a contradiction unless R is zero. Therefore, $R = 0$ and $[A, B]$ divides M.

We shall next prove a theorem that, for any two natural numbers A and B, associates their GCD, their LCM, and their product. For example, we have seen that the GCD of 4802 and 36 is

$$(4802, \ 36) \ = \ 2$$

and that their LCM is

$$[4802, \ 36] = 86436$$

and we observe that

$$(4802, 36)[4802, 36] = [4802, 36](4802, 36)$$

$$= 2 \times 86436$$

$$= 86436 \times 2$$

$$= 172872$$

This product of the GCD and the LCM of 4802 and 36 is the product of 4802 and 36

$$172872 = 4802 \times 36$$

This example is generalized by the following theorem.

THEOREM 7.14 If $(A, \ B)$ and $[A, \ B]$ are respectively the GCD and LCM of A and B, then

$$[A, B](A, B) \ = \ (A, B)[A, B] = AB$$

Proof: Using Theorem 7.9, we write

$$A \ = \ A'D \qquad \text{and} \quad B \ = \ B'D$$

where
$$D \ = \ (A, \ B) \quad \text{and} \quad (A', \ B') \ = 1$$

We observe that any multiple of A, say kA, can be written

$$kA \ = \ kA'D$$

If kA is to be divisible by B, where $B = B'D$, then clearly kA' must be divisible by B'. But A' and B' are relatively prime and, thus, k must be divisible by B'. Hence, k is a multiple of B', say $k = h \cdot B'$. Therefore, *any* common multiple M of A and B has the form

$$M = hB'A = hA'B'D = hA'B = h\frac{AB}{D} = h[A, B]$$

With $h = 1$, we therefore obtain the desired result, namely

$$[A, B] = \frac{AB}{D} = \frac{AB}{(A, B)}$$

We leave it as an exercise for the reader to illustrate the consecutive steps of this argument for the two integers 4802 and 36 that have been employed in the preceding examples.

The following theorem follows as an obvious corollary from Theorem 7.14.

THEOREM 7.15   The LCM of A and B equals the product AB if and only if $(A, B) = 1$.

We proved in Theorem 7.8 that

$$(kA, kB) = k(A, B)$$

We now prove the following theorem.

THEOREM 7.16   If k is any integer, $[kA, kB] = k[A, B]$.

Proof: From Theorems 7.8 and 7.14 we have

$$[kA, kB] = \frac{kA \cdot kB}{(kA, kB)} = k\frac{AB}{(A, B)} = k[A, B]$$

EXERCISES

1. In 1742, Goldbach made the following conjecture in a letter to Euler: "Every even number six or larger is the sum of two odd primes, and every odd number nine or larger is the sum of three odd primes." Verify both parts of the conjecture for several integers. We know that the conjecture is true for integers as large as 100,000, but it nevertheless remains unproved. Comment on the consequent mathematical viewpoint that the Goldbach conjecture today remains only a conjecture. Consider any odd number and subtract a smaller prime. Is the result even or odd? If it is even, can you show that the second part of the conjecture implies the truth of the first part?

2. We have defined the GCD of any two natural numbers A and B, and have designated it by the symbol (A, B). If we were given three numbers, A, B, and C, instead of only two, we would of course call any number that divides all three a common divisor. Certainly among these common divisors there is a greatest one; namely, the GCD of A, B, and C. Designate it by the symbol (A, B, C) and prove that

$$(A, B, C) = ((A, B), C)$$

Then establish the "associative law" for the GCD, namely that

$$((A, B), C) = (A, (B, C))$$

3. Find the GCD of the following
   (a) 561;   105;   30
   (b) 4662;   222;   228
   (c) 71162;   28405;   14859
   (d) 54989;   1122;   418;   143

4. Given any two natural numbers A and B, state a formal procedure based on the fundamental theorem of arithmetic by which one may determine their LCM.

5. We have defined the LCM of any two natural numbers A and B, and have designated it by the symbol $[A, B]$. Extend this definition to define the LCM of any three natural numbers A, B, and C using the symbol $[A, B, C]$ to represent it. Prove that

$$[A, B, C] = [[A, B], C]$$

and establish the following "associative law" for the LCM

$$[[A, B], C] = [A, [B, C]]$$

6. Find the LCM of each of the following
   (a) 187;   148;   35
   (b) 561;   105;   30
   (c) 4662;   222;   228
   (d) 54989;   1122;   418;   143

7. Find the least common denominator of the following fractions

   (a) $\dfrac{1}{13} + \dfrac{1}{17} + \dfrac{1}{26}$ (b) $\dfrac{7}{561} + \dfrac{2}{105} + \dfrac{11}{30}$ (c) $\dfrac{1}{A} + \dfrac{1}{B} + \dfrac{1}{C}$

   where A, B, and C are any three natural numbers. State your result formally as a theorem with any appropriate generalization.

8

**THE
REAL
NUMBER
SYSTEM**

8.1 The Inadequacy of the Rational Numbers

It might appear that in the rational numbers we have a number system adequate for all our needs. It is a very rich system, closed with respect to addition, subtraction, multiplication, and division by all numbers except zero. Also, it is adequate for counting and purposes of practical measurement.

For any given practical purpose one has neither the need nor the ability to measure quantities beyond certain tolerances, and hence can express any measurement he may make by using rational numbers. But there still remains the question, "If we would measure with complete precision, would our measurements always be expressible as rational numbers?" This question concerned the early Greek mathematicians, and even as early as the time of Pythagoras they knew that the answer was negative.

As an example, consider the following situation. We are given a square

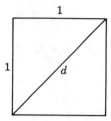

1

1

d

Figure 8.1   Unit square with diagonal d.

of one unit on a side, and we wish to find the length d of a diagonal. To compute this length we use the Theorem of Pythagoras concerning right triangles. In the present case this theorem says that $d^2 = 1^2 + 1^2 = 2$. So we are seeking a positive number whose square is two. Such a number we call the square root of 2 and denote by the symbol $\sqrt{2}$.

The only numbers we have studied so far are the rational numbers. Any nonzero rational number may be expressed as the ratio or quotient a/b of two integers a and b ($b \neq 0$) which are relatively prime. Thus, we may restate our problem as the question, "Do there exist relatively prime positive integers a and b such that $(a/b)^2 = 2$?"

Let us suppose that such relatively prime positive integers a and b exist. From $(a/b)^2 = 2$, we obtain $a^2 = 2b^2$. Now $2b^2$ is an even integer; hence, a^2 is even and, therefore, a itself is even. Thus, $a = 2c$ for some integer c. Substituting this into $a^2 = 2b^2$, we obtain $a^2 = (2c)^2 = 4c^2 = 2b^2$. This implies that $b^2 = 2c^2$, so that b^2 is even and b must also be even. Thus, a and b are both divisible by 2, contrary to the assumption that $(a, b) = 1$. Hence, there is no rational number whose square is 2.

The argument we have just given is commonly ascribed to Pythagoras. We shall now give a second proof that there is no rational number whose square is 2 and this proof is easier to generalize.

As before, we assume that there exist relatively prime integers a and b such that $(a/b)^2 = 2$, and obtain a contradiction. Clearly b is not 1 since there is no integer a whose square is 2. Therefore, b must be divisible by some prime p, say $b = pq$. From $(a/b)^2 = 2$, we then obtain $a^2 = 2b^2 = 2p^2q^2$ and a^2 is divisible by p. But if a^2 is divisible by the prime p, then a must also be divisible by p. Thus, a and b are both divisible by the prime p, which contradicts the assumption that $(a, b) = 1$.

As a generalization of this argument, let us show that there is no rational number whose square is n, where n is any positive integer which is not itself a perfect square. If there is a rational number whose square is n, then as before we can write the rational number in the form a/b with a and b relatively prime and with $b \neq 1$ since n is not a perfect square. Hence, b is divisible by some prime p. From $(a/b)^2 = n$, we have $a^2 = nb^2$ and as before a^2 is divisible by p. This contradicts the assumption that a and b are relatively prime. Therefore, there is no rational number whose square is n unless the integer n is itself the square of some integer.

We may further generalize this argument by replacing the word *square* throughout by *cube:* there is no rational number a/b whose cube is the integer n unless n is the cube of some integer. The crux of the argument is again that under the given condition b is not 1 since this would imply that $a^3 = n$ contrary to assumption. Then b is divisible by some prime p and $a^3 = nb^3$ is divisible by p. Hence, a is divisible by p. But any rational number can be written in the form a/b with a and b relatively prime, and a contradiction is again obtained.

Finally, we may show that there is no rational number whose kth power is the integer n, where n is not the kth power of an integer. For if relatively prime integers a and b exist with $(a/b)^k = n$ and $b \neq 1$, then b is divisible by some prime p, a^k is divisible by p, a is divisible by p, and we have a contradiction.

Considerations such as these lead us once again to extend our number system.

EXERCISES

1. Show that there is no rational number whose square is 3.
2. Give an argument, patterned after Euclid's argument that $\sqrt{2}$ cannot be a rational number, to show that there is no rational number whose cube is 2.
3. Show that there is no rational number whose cube is 4.
4. Show that there is no rational number whose square is $\frac{1}{2}$.
5. Show that there is no rational number whose square is $\frac{3}{4}$.
6. Show that there is no rational number whose square is $\frac{4}{3}$.
7. What positive rational numbers will have rational numbers as square roots?
8. What positive rational numbers will have rational numbers as cube roots?

8.2 Decimal Representation of Rational Numbers

In seeking an appropriate extension of our number system, we may first observe what happens when we write ordinary fractions in decimal form. For example, the fraction or rational number $\frac{1}{3}$ appears in the following nonterminating decimal form

$$\frac{1}{3} = 0.333 \cdots$$

where the dots indicate a never ending string of 3's. The reader will be familiar with many similarly unending decimal expressions for other simple rational numbers.

From this observation we may conclude that some unending decimal expressions represent rational numbers. Since these rational numbers were introduced for purposes of measurement, let us see what such a decimal as $n = 0.333 \ldots$ means in terms of measuring. The first digit after the decimal point tells us that n is at least $\frac{3}{10}$ but less than $\frac{4}{10}$, or $\frac{3}{10} \leq n < \frac{4}{10}$, which is all the accuracy we could obtain from a ruler divided into tenths. If we now use a ruler ten times as accurate, thus taking into account the second significant digit of n, we would obtain $\frac{33}{100} = \frac{3}{10} + \frac{3}{100} \leq n < \frac{3}{10} + \frac{4}{100} = \frac{34}{100}$. Using successively finer rulers, each ten times as accurate as its predecessor, would give successively better approximations to the number n, which correspond to taking into account successive digits in the decimal form of n.

If we consider the maximum possible errors at each stage of approximation in our example, we see that these errors form a sequence $\frac{1}{10}$, $\frac{1}{100}$, $\frac{1}{1000}$, ..., each $\frac{1}{10}$ of its predecessor. It certainly seems reasonable that if we continue forever to shrink the possible error by considering the infinite decimal $n = 0.333 \ldots$, we would arrive by this infinite process at exactly the length that we usually designate by $\frac{1}{3}$.

EXERCISES

1. Compute the first four digits to the right of the decimal point in the decimal expression for $\frac{1}{6}$.

2. Compute the first 10 digits in the decimal expression for $\frac{1}{7}, \frac{2}{7}, \frac{3}{7}, \frac{4}{7}, \frac{5}{7},$ and $\frac{6}{7}$. Do you find any pattern here?

3. Compute the first 10 digits in the decimal expressions for $\frac{1}{8}, \frac{1}{9}, \frac{1}{11}, \frac{1}{12},$ and $\frac{1}{13}$.

4. Construct a table of 10-digit decimal approximations to the first twelve unit fractions $(\frac{1}{2}, \frac{1}{3}, \frac{1}{4}, \ldots, \frac{1}{13})$ showing the denominators in factored form. From this table, can you guess which unit fractions will have decimal expressions that "come out even?"

8.3   Convergence and Limit of a Sequence

We now need to make definite the notions involved in the preceding section. These will serve as a foundation upon which we can build a number system adequate for the purposes of geometry. This involves defining a convergent sequence of rational numbers and the limit of such a sequence.

DEFINITION 8.1 Let r_1, r_2, r_3, ..., r_n, ... be an infinite sequence of rational numbers. The sequence is said to converge, or to be convergent, if for any positive rational number a, no matter how small, there is a natural number N such that $|r_m - r_n| < a$ whenever both m and n exceed N.

Thus, in a convergent sequence of rational numbers, the terms of the sequence differ from each other by as small an amount as we please, provided that we restrict attention to those terms sufficiently far along in the sequence. For example, consider the sequence $\frac{1}{2}$, $\frac{3}{4}$, $\frac{7}{8}$, $\frac{15}{16}$, $\frac{31}{32}$, ... Here, all terms beyond the third differ from each other by less than $\frac{1}{8}$; all beyond the fifth differ by less than $\frac{1}{32}$; and in general all terms beyond the nth differ by less than $1/2^n$. Thus, we can conclude that the sequence $\frac{1}{2}$, $\frac{3}{4}$, $\frac{7}{8}$, ... is convergent.

As another example, consider the sequence of successive decimal approximations to $\frac{1}{3}$, namely

$$r_1 = 0.3, \ r_2 = 0.33, \ ..., \ r_7 = 0.3333333, \ ...$$

For $N = 1$ we have that r_m and r_n both begin with 0.33 if m and n both exceed N; hence, r_m and r_n differ by less than 0.01 or $|r_m - r_n| < 0.01$. Similarly, if $N = 3$ and m and n both exceed N, then r_m and r_n both begin with 0.3333; hence, $|r_m - r_n| < 0.0001$. Clearly, we can guarantee that $|r_m - r_n|$ is as small as we please, provided that we take both m and n greater than some sufficiently large N. We thus have that this sequence is convergent.

Now suppose that we are given any nonterminating decimal. From it we may obtain a convergent sequence of rational numbers as follows. We let r_1 be that rational number obtained by deleting all but the first of the digits to the right of the decimal point; r_2 be that rational number obtained by deleting all but the first two of these digits; and so forth. Just as in the case of the sequence of decimal approximations to $\frac{1}{3}$, we have that, if m and n both exceed 1, then $|r_m - r_n| < 0.01$; if m and n both exceed 3, then $|r_m - r_n| < 0.0001$; or in general, if m and n both exceed N, then $|r_m - r_n| < 1/10^N$. Thus any nonterminating decimal determines a convergent sequence of rational numbers.

When we use the term *converge* in everyday speech, it is in the sense of *converge to something* as, "The two rails of a long straight level railroad appear to converge to a point on the horizon." The question of what, if anything, a convergent sequence of rational numbers converges to is, therefore, a natural one. In the case of the sequence 0.3, 0.33, 0.333, ..., we would naturally wish to say that the sequence *converges to* $\frac{1}{3}$. We now make this more precise.

DEFINITION 8.2   The infinite sequence of rational numbers r_1, r_2, ..., r_n, ... is said to converge to the rational number r, and r is said to be the limit of the sequence, if for any positive rational number b, no matter how small, there is some N such that for all $n > N$ we have $|r_n - r| < b$.

In other words, r is the limit of the sequence r_1, r_2, ..., r_n, ... if all the terms of the sequence from some point on differ from r by as small an amount as we please. Thus, 1 is the limit of the sequence $\frac{1}{2}$, $\frac{3}{4}$, $\frac{7}{8}$, ..., and $\frac{1}{3}$ is the limit of the sequence 0.3, 0.33, 0.333, ...

It is not difficult to show that if a sequence converges to a limit, then the sequence is convergent in the sense of Definition 8.1. Suppose that we are given a sequence r_1, r_2, ..., r_n, ..., converging to r, and also a positive rational number a. We let $b = a/2$ and b is also a positive rational number. Since the sequence converges to r, we know that there is an N such that for all $n > N$ we have $|r_n - r| < b = a/2$. Then, if m and n both exceed N, we have

$$|r_m - r_n| = |(r_m - r) + (r - r_n)| \leq |r_m - r| + |r_n - r|$$

$$< \left(\frac{a}{2} + \frac{a}{2}\right) = a$$

and the sequence is convergent.

Moreover, if the sequence r_1, r_2, ..., r_n, ... converges to the limit r, then r is unique. For if the sequence also converges to s, with $s \neq r$, we may suppose that $r > s$. Then $r - s = 2a > 0$ for some rational number a. From some point on, all terms r_n of the sequence must be within less than a of r and, likewise, within less than a of s. But this would be a contradiction since r and s differ by $2a$. Thus, the limit of a convergent sequence is unique if it exists at all.

However, not all convergent sequences of rational numbers converge to rational numbers as limits. For example, we may obtain a convergent sequence of rationals by calculating approximations to $\sqrt{2}$. One method of doing this is the following. Since $1^2 < 2 < 2^2$, we know that $1 < \sqrt{2} < 2$ and we take $r_1 = 1$ as our first approximation. Now, computing $(1.1)^2 = 1.21$, $(1.2)^2 = 1.44$, $(1.3)^2 = 1.69$, $(1.4)^2 = 1.96$, and $(1.5)^2 = 2.25$, we see that $(1.4)^2 < 2 < (1.5)^2$. Hence, $1.4 < \sqrt{2} < 1.5$ and we take $r_2 = 1.4$ as our second approximation. The next stage of computation yields

$$(1.41)^2 = 1.9881 < 2 < 2.0164 = (1.42)^2 \quad \text{or} \quad 1.41 < \sqrt{2} < 1.42$$

so our third approximation is $r_3 = 1.41$. At this point we may observe that 2 is roughly halfway between $(1.41)^2$ and $(1.42)^2$. It thus seems reasonable to try computing $(1.415)^2$, which we find to be 2.002225, which is a bit too large. We then compute

$$(1.414)^2 = 1.999396 < 2 < 2.002225 = (1.415)^2$$

and our fourth approximation is $r_4 = 1.414$. Continuing in this manner, we could obtain a convergent sequence of rationals: $r_1, r_2, \ldots, r_n, \ldots$. But since there is no rational number whose square is 2, we see that this particular sequence of rationals, although convergent, does not converge to any rational number.

EXERCISES

1. Which of the following sequences of rational numbers are convergent?

(a) $2 + 1, \quad 2 - \dfrac{1}{2}, \quad 2 + \dfrac{1}{3}, \quad 2 - \dfrac{1}{4}, \quad 2 + \dfrac{1}{5}, \quad \ldots$

(b) $2, \quad -1.1, \quad 1.01, \quad -1.001, \quad 1.0001, \quad \ldots$

(c) $1, \quad 1.1, \quad 1.11, \quad 1.111, \quad 1.1111, \quad \ldots$

(d) $\dfrac{1}{2}, \quad -\dfrac{3}{4}, \quad \dfrac{5}{6}, \quad -\dfrac{7}{8}, \quad \dfrac{9}{10}, \quad -\dfrac{11}{12}, \quad \ldots$

(e) $3, \quad 3.09, \quad 3.0909, \quad 3.090909, \quad \ldots$

2. For each of the convergent sequences in Exercise 1, how large must m and n be to guarantee that $|r_m - r_n| < \frac{1}{10}$? $< \frac{1}{100}$? $< \frac{1}{1000000}$?

3. A famous problem, one of Zeno's paradoxes, concerns Achilles and a tortoise. In slightly modified form we have the following situation. Achilles is some distance, say a block, from a tortoise, and runs to catch it. Meanwhile the

tortoise moves away, so that when Achilles arrives at the point where the tortoise started, the tortoise has moved $\frac{1}{10}$ block. When Achilles arrives at this new position, the tortoise has moved an additional $\frac{1}{100}$ block; and so on. Can Achilles ever catch the tortoise?

4. Another method of computing $\sqrt{2}$ is the following. Suppose $x = \sqrt{2}$. Then $x \cdot x = 2$ or $x = 2/x$, and $2x = x + 2/x$ or $x = (x + 2/x)/2$. Now if we start with some y slightly less than $\sqrt{2}$, then $2/y$ is slightly greater than $\sqrt{2}$ and $(y + 2/y)/2$, the average of y and $2/y$, will be between y and $2/y$, and closer to $\sqrt{2}$ than y. Thus, if we start with some guess y_0 and let $y_1 = (y_0 + 2/y_0)/2$, $y_2 = (y_1 + 2/y_1)/2$, and so forth, we would expect to get closer and closer to $\sqrt{2}$. Start with $y_0 = \frac{5}{4} = 1.25$ and compute y_1 and y_2. Compare this procedure for computing $\sqrt{2}$ with that given in the text.

5. Use the method of the text to compute $\sqrt{5}$ to the nearest $\frac{1}{100}$.

6. Modify the method of Exercise 5 to compute $\sqrt{5}$ to the nearest $\frac{1}{100}$, taking 2 as the first approximation.

8.4 Definition of the Real Numbers

As we have seen, each nonterminating decimal determines a convergent sequence of rational numbers in a natural way. In particular, let us consider the sequences determined by 0.999 ... and by 1.000 ...; that is, the sequences 0.9, 0.99, 0.999, ... and 1.0, 1.00, 1.000, ... Since every member of the latter sequence is the rational number 1, this sequence clearly converges to 1. Moreover, it is easy to see that the first sequence also converges to 1. We shall, therefore, define the nonterminating decimals 0.999 ... and 1.000 ... to be equal. Similarly, any non-terminating decimal ending with an infinite string of 9's is defined to be equal to the appropriate nonterminating decimal ending with an infinite string of 0's. For example

$$12.23999\ldots = 12.24000\ldots \quad \text{and} \quad 0.0637999\ldots = 0.0638000\ldots$$

Whenever we obtain, by some computational procedure, a decimal with an infinite string of 9's, we will replace it by the equal decimal with an infinite string of 0's.

DEFINITION 8.3 The real number system consists of the set of all non-terminating decimals; that is, expressions consisting of an integer followed by a decimal point, and then an infinite succession of digits, which do not include an infinite succession of 9's. Also, there are relations of *equal to* and *less than*, and operations called *addition* and *multiplication*. The relations and operations are defined as follows:

1. Two real numbers x and y are equal if they are identical; i.e., if, in the rational sequences $x_1, x_2, \ldots, x_n, \ldots$, and $y_1, y_2, \ldots, y_n, \ldots$, determined by x and y respectively, we have $x_n = y_n$ for every n.

2. We define $x + y$ to be that real number corresponding to the convergent sequence of rationals $x_1 + y_1, x_2 + y_2, \ldots, x_n + y_n, \ldots$. Similarly, we define xy to be that real number corresponding to the convergent sequence of rationals $x_1y_1, x_2y_2, \ldots, x_ny_n, \ldots$.

3. Finally, we define an order relation for real numbers by $x < y$ if $x_n < y_n$ for some n.

That these sequences $x_1 + y_1, x_2 + y_2, \ldots$, and $x_1y_1, x_2y_2, \ldots$, are convergent can be proven, but we shall omit the proofs. The definitions of $x - y$ and x/y, when $y \neq 0$, are obvious. As examples of this addition and multiplication, suppose that $x = 1.090909\ldots$ and that $y = 2.3333 \ldots$. To determine $x + y$, we compute

$$x_1 + y_1 = 1.0 + 2.3 = 3.3$$
$$x_2 + y_2 = 1.09 + 2.33 = 3.42$$
$$x_3 + y_3 = 1.090 + 2.333 = 3.423$$
$$x_4 + y_4 = 1.0909 + 2.3333 = 3.4242$$

etc.; and we quickly see that $x + y = 3.424242\ldots$. To determine xy, we compute

$$x_1y_1 = 2.3; \quad x_2y_2 = 2.5397; \quad x_3y_3 = 2.54297;$$
$$x_4y_4 = 2.54539697; \quad x_5y_5 = 2.545429697$$

etc. While the computation isn't as easy in this case, after computing a few more values of x_ny_n we would conclude that $xy = 2.545454\ldots$.

From the definitions we have given, we could verify that the real numbers satisfy all of the properties R1 through R7 of Chapter 6, where we now replace the word "rational" by "real" throughout. Thus, the real numbers are an *ordered field*. Moreover, in a very natural sense, the real number field "contains" the rational number field. By this we mean that, although a ratio of integers is not a nonterminating decimal, nevertheless each rational number determines a unique nonterminating decimal and does so in such a manner that sums correspond to sums and products to products.

To determine the real number corresponding to a given rational number, it is only necessary to carry out the long division process. For example, if we are given the rational number $\frac{12}{11}$, we have

$$
\begin{array}{r}
1.0909\ldots \\
11 \,\overline{)\, 12.0000\ldots} \\
\underline{11} \\
1\ 00 \\
\underline{99} \\
100 \\
\underline{99} \\
1
\end{array}
$$

from which it is evident that we will obtain $1.0909\ldots = 1.\overline{09}$, where we have indicated that the block "09" repeats *ad infinitum* by overscoring it. In a similar manner, we would find that $\frac{7}{3}$ corresponds to $2.\overline{3}$, $\frac{2}{11}$ to $0.\overline{18}$, and $\frac{3721}{1998}$ to $1.8\overline{623}$.

Indeed, we will always obtain some such *repeating decimal* when we determine the real number corresponding to a given rational number. That is, in the division process, we will sooner or later obtain a block of digits which thereafter repeats itself indefinitely. To see that this is so, let us consider another example. If we are given the rational number $\frac{6}{13}$, we obtain

$$
\begin{array}{r}
.461538\ldots \\
13 \,\overline{)\, 6.000000\ldots} \\
\underline{5\ 2} \\
80 \\
\underline{78} \\
20 \\
\underline{13} \\
70 \\
\underline{65} \\
50 \\
\underline{39} \\
110 \\
\underline{104} \\
6
\end{array}
$$

Since at this point of the process we have a remainder of 6, we will next divide 13 into 60, obtaining a remainder of 8, etc., and must repeat all the steps we have already gone through. We thus conclude that the real number corresponding to $\frac{6}{13}$ is $0.\overline{461538}$.

More generally, suppose that we are given the rational number a/b, where a and b are integers. As we go through the division process of finding the decimal corresponding to a/b, we may ask how many distinct remainders are possible in all. This number is of course b, since $0, 1, 2, \ldots,$ $b - 1$ are the possible remainders. If 0 occurs as a remainder, then the real number corresponding to a/b will have all zeros from that point on; for example, $\frac{2}{5}$ corresponds to $0.4\overline{0}$. If 0 does not occur as a remainder, then some nonzero remainder must repeat. When this occurs, provided that on both occurrences of the remainder there are only zeros to "bring down" from the dividend, it follows that the entire process repeats itself. Thus, every rational number determines a unique repeating decimal.

Conversely, every repeating decimal corresponds to a rational number. Consideration of a specific case will make the general argument clear. For example, suppose we are given the repeating decimal $z = 3.\overline{42}$. Subtracting z from $100z$, we have

$$
\begin{aligned}
100z &= 342.\overline{42} \\
z &= 3.\overline{42} \\
\hline
99z &= 339.\overline{0}
\end{aligned}
$$

Now $339.\overline{0}$ is clearly the real number corresponding to 339, from which we see that z corresponds to $\frac{339}{99} = \frac{113}{33}$.

As another illustration, suppose $z = 2.3\overline{142}$. We then have

$$
\begin{aligned}
1000z &= 2314.\overline{2142} \\
z &= 2.3\overline{142} \\
\hline
999z &= 2311.9\overline{0} \\
9990z &= 23119.\overline{0}
\end{aligned}
$$

so that z corresponds to the rational number $\frac{23119}{9990}$.

We thus have a perfect correspondence between rational numbers and repeating decimals. Moreover, the correspondence preserves sums and products. For example, if $\frac{12}{11}$ corresponds to $x = 1.\overline{09}$ and $\frac{7}{3}$ to $y = 2.\overline{3}$, we have that $\frac{12}{11} + \frac{7}{3} = \frac{113}{33}$ corresponds to $x + y = 3.\overline{42}$ and that $\left(\frac{12}{11}\right)\left(\frac{7}{3}\right)$ corresponds to $xy = 2.\overline{54}$. Since we have this correspondence, *we shall identify a given rational number with its corresponding repeating decimal*. Thus, we write $\frac{7}{3} = 2.\overline{3}$; $\frac{12}{11} = 1.\overline{09}$; $624 = 624.\overline{0}$; and so forth; and in this way imbed the field of rational numbers in the field of real numbers.

Of course, there are many nonrepeating decimals; for example, $1.101001000100001\ldots$, or $0.123456789101112\ldots$, or $\pi = 3.14159265\ldots$. All such nonrepeating, nonterminating, decimals we call *irrational* numbers, meaning that they are *not* expressible as *ratios* of integers.

EXERCISES

1. Determine the infinite decimal expressions for each of the following rational numbers.

   (a) $\dfrac{-11}{3}$ (b) $\dfrac{43}{6}$ (c) $\dfrac{13}{7}$ (d) $\dfrac{-126}{11}$

2. Determine the ratio of integers a/b corresponding to each of the following.

   (a) $17.\overline{23}$ (b) $136.2\overline{46}$ (c) $-7.30\overline{201}$

   (d) $0.0\overline{12}$ (e) $203.\overline{8}$ (f) $-0.007\overline{42}$

3. Give the definitions for the difference $x - y$ and quotient x/y $(y \neq 0)$ of real numbers x and y.

4. For $x = 17.\overline{23}$ and $y = 0.0\overline{12}$, determine each of $x + y$, $x - y$, xy, and x/y by use of the definitions of addition, subtraction, multiplication, and division of real numbers.

5. For x and y as in Exercise 4, determine $x + y$, $x - y$, xy, and x/y by expressing x and y as ratios of integers, performing the required operation, and converting back into a repeating decimal.

8.5 Geometrical Representation of Certain Irrational Numbers

In Chapter 6, we considered the rational number line and the geometrical representation of rational numbers. In admitting infinite decimals into the number system, we were motivated by the desire to have a number to represent every possible length on such a scaled line. Although we cannot give geometrical representations of all irrational numbers, it is of interest to consider the representation of certain irrational numbers.

In particular, to represent $\sqrt{2}$ on the number line is very easy. As is shown in Fig. 8.2, we draw a line segment of unit length perpendicular to the number line at the point corresponding to 1. The point P is then

$\sqrt{2}$ units distant from O. By swinging an arc with center O from P to the number line, we obtain the point corresponding to $\sqrt{2}$.

Having located $\sqrt{2}$, we may represent square roots of other positive integers as indicated in Fig. 8.2. Draw a line segment of unit length

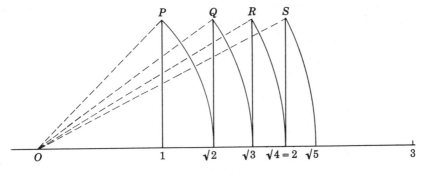

Figure 8.2

perpendicular to the number line at $\sqrt{2}$. From its end Q we swing an arc with center O to the number line. Since the sides of the right triangle $O\,\sqrt{2}\,Q$ are of length $\sqrt{2}$ and 1, the square of the hypoteneuse OQ is

$$(\sqrt{2})^2 + 1^2 = 2 + 1 = 3$$

Thus, $OQ = \sqrt{3}$, and we have located $\sqrt{3}$ on the number line. Erecting a unit perpendicular at $\sqrt{3}$ and again swinging an arc, we obtain the square root of

$$(\sqrt{3})^2 + 1^2 = 3 + 1 = 4$$

which of course is 2. We may proceed in this manner to locate on the number line the square root of any positive integer.

We may also represent the square root of any given positive number. Referring to Fig. 8.3, we proceed as follows.

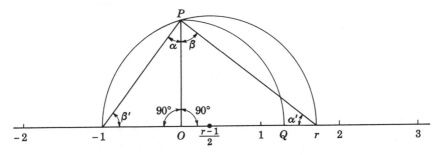

Figure 8.3

Given the positive number r on the number line, we first locate $(r-1)/2$ and draw a semicircle with center $(r-1)/2$ and radius $(r+1)/2$. This semicircle will meet the number line at the points corresponding to -1 and r. Now draw the perpendicular to the number line at O, meeting the semicircle at P. From P, swing an arc with radius OP meeting the number line at Q, the point corresponding to $\sqrt{r}$.

To prove that this construction is valid, we must show that OP has length $\sqrt{r}$. The angle formed by drawing, from a point on a circle, lines to the two ends of a diameter of the circle is a right angle. Thus, the angle $(-1)Pr$ is a 90° angle. We then have $\alpha + \beta = 90°$. Since in any triangle the angles add up to 180°, we also have that $\alpha + \beta' = 90°$ and $\beta + \alpha' = 90°$. It follows that $\alpha = \alpha'$ and $\beta = \beta'$. Thus, the triangles $(-1)OP$ and rOP are similar and their sides are proportional; hence, $1/OP = OP/r$. This says that $(OP)^2 = r$ or that $OP = \sqrt{r}$ as required.

Having seen that we can construct square roots of any positive numbers that we are given, it is natural to ask if one can also construct cube roots. (We call s a cube root of r, $s = \sqrt[3]{r}$, if $s^3 = r$.) Whereas any real number has a real number for a cube root, we cannot in general construct cube roots by the use of straightedge and compass. However, the proof that we cannot do so lies well beyond the scope of this book. We can of course construct fourth roots by repeated construction of square roots. That is, if r is any positive real number, then $s = \sqrt[4]{r} = \sqrt{\sqrt{r}}$ satisfies $s^4 = r$, since $s^4 = (\sqrt{\sqrt{r}})^4 = [(\sqrt{\sqrt{r}})^2]^2 = (\sqrt{r})^2 = r$.

EXERCISES

1. Find geometrical representations for $\sqrt{3}$ and $\sqrt{5}$, and then use the method of Chapter 6 to represent $\sqrt{15} = \sqrt{3}\sqrt{5}$.

2. Use the method of Exercise 1 to represent $\sqrt{105}$.

3. Represent geometrically $\sqrt[4]{6}$ by the method of this section.

4. Represent geometrically $1/\sqrt{2}$.

8.6 Some Properties of the Real Number System

One reason for introducing the real number system was a desire to have a number to represent the length of every possible segment of a scaled line. Equivalently, we wished to have a number associated with each point on a scaled line. We shall accept as a postulate of geometry that there is a unique point on a scaled line common to all of any infinite sequence of nested rational intervals, whose lengths form a sequence approaching zero. By a rational interval, we mean that segment of the scaled line lying between the points corresponding to two distinct rational numbers a and b, and including the points corresponding to a and b. We will denote such an interval, with $a < b$, by the symbol $[a, b]$. By a sequence of nested intervals, we mean that each interval completely contains its successor. For example, the rational intervals $[0, 1]$, $[0.3, 0.4]$, $[0.33, 0.34]$, $[0.333, 0.334]$, ... form a nested sequence determining the point corresponding to the rational number $\frac{1}{3}$.

Suppose that we are given any sequence of nested rational intervals whose lengths approach zero, say $[a_1, b_1]$, $[a_2, b_2]$, $[a_3, b_3]$, ... where the sequence $b_1 - a_1$, $b_2 - a_2$, ... approaches zero, and $a_i \leq a_{i+1} < b_{i+1} \leq b_i$ for all indices i. We then form the sequence of rational numbers $a_1, b_1, a_2, b_2, a_3, b_3, \ldots$. It is clear that this sequence is convergent, and hence determines a unique real number.

For example, the point on a scaled line that is the length of the diagonal of a unit square to the right of 0 is determined by the nested sequence of rational intervals $[1, 2]$, $[1.4, 1.5]$, $[1.41, 1.42]$, $[1.414, 1.415]$, ..., and the sequence 1, 2, 1.4, 1.5, 1.41, 1.42, ... converges to $\sqrt{2}$.

Not only is there a real number corresponding to each point on a scaled line, but conversely, every real number determines a unique point on a scaled line. For suppose that we are given any real number r, where $r_1, r_2, \ldots, r_n, \ldots$ is the sequence of terminating decimals (hence, rational numbers) formed by deleting all but the first digit to the right of the decimal point, all but the first two, and so forth. Now let $a_1 = r_1$ and $b_1 = (r_1 + 0.1)$, $a_2 = r_2$ and $b_2 = (r_2 + 0.01)$, and so forth. Each of the rational intervals $[a_n, b_n]$ contains its successor and the sequence of lengths 0.1, 0.01, 0.001, ... clearly approaches zero. Since for every n we have $a_n \leq r < b_n$, the point corresponding to r is in each of these intervals. Since there is but one point common to all these intervals, the point corresponding to r is uniquely determined.

We have already noted that the real numbers form a field; that is, they satisfy all of the properties F1–F7 of Chapter 6. Thus, we may add, subtract, multiply, and divide real numbers using the same basic laws that apply to the rational numbers. And, since the order properties of the rational numbers also hold for the real numbers, we may manipulate inequalities involving real numbers according to the familiar rules.

There are many algebraic problems unsolvable in the rational number system which can be handled in the real number system. We have already seen that there will be exactly one positive real number, $\sqrt{2}$, whose square is 2. Similarly, if r is any given positive real number, then there is exactly one positive real number, $\sqrt{r}$, whose square is r. We may calculate rational approximations to $\sqrt{r}$ in a manner similar to that used to approximate $\sqrt{2}$. Note that if r is a positive real number, then both $\sqrt{r}$ and $-\sqrt{r}$ satisfy the equation $x^2 = r$. However, the symbol $\sqrt{r}$ will always denote the positive real number whose square is r. Thus, if we want to refer to the negative solution of $x^2 = r$, we must denote it by $-\sqrt{r}$.

The real numbers are adequate for solving more algebraic equations than just those of the form $x^2 = r$ where $r \geq 0$. For example, if q is any real number, then there is exactly one real number whose cube is q; i.e., exactly one real number, $\sqrt[3]{q}$, satisfying $x^3 = q$. Similarly, there is exactly one real number satisfying $x^m = q$, where q is any real number and m is any *odd* natural number.

When we consider equations $x^m = r$, where m is an *even* natural number, the situation is very like that of $x^2 = r$. If r is negative, then there is no real number that satisfies the equation. But if r is positive, then there are always two real numbers satisfying the equation, one positive real and denoted by $\sqrt[m]{r}$, and one negative and denoted by $-\sqrt[m]{r}$. Any such real solution of an equation of the form $x^m = r$, with r a real number, can be approximated by rational numbers to any desired degree of accuracy.

Before closing our discussion of the real number system, we must mention one of its most important properties: the real number system is *complete*. By this we mean that any convergent sequence of real numbers converges to a real number as a limit.

DEFINITION 8.4   The infinite sequence $r_1, r_2, \ldots, r_n, \ldots$ of real numbers is said to be convergent if, for any given positive rational number a, there is some positive integer N such that whenever m and n both exceed N, then $|r_m - r_n| < a$. The real number r is said to be the limit of the sequence if, for any given positive rational number b, there is an M such that $|r - r_m| < b$ for all $m > M$.

Suppose that we have a convergent sequence $r_1, r_2, \ldots, r_n, \ldots$ of real numbers (nonterminating decimals). The only situation in which two nonterminating decimals x and y could differ in their integral parts, and yet differ from each other by an amount less than any positive rational number, would be in a situation such as $x = 1.\bar{0}$ and $y = 0.\bar{9}$, which we have agreed to identify. Thus, there is some N_0 such that all the r_n for $n > N_0$ agree in their integral parts. Likewise, there is an N_1 such that, for $n > N_1$, all the r_n must agree in their integral parts and first decimal places. Continuing this way we see that, provided we go far enough in the sequence, all the nonterminating decimals of the sequence will agree to as many decimal places as we choose. Thus, the convergent sequence $r_1, r_2, \ldots, r_n, \ldots$ determines a (unique) real number r to which it converges. This property of the real number system is called *completeness* and we say that the real numbers are a *complete ordered field*. It is this completeness of the real number system that underlies many of its most important uses. In particular, the development of the calculus is highly dependent upon this property of the real numbers.

EXERCISES

1. Prove that if r is a negative number, then there is no real number whose square is r.

2. Consider the following statements:

(a) x is a rational number

(b) x^2 is a rational number

(c) x is an irrational number

(d) x^2 is an irrational number

Which of these statements implies which others?

3. Let u and v be nonzero irrational numbers. Can you conclude that $u + v$ is irrational? What about uv? $1/u$? Prove your answers.

4. Let r be a rational number and x an irrational number. Is $r + x$ rational or irrational? What about rx?

5. Show that there is no smallest positive rational number. Is there a smallest positive real number?

6. Argue that if x and y are real numbers with $x < y$, then there is a rational number r such that $x < r < y$.

7. Argue that if r and s are rational numbers with $r < s$, then there is an irrational number x such that $r < x < s$.

ANSWERS

TO
SELECTED
PROBLEMS

CHAPTER 1

1.9

3. The numbers corresponding to $p = 2$, 3, 5, and 7 are, respectively 6, 28, 496, and 8128. Thus $1 + 2 + 3 = 6$; $1 + 2 + 4 + 7 + 14 = 28$; the sum of 1, 2, 4, 8, 16, 31, 62, 124, and 248 is 496; and the sum of 1, 2, 4, 8, 16, 32, 64, 127, 254, 508, 1016, 2032, and 4064 is 8128.

1.11

4. One observes that $999 = 1000 - 1$, $1436 + 999 = 1436 + (1000 - 1)$, $1436 - 999 = 1436 - (1000 - 1)$, and $1436 \times 999 = 1436 \times (1000 - 1)$.

1.13

Page 29

1. 10000101010
3. 10001000111

5. 11000011100
8. 11010101011
10. 11100110101

Page 31

1.   (1) (1) (1)
    1 0 1 1
        1 0 1
  —————————
  1 0 0 0 0

(In base ten, $11 + 5 = 16$)

4.   (1) (1)
    (1) (1) (1) (1)
  (1) (1) (1) (1) (1)
        1 0 1 1
        1 1 0 1
        1 1 1 1
          1 1 0
          1 0 1
  —————————————
  1 1 0 0 1 0

(In base ten, $11 + 13 + 15 + 6 + 5 = 50$)

7. 1 0 1 1
      1 0 1
  —————————
   (10) 1   1
     1 0 1
  —————————
    1 1 0

(In base ten, $11 - 5 = 6$)

9. 1 0 0 0
        1   1
  —————————
  (10) 0   0
      1   1
  —————————
  1 (10) 0
      1 1
  —————————
  1 1 (10)
      1 1
  —————————
  1 0 1

(In base ten, $8 - 3 = 5$)

11. 1   1   1   0   0   0   0
         1   1   1   0   1
    ─────────────────────────────
     1   1   0 (10)   0   0   0
         1   1   1   0   1
    ─────────────────────────────
     1   0 (10)   1 (10)   0   0
         1   1   1   0   1
    ─────────────────────────────
     1   0 (10)   1   1 (10)   0
         1   1   1   0   1
    ─────────────────────────────
     1   0 (10)   1   1   1 (10)
         1   1   1   0   1
    ─────────────────────────────
     1   0   1   0   0   1   1

(In base ten, $112 - 29 = 83$)

1.14

Page 34

1. $(6561)_T = (100000000)_3$
3. $(1492)_T = (2001021)_3$
5. $(186000)_T = (100110010220)_3$

Page 38

1. (1) (1) (1)
          2   2   2
          2   2   1
    ─────────────────
      1   2   2   0

(In base ten, $26 + 25 = 51$)

3.   (1)
      (1) (1) (1)
      (1) (1) (1) (1) (1)
            2   2   2   1   0
            2   1   2   0   1
            2   0   1   2   2
            1   2   2   1   2
    ─────────────────────────
      1   0   0   1   2   2   2

(In base ten, $237 + 208 + 179 + 158 = 782$)

1. 1220
3. 1001222
5. 102
7. 111112
9. 1122201
11. 2120111121
13. 1200
15. 11
17. 2120

1. 1110
3. 33424
5. 21031
7. 2304433
9. 10111000000

CHAPTER 2

2.4

1. The sets of numbers in parts a, b, e, and f are closed under the indicated operation.
2. (b) When a and b are both odd or both even.
4. (b) No, since $1 + 1 = 2$ is not in T.
   (c) Yes.
   (d) Yes.

2.5

1. No; for example, $5 - 3 \neq 3 - 5$.
4. (c) No; for example, $7 \bigcirc 6 \neq 6 \bigcirc 7$.
   (d) When $a = b$.

2.6

2. $(5 + 7) + 4$, $5 + (7 + 4)$, $4 + (5 + 7)$, $5 + (4 + 7)$, $(7 + 4) + 5$, and $7 + (5 + 4)$.
4. Yes, $(12 \div 6) \div 1 = 12 \div (6 \div 1)$. In order that this be so, we must have $c = 1$.
5. No; for example, $(4 * 12) * 8 = 8 * 8 = 12$ and $4 * (12 * 8) = 4 * 10 = 7$.
   A simple instance where the law fails suffices to show that it is not generally valid.
7. In five ways.

2.7

2. Yes, the law of trichotomy holds in S.
3. (a) 1, 1, 1, 1.
   (e) No; for example, $1 = 1$ and $1 = 1 + 4$. This violates the law of trichotomy.

2.8

1. Yes.
3. Yes. You can deduce this from the cancellation law for addition of natural numbers, since $a \bigcirc b = a \bigcirc c$ if and only if $2a + b = 2a + c$, and this is true if and only if $b = c$.
4. No, since $3 \oplus 1 = 3 \oplus 4$ and $1 \neq 4$.
5. (a) $x = 7$.
   (d) $x = 126$.
6. (b) Not justified.
   (c) Justified by the cancellation law and the commutative law for addition of natural numbers since $x + 7 = 7 + x$.

2.10

1. Since there are 56 squares and two triangles in each sqaure, there must be $56 \cdot 2 = 112$ triangles in all.
3. The number is $7 + 7^2 + 7^3 + 7^4 = 2790$.
4. (b) Since $451 = 11 \cdot 41$, it follows that $x = 41$.
   (c) Since $x \cdot 7 = 7x$ and $1001 = 7 \cdot 143$, it follows that $7x = 7 \cdot 143$ and $x = 143$.
7. (a) $x = 3$. This checks since, for $x = 3, 7x + 14 = 7 \cdot 3 + 14 = 21 + 14 = 35$.
   (c) $x = 4$.

2.12

1. No.
2. Yes, since 1 is such a number.
3. No.
6. Yes, 4 is the identity.
7. Zero is a right identity for subtraction.

2.14

1. (a) All from the third one on will fall down.
   (b) It contains all natural numbers from three on.

2.15

1. (a) 6
   (c) 2
   (e) 8
   (g) 12

2. (a) 6 and 6
   (c) 6 and 6
   (e) 12 and 12

3. (a) 3 and 3
   (d) No. In fact, $5 \boxplus_{12} (6 \boxtimes_{12} 3) = 11$ and $(5 \boxplus_{12} 6) \boxtimes_{12} (5 \boxplus_{12} 3) = 9$. Thus, the supposed rule does not hold in every case.

5. For $a = 1, 5, 7,$ or 11; those numbers in clock arithmetic that have no factor in common with 12 other than 1. It does not hold if a is a divisor of zero.

7. (b) $x = 5$. This checks since, for $x = 5$, $(5 \boxtimes_{12} x) \boxplus_{12} 1 = (5 \boxtimes_{12} 5) \boxplus_{12} 1 = 1 \boxplus_{12} 1 = 2$.
   (d) $x = 10$.

9. (a) Yes.
   (c) Yes.
   (e) No. For example, $2 \boxplus_7 6 = 8$ and $8 \boxplus_7 1 = 2$. This violates the law of trichotomy for seven hour clock arithmetic.
   (g) For $a = 1, 2, 3, 4, 5,$ and 6.
   (i) Yes, with any number in the arithmetic other than 7.
   (k) Yes, 7 is the additive identity.
   (l) No. There are no divisors of zero, since $a \boxtimes b = 7$ if and only if $a = 7$ or $b = 7$.

11. (a) For clocks with a prime number of hours. Note that a prime is a natural number other than 1 that is evenly divisible only by itself and 1.
    (b) For those values of a that have no factor in common with n other than 1.
    (c) For prime values of n.
    (d) Those numbers that have no factor in common with n other than 1.

12. (b) Yes, since the table is symmetric about a line drawn from the upper left to the lower right hand corner.
    (c) No. For example, $\alpha \odot \nu = \alpha \odot \delta$ in violation of the cancellation law.

CHAPTER 3

3.4

1. $U = \{1, 2, 3\},\ \ \{1, 2\},\ \ \{1, 3\},\ \ \{2, 3\},\ \ \{1\},\ \ \{2\},\ \ \{3\},\ \ Z.$
2. 2; 4; 8; 16; 128.
5. The set of people who are both adult and either busy or in college is the same as the set of people who are either adult and busy or adult and in college. The set of people who are either adult or both busy and in college is the same as the set of people who are both adult or busy and adult or in college.
7. The set of people who are neither busy nor in college is the same as the set of people who are both not busy and not in college. The set of people who are not both busy and in college is the same as the set of people who are either not busy or not in college.
10. A.
11. $\bar{A}$.
12. Let W = set of worthwhile activities, E = set of activities involving effort, and F = the set of activities that are lots of fun. Then we have
(a) $W \cap \bar{E} = Z$ or $W \subset E$.
(b) $W \cap F \neq Z$.
14. (b), (d), (f), and (g) must be true.

3.5

1. B2.

   B5.

3. (a) $P \rightarrow P$ (b) $\overline{P \rightarrow P}$.
5. $A \cup U = U$: a switch in parallel with a permenently closed switch is equivalent to a permanently closed switch.

   $A \cap Z = Z$: A switch in series with a permanently open switch is equivalent to a permanently open switch.

   $A \cup U = U$: The proposition "either A or a tautology" is a tautology.

   $A \cap Z = Z$: The proposition "both A and a self-contradiction" is a self-contradiction.

A	U	A	$U = U$		A	Z	$A \cap Z = Z$	
$+$	$+$	$+$	$+$ $+$		$+$	$-$	$-$	$+$ $-$
$-$	$+$	$+$	$+$ $+$		$-$	$-$	$-$	$+$ $-$

9. Conclusions: No automobiles are necessary.
   No paintings are necessary.

10. Conclusions: No fools are teachers.
    All fools are rich.

3.6

1. **G1.** For any line b and point A, b lies on A if and only if A lies on b.
   G2. Each point is determined by the lines that lie on it.
   G3. For any two distinct lines there is a unique point that lies on both lines.
   G4. For any point there is a line that lies on the point and a line that does not lie on the point.
   G5. For any point A and line c that does not lie on A, there is a unique point B such that c lies on B and no line lies on both A and B.
   G6. There are exactly four lines.

3. Points a, b, c, d, e, and f and lines A, B, C, D, E, F, and G, as in either of the following figures.

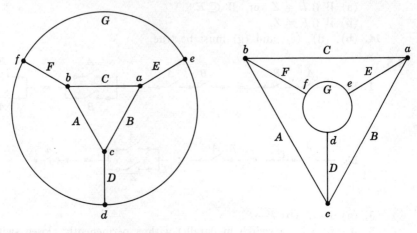

5. This geometry is self-dual; i.e., the dual is the same figure with points and lines renamed.

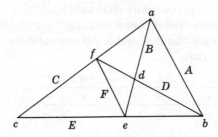

6. No. For example, the point A is not on the line c, but every line through A has some point in common with line c.

CHAPTER 4

4.3

1. N1, N2, N4, N5, and N7 are true. N3 fails to hold since, for example, $(1 * 2) * 3 = 6 * 3 = 18$, but $1 * (2 * 3) = 1 * 10 = 22$. N6 fails to hold since, for example, $2 \neq 3$, $2 * a \neq 3$, and $2 \neq 3 * a$ for all natural numbers a.
   N8 fails to hold since, starting with 1, we obtain $1 * 1 = 4$, $4 * 1 = 10$, $10 * 1 = 22$, etc., and clearly do not obtain all the natural numbers.

3. N1, N4, N5, and N7 are ture. N2 fails to hold since, for example, $1 * 2 = 5$, but $2 * 1 = 4$. N3 fails to hold since, for example, $(1 * 2) * 3 = 5 * 3 = 13$, but $1 * (2 * 3) = 1 * 8 = 17$. No fails to hold since, for example, $2 \neq 3$, $2 * a \neq 3$, and $2 \neq 3 * a$ for all natural numbers a. N8 fails to hold since $1 * 1 = 3$, $3 * 1 = 5$, $5 * 1 = 7$, etc., so that by this process we obtain only the odd natural numbers.

5. N1, N2, N3, N4, and N7 are true. N5 fails to hold since, for example, $2 * 3 = 2 = 2 * 4$, whereas $3 \neq 4$. N6 fails to hold since, for example, $2 = 2$ and $2 * 1 = 2$ both hold. N8 fails to hold since $1 * 1 = 1$

7. N1, N2, N3, N4, N7, and N8 are true. N5 fails to hold since $a + b = b + b$, but $a \neq b$. N6 fails to hold since $b = b$ and $b = a + b$. (Notice that b is the multiplicative identity, or "1", of this system.)

9. N1, N2, N3, N4, N7, and N8 are true.

12. N1, N2, N3, N4, N6, and N8 together with the following postulates:

   A. The system consists of seven elements, $S = \{1, 2, 3, 4, 5, 6, 7\}$
   B. For any a in S, $a + 7 = a$.
   C. For any a, b, and c in S, if $a + b = a + c$, then $b = c$, and if both $ab = ac$ and $a \neq 7$, then $b = c$.

   Other, equivalent lists of postulates are, of course, also possible.

4.4

2. Let U be the universe set and Z the empty subset of U.
   Then we have $U \cup U = U \cup Z$ and $Z \cap U = Z \cap Z$, but certainly $U \neq Z$ in general.

5. $ab = ba$ (N2)
      $= ca$ (Hypothesis)
      $= ac$ (N2)
   $b = c$ (N5)

7. Suppose a and b are least natural numbers. By N6 (trichotomy), exactly one of $a = b$, $a < b$, or $b < a$ holds. But $a < b$ contradicts the assumption that b is a least natural number, and $b < a$ contradicts the assumption that a is a least natural number. Hence, we must have $a = b$, and there can be only one least natural number.

10. (a) Suppose x is a natural number such that $3x + 1 = x + 5$. Then

$$3x + 1 = x + 5 \qquad \text{(Hypothesis)}$$
$$= x + (4 + 1) \qquad \text{(Addition fact)}$$
$$= (x + 4) + 1 \qquad \text{(N3)}$$
$$3x = x + 4 \qquad \text{(N5)}$$
$$(1 + 2)x = x + 4 \qquad \text{(Addition fact)}$$
$$1 \cdot x + 2 \cdot x = x + 4 \qquad \text{(T1)}$$
$$x + 2 \cdot x = x + 4 \qquad \text{(N7)}$$
$$2 \cdot x = 4 \qquad \text{(N5)}$$
$$= 2 \cdot 2 \qquad \text{(Multiplication fact)}$$
$$x = 2 \qquad \text{(N5)}$$

(b) Suppose $x = 2$.

$$3x + 1 = 3x + 1 \qquad \text{(Identity)}$$
$$= 3 \cdot 2 + 1 \qquad \text{(Hypothesis and substitution)}$$
$$= 7 \qquad \text{(Multiplication and addition facts)}$$
$$= 2 + 5 \qquad \text{(Addition fact)}$$
$$= x + 5 \qquad \text{(Hypothesis and substitution)}$$

11. $26 \times 37 = 26 \times (3 \times 10 + 7)$ (Positional notation, base 10)

$$= 26 \times (3 \times 10) + 26 \times 7 \qquad \text{(N1 and N4)}$$
$$= (26 \times 3) \times 10 + 26 \times 7 \qquad \text{(N3)}$$
$$= [(2 \times 10 + 6) \times 3] \times 10 \qquad \text{(Positional notation)}$$
$$+ (2 \times 10 + 6) \times 7$$
$$= [(2 \times 10) \times 3 + 6 \times 3] \times 10 \qquad \text{(N1 and T1)}$$
$$+ [(2 \times 10) \times 7 + 6 \times 7]$$
$$= [(2 \times 3) \times 10 + 6 \times 3] \times 10 \qquad \text{(N2 and N3)}$$
$$+ [(2 \times 7) \times 10 + 6 \times 7]$$
$$= [6 \times 10 + (1 \times 10 + 8)] \times 10 \qquad \text{(Multiplication facts)}$$
$$+ [(1 \times 10 + 4) \times 10$$
$$+ (4 \times 10 + 2)]$$
$$= [6 \times 10 + (1 \times 10 + 8)] \times 10 \qquad \text{(N1 and T1)}$$
$$+ \{[(1 \times 10) \times 10 + 4 \times 10]$$
$$+ (4 \times 10 + 2)\}$$
$$= [(6 \times 10 + 1 \times 10) + 8] \times 10 \qquad \text{(N1 and N3)}$$
$$+ [1 \times 10^2 + (4 \times 10 + 4 \times 10)$$
$$+ 2]$$

$$= [(6 + 1) \times 10 + 8] \times 10 \qquad \text{(N4)}$$
$$+ [1 \times 10^2 + (4 + 4) \times 10$$
$$+ 2]$$
$$= (7 \times 10 + 8) \times 10 + [1 \times 10^2 \qquad \text{(Addition facts)}$$
$$+ 8 \times 10 + 2]$$
$$= [(7 \times 10) \times 10 + 8 \times 10] \qquad \text{(N1 and T1)}$$
$$+ [1 \times 10^2 + 8 \times 10 + 2]$$
$$= [7 \times 10^2 + 8 \times 10] + [1 \times 10^2 \qquad \text{(N3)}$$
$$+ 8 \times 10 + 2]$$
$$= (7 \times 10^2 + 1 \times 10^2) \qquad \text{(N1, N2 and N3)}$$
$$+ (8 \times 10 + 8 \times 10) + 2$$
$$= (7 + 1) \times 10^2 + (8 + 8) \times 10 + 2 \text{ (T1)}$$
$$= 8 \times 10^2 + (1 \times 10 + 6) \times 10 + 2 \text{ (Addition fact)}$$
$$= 8 \times 10^2 + [(1 \times 10) \times 10 \qquad \text{(N1 and T1)}$$
$$+ 6 \times 10] + 2$$
$$= 8 \times 10^2 + (1 \times 10^2 + 6 \times 10) \qquad \text{(N3)}$$
$$+ 2$$
$$= (8 \times 10^2 + 1 \times 10^2) + 6 \times 10 \qquad \text{(T1)}$$
$$+ 2$$
$$= 9 \times 10^2 + 6 \times 10 + 2 \qquad \text{(Addition fact)}$$
$$= 962 \qquad \text{(Positional notation)}$$

CHAPTER 5

5.3

1. (a) $\dfrac{3}{4}$

(c) $\dfrac{3}{4}$

(e) $\dfrac{3}{4}$

(g) $\dfrac{63}{89}$

3. No, since $205 \cdot 9 \neq 451 \cdot 4$.

5.4

1. (a) $\dfrac{5}{6}$

   (c) $\dfrac{5}{6}$

   (e) $\dfrac{23}{102}$

   (g) $\dfrac{473}{5400}$

3. (a) $\dfrac{51}{40}$ and $\dfrac{51}{40}$

   (c) $\dfrac{23}{12}$ and $\dfrac{23}{12}$

4. (b) $\dfrac{11}{18}$ and $\dfrac{11}{18}$

5.5

1. (a) $\dfrac{7}{20}$

   (c) $\dfrac{5}{26}$

   (d) $\dfrac{1}{4}$

2. (a) $\dfrac{3}{10}$

   (c) $\dfrac{4}{75}$

3. (b) $\dfrac{1}{1}$ and $\dfrac{1}{1}$

5. (a) $\dfrac{3}{10}$ and $\dfrac{3}{10}$

5.6

1. Since $ab = ab$, it follows from Definition 2 that $\dfrac{a}{a} = \dfrac{b}{b}$ for any natural numbers a and b.

2.
$$\frac{c}{c} \cdot \frac{a}{b} = \frac{ca}{cb} \qquad \text{by Definition 4}$$

$$= \frac{ac}{bc} \qquad \text{by N2}$$

$$= \frac{a}{b} \qquad \text{by Theorem 5}$$

5. Yes.

7. (b) $\dfrac{14}{29}$

   (d) $\dfrac{3}{35}$

8. (b) $\dfrac{2}{5}$

   (d) $\dfrac{85}{72}$

9. (b) $\dfrac{2}{5}$

5.7

2. (a) $\dfrac{8}{9}$

   (c) $\dfrac{2}{1}$

   (e) $\dfrac{3173}{1491}$

3. (b) $x = \dfrac{15}{17}$

4. (c) $\dfrac{42}{5}$

5.

$$\left(\frac{a}{b}+\frac{c}{d}\right) \div \frac{e}{f} = \left(\frac{a}{b}+\frac{c}{d}\right)\frac{f}{e} \qquad \text{by Theorem 9}$$

$$= \frac{f}{e}\left(\frac{a}{b}+\frac{c}{d}\right) \qquad \text{by Theorem 1}$$

$$= \frac{f}{e}\cdot\frac{a}{b}+\frac{f}{e}\cdot\frac{c}{d} \qquad \text{by Theorem 7}$$

$$= \frac{a}{b}\cdot\frac{f}{e}+\frac{c}{d}\cdot\frac{f}{e} \qquad \text{by Theorem 1}$$

$$= \frac{a}{b}\div\frac{e}{f}+\frac{c}{d}\div\frac{e}{f} \qquad \text{by Theorem 9}$$

6. The numbers in 12 hour clock arithmetic that have multiplication inverses are 1, 5, 7, and 11. Each of these numbers is its own multiplicative inverse.

9. No. If Z is the additive identity in a given clock arithmetic, then $Za = Z$ for any a in that arithmetic. Thus, there can exist no u in the arithmetic such that $Zu = 1$ and, thus, Z cannot have a multiplicative inverse.

5.8

1. We already know that $1/1$ is a multiplicative identity for the set of positive rational numbers. Thus, $1/1 \cdot a/b = a/b$. On the other hand, if a/b is also a multiplicative identity, then $a/b \cdot 1/1 = 1/1$. Since $a/b \cdot 1/1 = 1/1 \cdot a/b$ by Theorem 1, it therefore follows that $a/b = 1/1$.

5.9

1. (a) $3+\dfrac{4}{5}=\dfrac{19}{5}$

(c) $3+\dfrac{11}{9}=\dfrac{38}{9}$

(e) $5\cdot\dfrac{3}{4}=\dfrac{15}{4}$

(g) $\dfrac{3}{4} \div 5 = \dfrac{3}{20}$

(i) $\dfrac{5/7}{1 + 1/5} = \dfrac{25}{42}$

3. Since we have identified t and $t/1$, we have that

$$\frac{r}{s} \div t = \frac{r}{s} \div \frac{t}{1} = \frac{r}{s} \cdot \frac{1}{t} = \frac{r}{st}$$

5. Since $a = a/1$ and $b = b/1$, we have that

$$a \div b = \frac{a}{1} \div \frac{b}{1} = \frac{a}{1} \cdot \frac{1}{b} = a\left(\frac{1}{b}\right).$$

7. (a) $x = 10$
(c) $x = 10$

9. As shown in the accompanying figure, the height of the church steeple, x, is proportional to the height of the telephone pole. Thus, we have

$$x : 45 = 18 : 10 \text{ so that } x = \frac{18 \cdot 45}{10} = 81 \text{ feet.}$$

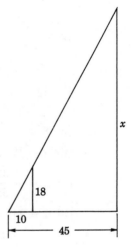

CHAPTER 6

6.5

1. (a) 4
(c) -10

(e) $-\dfrac{22}{5}$

(h) $-\dfrac{13}{28}$

(k) -2

(m) $\dfrac{3}{5}$

2. (a) 4
   (c) -10

   (e) $\dfrac{32}{7}$

   (g) $-\dfrac{32}{7}$

   (i) $\dfrac{17}{12}$

   (l) -2
   (n) 8

3. (a) $x = 19$

   (c) $x = -\dfrac{47}{55}$

   (e) $x = 11$

5.
$$
\begin{aligned}
(r - s) + t &= (r + s') + t && \text{by Theorem 7} \\
&= r + (s' + t) && \text{by R3} \\
&= r - (s' + t)' && \text{by Theorem 7} \\
&= r - (s'' + t') && \text{by Theorem 6} \\
&= r - (s + t') && \text{by Theorem 4} \\
&= r - (s - t) && \text{by Theorem 7.}
\end{aligned}
$$

7. (a) $12 - (5 - 7) = (12 - 5) + 7 = 7 + 7 = 14.$
   (c) $(15 - 8) - 21 = 15 - (8 + 21) = 15 - 29 = -14.$

6.7

1. (a) $\dfrac{7}{12}$

   (c) $-\dfrac{30}{77}$

   (e) 0
   (g) 8

   (i) $\dfrac{4}{7}$

(k) $-\dfrac{1}{14}$

(l) undefined

(n) $-\dfrac{3}{2}$

(p) 0

(r) -33

(t) $\dfrac{35}{9}$

2. Let $r/s = q$. Then $r = sq$ and $rt = (sq)t = (qs)t = q(st)$.
Therefore

$$\frac{rt}{st} = q = \frac{r}{s}$$

The reader should supply a reason for each of these steps and should also show that $tr/ts = r/s$.

3. (a) 1   (c) $-\dfrac{47}{50}$ (e) $\dfrac{362}{143}$

5. (a) 2 and 2

6.8

2. (a)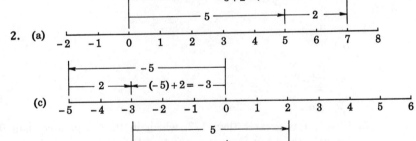

(c)

(e)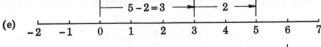

(g)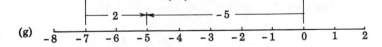

6.9

1. (a) False
   (c) True, since $(-2)(-3) = 6$ and $(-2) + 8 = 6$.
   (e) False
3. Since $0 < 1$ and $1 < a$, it follows that $0 < a$. Therefore, by Theorem 18, $a \cdot 1 < a \cdot a$. But $a \cdot 1 = a$ and $a \cdot a = a^2$. Thus, $a < a^2$.
5. No. If $a \leq 0$, then $a^2 \geq a$. The reader should show this in detail.
7. By Definition 4, there exists a rational number $r > 0$ such that

$$\frac{c}{d} + r = \frac{a}{b}$$

Thus, by Definition 1 and Theorem 9

$$r = \frac{a}{b} - \frac{c}{d} = \frac{ad - bc}{bd}$$

Hence, by the definition of division, we obtain

$$ad - bc = r(bd)$$

Finally $r(bd) > 0$ since $r > 0$, $b > 0$, and $d > 0$; and so $ad - bc > 0$.

9. (a) For all rational x with $x < 3$.
   (c) For all rational x with $x > -3$.
   (e) For all rational x with $x < 7$.
   (g) For all rational x with $x > 9$.
   (i) For all rational x with $x < -1$.

11. *Case 1.* If $a = b$, then $ac = bc$ by substitution.
    Case 2. If $a < b$, then $ac < bc$ by Theorem 18.
    Combining Cases 1 and 2 we have the desired result.

6.10

1. (a) 9
   (c) 29

   (e) $\dfrac{19}{2}$

   (g) 349

3. Clearly 1 is greater than $1/2$, which in turn is greater than 0. In symbols, these two inequalities are combined into the single statement

$$1 > \frac{1}{2} > 0$$

Since $x < 0$, it follows from Theorem 18, that

$$x < x \cdot \frac{1}{2} < x \cdot 0$$

But $x \cdot 1/2 = x/2$ and $x \cdot 0 = 0$. Thus, we have

$$x < \frac{x}{2} < 0$$

as required.

4. Suppose that the assertion of the exercise is true. Then, if we were to plot x, y and $(x + y)/2$ on a number line, it would appear as in the accompanying diagram

This suggests that we consider the differences $(x + y)/2 - x$ and $y - (x + y)/2$, which give the distances from x to $(x + y)/2$ and from $(x + y)/2$ to y respectively. We obtain

$$\frac{x + y}{2} - x = \frac{x + y}{2} - \frac{2x}{2} = \frac{(x + y) - 2x}{2} = \frac{y - x}{2}$$

$$y - \frac{x + y}{2} = \frac{2y}{2} - \frac{x + y}{2} = \frac{2y - (x + y)}{2} = \frac{y - x}{2}$$

Since the distance is the same in each case, it follows that $(x + y)/2$ lies mid-way between x and y.

To see that $(x + y)/2$ is rational, we have only to note that x, y, and 2 are rational and that the rational numbers are closed with respect to both addition and division (except for division by zero).

6.11

1. Postulates F1–F5 are true in any clock arithmetic. Thus, we have only to show that 1 and 2 both have additive inverses and that 1 has a multiplicative inverse in two hour clock arithmetic. Since $1 + 1 = 2$, $2 + 2 = 2$, and $1 \cdot 1 = 1$, it follows that each element is its own inverse in each case.

2. The element 2 has no multiplicative inverse in 4 hour clock arithmetic.

3. (a) $\dfrac{3}{5} = 2$

   (c) $\dfrac{1}{5} = 3$

   (e) 6/7 undefined since 7 is the additive identity in 7 hour clock arithmetic.

4. (a) $x = 3$
   (c) $y = 5$

CHAPTER 7

7.2

   2. $154 = 2 \cdot 7 \cdot 11,$ $8470 = 2 \cdot 5 \cdot 7 \cdot 11^2$

7.7

   Observe that if $p = 13$, $W = (3,628,800 \times 11 \times 12) + 1$

7.9

   $(41213, 539) = 7$

7.12

   $1037232 = 2^4 \cdot 3^3 \cdot 7^4$

7.13

   3. (a) 3   (c) 13
   6. Calculate and check your results using different theorems given in the text.

CHAPTER 8

8.1

   2. Suppose that there are relatively prime positive integers a and b such that $(a/b)^3 = 2$. Then $b \neq 1$ since 2 is not the cube of any integer. Hence, b is divisible by some prime p. Thus, $a^3 = 2b^3$ is also divisible by p and a must be divisible by p, contrary to the assumption that $(a, b) = 1$. But any positive rational can be written in the form a/b with $(a, b) = 1$. Hence, there is no rational number whose cube is 2.
   5. Suppose there is a rational number a/b, $(a, b) = 1$ such that $(a/b)^2 = \frac{3}{4}$. Then $4a^2 = 3b^2$ and $a \neq 1$ since 4 is not divisible by 3. Hence, a is divisible by some prime p, and p^2 divides $4a^2 = 3b^2$. But then, since 3 is prime, 3 is not divisible by p^2. Hence, b must be divisible by p. This contradicts $(a, b) = 1$ and no such rational can exist.
   8. The rational number r will have a rational number as a cube root if and only if $r = (a/b)^3$ for some integers a and b.

8.2

   1. $\frac{1}{6} = 0.166666 \cdots$
   3. $\frac{1}{8} = 0.1250000000 \cdots$ $\frac{1}{9} = 0.1111111111 \cdots$ $\frac{1}{11} = 0.0909090909 \cdots$
      $\frac{1}{12} = 0.0833333333 \cdots$ $\frac{1}{13} = 0.0769230769 \cdots$

8.3

1. (a), (c), and (e) are convergent.
3. Yes, Achilles will catch the tortoises after running 10/9 blocks.
6. $y_0 = 2, y_1 = (2 + 5/2)/2 = 9/4 = 2.25, y_2 = (9/4 + 20/9)/2 = 161/72 = 2.236\overline{1}, \sqrt{5} = 2.236068\cdots$

8.4

1. (a) $-11/3 = -3.\overline{6}$, (c) $13/7 = 1.\overline{857142}$.
2. (a) $17.\overline{23} = 1706/99$, (c) $-7.30\overline{201} = -739471/99900$, (e) $203.\overline{8} = 20180/99$.
4. $17 \cdot \overline{23} + 0.0\overline{12} = 17.2\overline{4}, 17.\overline{23} - 0.0\overline{12} = 17.2\overline{20}$
   $(17.\overline{23})(0.0\overline{12}) = 0.208876644\cdots, (17 \cdot \overline{23})/(0.0\overline{12}) = 1421.\overline{6}$.

8.6

2. (a)→(b), (d)→(c)
3. $u + v$ need not be irrational. uv need not be irrational. $1/u$ must be irrational.
5. Let r be a positive rational number so that $r = a/b$, with a and b positive integers. Then $a/2b$ is also a positive rational and $a/2b < a/b$ since $ab < 2ab$ for positive integers a and b. Similarly, there is no smallest positive real number.

INDEX